QUANTUM MECHANICS

for Mathematicians
and Physicists

QUANTUM MECHANICS

FOR MATHEMATICIANS
AND PHYSICISTS

ERNEST IKENBERRY

RESEARCH PROFESSOR
AUBURN UNIVERSITY

NEW YORK

OXFORD UNIVERSITY PRESS

1962

© 1962 by Oxford University Press, Inc.

Library of Congress Catalogue Card Number: 61-13565

Printed in the United States of America

PREFACE

This text is written for mathematicians with little or no background in physics and for physicists, including nuclear engineers in a physics curriculum, with a minimum of mathematics. It has been class-tested with great success on first-year graduate students who are proceeding to the doctorate in mathematics or in physics. As a teacher of both physics and mathematics, the writer believes that a basic course in quantum mechanics should be available to mathematics and physics majors alike. Such a course must perforce introduce many physical concepts new to each class of students and it must be at a mathematical level understandable by both. Its success may be judged by the interest it creates in students of diverse preparation and, further, by the ability of graduates to read independently from texts and research papers in this most exciting of scientific disciplines.

The mathematical theory of quantum mechanics is introduced in this book by a brief historical study. The accompanying descriptions of certain basic phenomena and their associated theories provide the background necessary for the understanding and appreciation of Schroedinger's wave mechanics. The presentation is axiomatic, statements of principles generally preceding explanations and clarifying examples. The basic properties of linear operators over inner product spaces are given at an early stage. These concepts and those involved in the $\psi^*\psi$ hypothesis are immediately illustrated in a chapter on sectionally constant potentials. Approximation of smooth potentials by sectionally constant potentials makes plausible certain specifically quantum effects, such as the existence of discrete energy states for bound systems. There follows a general treatment of the eigenvalue problem, accompanied by discussions of degeneracy, Gram-Schmidt orthogonalization, the expansion problem, completeness, and extremal properties of eigenvalues. These are illustrated in a chapter on the harmonic oscillator, where the wave equation is solved by the power series method and by the factorization method. Here Dirac's bra and ket symbols are introduced and matrix elements are calculated.

The student is now prepared for Born's statistical interpretation of the wave function, for formal statement of the postulates of quantum mechanics, and for a discussion of the quantum theory of measurement. At

v

this point, commuting operators, complete sets of simultaneous eigenfunctions, and sets of compatible constants of the motion become of central importance. The utility of these concepts is illustrated in a chapter on
angular momentum which is concluded with their application to the
Stern-Gerlach experiment.

A solution of the wave equation for the hydrogen atom follows. "Separation" of the variables in the wave equation is replaced by a search for
simultaneous eigenfunctions of commuting operators. The radial equation
is solved by the power series method and by the factorization method.
These solutions are followed by a brief description of the semi-classical
theory of radiation, by the calculation of selection rules, and by a description of the normal Zeeman effect.

The succeeding chapter presents Schroedinger's time-independent perturbation theory and its application to the normal Zeeman effect and to
the Stark effect.

A chapter on matrix representations, containing a development of the
formal relationship between the Schroedinger and the Heisenberg pictures, precedes a chapter on Pauli's theory of electron spin.

The final chapter introduces the student to relativistic wave mechanics.
Here plane wave solutions for the Dirac electron are obtained and Dirac's
theories of the positron and of the spinning electron are presented. Four-
component energy eigenfunctions and Sommerfeld's formula for the
energy levels of the hydrogen atom are obtained.

In this book 352 problems appear. Though many of these are quite simple, most of them form an integral part of the text. Abundant references
are provided at the end of each chapter for supplementary reading.

The author wishes to express his deep obligation to the authors of many
texts and original papers in atomic physics and quantum mechanics, only
a part of which could be listed in the bibliography and in the footnotes.
The author also wishes to express his appreciation to Dean W. V. Parker
and Professor H. E. Carr for their co-operation in arranging for him to
present courses in quantum mechanics to majors in mathematics and in
physics.

AUBURN UNIVERSITY   E. I.
SEPTEMBER 1961

CONTENTS

CONTENTS

QUANTUM MECHANICS

for Mathematicians
and Physicists

CHAPTER 1

THE DUAL NATURE OF LIGHT

1.1. Brief Historical Outline, Prior to 1900. The Roman philosopher Lucretius, (95–51? B.C.) in his poem *De Rerum Natura* (Book IV) summed up his theory of light 2000 years ago in the words: "Know then that bodies have, as we call them, their semblances which are slender membranes detaching themselves from their surface and flying in every direction in the air . . . These semblances must traverse incalculable distances in a flash; first, because they are exceedingly small elements, and secondly they fly in swarms so subtle that they can easily penetrate and as it were pour through the air."

This theory of light was an ingenious part of the attempt to explain all natural phenomena by the motion and interaction of indivisible corpuscles, that is, of atoms (Gr. *atomos:* an exceedingly small particle or thing, an iota). This ancient theory, which was developed by people who were capable of making precise observations, but were unwilling to experiment,[1] was strengthened by the experiments and the theories of the eighteenth and early nineteenth centuries. A study of quantitative relations led J. Dalton (1766–1844), Proust (1760–1826), and Lavoisier (1743–1794) to the establishment of atomic and molecular theories of chemistry. Prior to this, Newton (1642–1727) had shown that the idea that light consists of corpuscles permitted an interpretation of the rectilinear propagation of light, its reflection in mirrors, and its refraction in transparent media.

In spite of the popularity and the apparently complete success of the Atomic Theory of Nature, the Dutch scientist Christian Huyghens (1629–1695), a contemporary of Newton's earlier period, advanced a theory that the propagation of light should be compared with the traveling of ripples on a disturbed water surface. However, Newton had abandoned his own attempts to combine corpuscular and undulatory concepts, and his authority led the scientific world to reject temporarily Huyghens's ideas. In the eighteenth century, the only prominent writers who advocated the undulatory theory were the Swiss mathematician Leonard Euler (1707–1783) and the American statesman Benjamin Franklin (1706–1790). A

---

[1] See A. d'Abro, *The Rise of the New Physics*, Dover, 1951, Vol. 1, p. 7.

German writer of the time stated that Euler's views were not held "by a single physicist of prominence." Thus Newton's corpuscular theory of light held sway for more than a century because of his dominating influence on the scientific world and because of the absence of any contradictory experiments.

Fortunately for the further advancement of the theory of light there were discovered by the English physicist Thomas Young (1773–1829) and the French scientist Augustine Fresnel (1788–1827) certain phenomena, those of interference and diffraction, which could not be explained by corpuscular concepts. Then Fresnel demonstrated that Huyghens's wave theory of light accounted not only for reflection, refraction, and rectilinear propagation, but also for the phenomena of diffraction and interference. As a consequence, the corpuscular theory of light was temporarily abandoned in favor of the wave theory.

Whereas the corpuscular theory of light remained discredited throughout the nineteenth century, the corpuscular theory of matter became more firmly established. This theory, upon which the foundations of chemistry were firmly laid, was applied with limited success in explaining characteristic properties (such as thermal conductivity, viscosity, and compressibility) of the three states of matter in bulk: gaseous, liquid, and solid. The great James Clerk Maxwell (1831–1879) and perhaps equally great Ludwig Boltzmann (1844–1906) and John Willard Gibbs (1839–1903) laid the foundations of statistical mechanics in their work on the kinetic theory of matter. Even today, success of the theory appears to be more limited by the complexity of the mathematical calculations than by the theory *per se*.

In this brief historical outline the monistic philosophy which attempts to explain all natural phenomena by an atomistic theory has been traced from Greek attempts to explain the phenomena of vision to the temporary success of Newton and his contemporaries in developing atomistic theories of bulk matter and of light. After Newton, the successes of Fresnel and Young in explaining the newly discovered phenomena of interference and diffraction by undulatory concepts, and the continued successes of other scientists in developing corpuscular theories of bulk matter, forced scientists to accept a dualistic philosophy about Nature: bulk matter consists of atoms or corpuscles whereas light consists of waves.

Toward the end of the nineteenth century, optimism about the fruitfulness of adhering strictly to these parallel philosophies began to fall: all attempts to obtain a satisfactory wave-theory for black body radiation met with failure. However, as we shall see, these attempts, although unsuccessful, are not to be regarded as fruitless since they pointed the way toward the modern wave-particle interpretation of light and of matter.

1.2. Properties of Black Body Radiation. Different portions of the interior boundary of an enclosure and of any matter in the enclosure exchange energy by emitting and absorbing radiation. After the temperature within the enclosure has become uniform, a balance is reached in which the rates of emission and absorption by any portion are equal. The system may be said to be in *radiative equilibrium*. The peculiar mixture of monochromatic radiations in the enclosure is characterized by a function E_ν giving the density of radiative energy per unit volume, per unit frequency interval (see Fig. 1.1). By analyzing the radiation which streams from an aperture in such an enclosure, experimenters have found that:

(a) E_ν depends only on the frequency ν and the temperature T of the

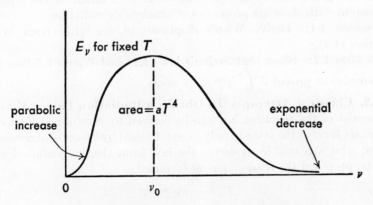

Fig. 1.1. Energy distribution of black body radiation.

enclosure, and is not affected by the shape of the enclosure or the material of which it is made or which it contains:

(1.1) $$E_\nu = f(\nu, T);$$

(b) For small values of ν, E_ν is proportional to ν^2;

(c) At sufficiently high ν, E_ν decreases exponentially as ν increases;

(d) The total amount of radiative energy per unit volume of enclosure is proportional to T^4 (the Stefan-Boltzmann law[2]):

(1.2) $$\int_0^\infty E_\nu \, d\nu = a \cdot T^4.$$

Experimentally, $a = 7.6 \times 10^{-15}$ erg/cc/deg^4.

(e) The frequency ν_0 at which E_ν has its maximum value is propor-

[2] The Stefan-Boltzmann law was deduced experimentally by Stefan in 1879, theoretically by Boltzmann in 1884: J. Stefan, *Wiener Berichte*, **79**, 391 (1879); L. Boltzmann, *Ann. Physik*, **22**, 31 291, 616 (1884).

tional to the absolute temperature (Wien's displacement law):

(1.3) $\nu_0 = bT.$

Experimentally, $b = 1.96\, c \sec^{-1} \deg^{-1}$, where c is the velocity of light *in vacuo*.

(f) The energy density function E_ν may be written in the form (Wien's relation)

(1.4) $E_\nu = \dfrac{\nu^3}{c^2} f\left(\dfrac{\nu}{T}\right).$

This functional relation was suggested by Wien (1864–1928) from thermodynamical arguments.

An acceptable theory of light must lead to a radiation law which is consistent with these six properties of black body radiation.

Problem 1.1:   Derive Wien's displacement law (1.3) from Wien's relation (1.4).

Problem 1.2:   Show that Stefan's law (1.2) and Wien's relation (1.4) are consistent provided $\int_0^\infty x^3 f(x)\, dx$ exists.

1.3. Classical Attempts To Obtain a Radiation Law.   Although properties of the radiation law can be derived by careful measurements, the exact form of the law can only be established by theoretical reasoning. Wien, who was unable to derive the law from thermodynamical arguments, proposed the semi-empirical formula[3]

(1.5) $E_\nu = c_1 \nu^3 e^{-c_2 \nu/T},$

where c_1 and c_2 were to be determined so as to obtain "best fit." It is readily observable that (1.5) satisfies all except the second of the six characteristics of black body radiation listed in Section 1.2 above. Later we shall see that Wien's formula may be regarded as being a mollification of Boltzmann's law for the distribution of independent particles in statistical equilibrium in favor of the wave nature of light. We may here observe that the mere fact that E_ν depends on a wavelike property, the frequency ν, precludes a purely corpuscular explanation of black body radiation. Is a purely wave-theoretical explanation possible?

In view of the successes of Fresnel and Young in explaining interference, diffraction, etc., by means of wave concepts, Lord Rayleigh (John William Strutt, 1842–1919)[4] attempted to obtain a wave-theoretical explanation of black body radiation. His derivation was subsequently simplified by Jeans.[5] The following derivation, which is a composition of

[3] W. Wien, *Ann. Physik*, **58**, 662 (1896).
[4] Lord Rayleigh, *Phil. Mag.*, **49**, 539 (1900); *Nature*, **72**, 54 (1905).
[5] J. H. Jeans, *Phil. Mag.*, **10**, 91 (1905).

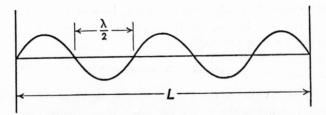

Fig. 1.2. Standing wave in one-space dimension.

the Rayleigh-Jeans derivation and of a quite different derivation given by Max Planck[6] (1858–1947) contains arguments of great importance even though the end result is incorrect.

According to the wave theory of light, when the radiation in an enclosure has reached equilibrium, only standing waves can be present. This assumes of course that the wavelengths involved are small compared to microscopic irregularities in the interior surface of the enclosure. As the first step in deriving the Rayleigh-Jeans formula, we determine the number of modes in which standing waves of transverse vibrations can be present in the enclosure, per unit frequency interval and per unit volume of enclosure.

In Fig. 1.2 we picture a standing wave in one-space dimension. Quite readily we see from this figure that the condition for a standing wave is

$$(1.6) \qquad n \cdot \left(\frac{\lambda}{2}\right) = L$$

where λ is the wavelength and n is a positive integer.

In Fig. 1.3 we picture the intersection of two successive wave fronts

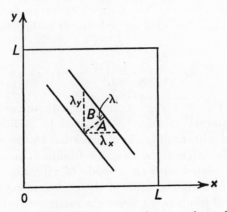

Fig. 1.3. The intersection of two successive wave fronts by a plane.

[6] M. Planck, *Verhandl. deut. physik. Ges.*, **2**, 202, 237 (1900); *Ann. Physik*, **4**, 553, 564, (1901); *Naturwissenschaften*, **31**, 153 (1943).

of a standing wave in a cubic box of edge L, by a plane parallel to one of the faces of the box. Letting A, B, and C be the direction angles of the normal to the wave fronts, we have

(1.7) $\lambda = \lambda_x \cos A = \lambda_y \cos B = \lambda_z \cos C,$

where λ_x, λ_y, and λ_z are the distances between the successive wave fronts, as measured parallel to the x, y, and z axes, respectively. Since

(1.8) $\cos^2 A + \cos^2 B + \cos^2 C = 1,$

this gives

(1.9) $\dfrac{1}{\lambda_x{}^2} + \dfrac{1}{\lambda_y{}^2} + \dfrac{1}{\lambda_z{}^2} = \dfrac{1}{\lambda^2}.$

However, in order that there be standing waves, we must have, as we see from (1.6) and Fig. 1.3,

(1.10) $n_x\left(\dfrac{\lambda_x}{2}\right) = n_y\left(\dfrac{\lambda_y}{2}\right) = n_z\left(\dfrac{\lambda_z}{2}\right) = L,$

where n_x, n_y, and n_z are positive integers. Eliminating λ_x, λ_y, and λ_z from (1.9) and (1.10), and replacing λ by c/ν, we find that

(1.11) $n_x{}^2 + n_y{}^2 + n_z{}^2 = \left(\dfrac{2L\nu}{c}\right)^2.$

Let $N_\nu \cdot d\nu$ be the number of modes of transverse vibration in the frequency interval $d\nu$, per unit volume of enclosure. From (1.11) we see that $L^3 N_\nu \, d\nu$, the number of modes of transverse vibration in the frequency interval $d\nu$, is equal to twice the number of lattice points in one octant of the spherical shell bounded by spheres of radii r and $r + dr$, where $r = 2L\nu/c$. Thus

(1.12) $N_\nu \, d\nu = 2 \cdot \dfrac{1}{8} \cdot \dfrac{4\pi r^2 \, dr}{L^3} = 8\pi \nu^2 \, d\nu/c^3.$

An expression for the energy associated with waves of frequencies in the frequency interval $d\nu$ may be obtained by multiplying the mean energy associated with each mode of vibration by the number of modes of vibration in the interval $d\nu$. In order to obtain an expression for the mean energy associated with each mode of vibration, Planck assumed that the matter forming the walls of the enclosure could be represented by oscillators of all frequencies. Since the oscillators exchange energy via the radiation field, the oscillators are in statistical equilibrium *inter se* when the radiation field is in radiative equilibrium. According to the *Classical Principle of Equipartition of Energy*, with each oscillator there may be associated, on the average, kT ergs of energy. Here k is the Boltzmann constant, 1.371×10^{-16} erg/°C. Planck therefore assumed that with each mode of transverse vibration there is associated, on the average, kT ergs of energy. By this means Planck obtained the Rayleigh-Jeans formula

$$(1.13) \qquad E_\nu \, d\nu = kT \cdot N_\nu \, d\nu = \frac{8\pi\nu^2 kT \, d\nu}{c^3}.$$

Thus the Rayleigh-Jeans formula for black body radiation is obtainable by multiplying the number of modes of transverse vibration, per unit frequency interval, per unit volume of enclosure, by the classical expression kT for the mean energy associated with each mode of vibration.

The Rayleigh-Jeans formula predicts a parabolic increase in the density of black body radiation over the entire frequency scale. Its failure to satisfy experimental requirements at high frequencies is frequently described as "the ultraviolet catastrophe."

Problem 1.3: Obtain N_ν for waves in two space dimensions (e.g., for water waves on a pond). Answer: $N_\nu = 2\pi\nu/c^2$.

Problem 1.4: With which of the six characteristics of black body radiation is Wien's formula (1.5) inconsistent?

Problem 1.5: With which of the six characteristics of black body radiation is the Rayleigh-Jeans formula (1.13) inconsistent?

1.4. Planck's Law of Black Body Radiation. In 1900, Planck, as a consequence of intensive efforts, succeeded in devising a new theory of black body radiation which he called the "quantum theory." The main feature of Planck's theory was his assumption that a "radiation oscillator" of frequency ν could have energy

$$(1.14) \qquad \epsilon_n = nh\nu$$

where n is a nonnegative integer and h is a positive numerical factor. Planck thought that he might be able to derive a satisfactory radiation law by ultimately letting h approach zero, but to his surprise he obtained the law by assigning h a definite positive value:

$$(1.15) \qquad h = 6.5 \times 10^{-27} \text{ erg sec.}$$

Planck obtained an expression for the total number of oscillators of frequency ν by starting with the Boltzmann distribution law, which states that the number $N(\epsilon)$ of independent oscillators of energy ϵ, in statistical equilibrium, is given by

$$(1.16) \qquad N(\epsilon) = Ce^{-\epsilon/kT},$$

where C is a proportionality factor, independent of ϵ. The mean energy of an oscillator of frequency ν is then

$$(1.17) \qquad U(\nu) = \frac{\sum\limits_{n=0}^{\infty} \epsilon_n N(\epsilon_n)}{\sum\limits_{n=0}^{\infty} N(\epsilon_n)} = \frac{h\nu}{e^{h\nu/kT} - 1}.$$

By multiplying $U(\nu)$ by the Rayleigh-Jeans expression (1.12) for $N_\nu \, d\nu$, the number of modes of transverse vibration in the frequency interval $d\nu$, per unit volume of enclosure, Planck obtained

$$(1.18) \quad E_\nu \, d\nu = U(\nu) \cdot N_\nu \, d\nu = \frac{h\nu}{e^{h\nu/kT} - 1} \cdot \frac{8\pi\nu^2 \, d\nu}{c^3} = \frac{8\pi h\nu^3 \, d\nu}{c^3(e^{h\nu/kT} - 1)}.$$

At first, the reaction of physicists to Planck's derivation was lukewarm, and Planck himself retained a cautious attitude for a long time. One unsatisfactory feature of Planck's derivation was the question raised as to how Maxwell's theory of continuous electro-magnetic fields could be correct if radiation is emitted from matter in "quanta." In discussing the "quantum theory" at the Solvay Congress of 1911, Planck stated: "When the emission by an oscillator occurs in 'quanta,' Maxwell's equations retain their validity in surrounding space, but only at a sufficient distance from the oscillator . . . they must be modified inside the oscillator and in its immediate vicinity." Thus Planck's view was that after leaving the oscillator the quanta of radiation merge, giving place to a continuous field. A very few years later Einstein (1879–1955) rejected this view in a revolutionary explanation of the photoelectric effect.

Looking briefly at Wien's formula (1.5) and at the derivation of the Rayleigh-Jeans law (1.13) and of Planck's law (1.18), we see that all three were obtained by multiplying an expression primarily associated with corpuscular concepts by an expression primarily associated with wavelike concepts. However, by making a slight modification in the method of deriving Planck's law, we can more closely portray the present-day theory as to the dual natures of light and of matter.[7] Let us set the number of oscillators of frequency ν, obtained by using the Boltzmann law (1.16) for the distribution of independent oscillators in statistical equilibrium, equal to the number of modes of transverse vibration in the frequency interval $d\nu$:

$$(1.19) \qquad \sum_{n=0}^{\infty} N(\epsilon_n) = N_\nu \, d\nu.$$

Substituting from (1.14) and (1.16) into (1.19), and making elementary

[7] E. Ikenberry, *Am. J. Phys.*, **27**, 359 (1959).

calculations (see Problem 1.6), we obtain an expression for the proportionality factor C in (1.16):

$$(1.20) \qquad C = (1 - e^{-h\nu/kT})N_\nu \, d\nu.$$

For the total energy in the frequency interval $d\nu$, per unit volume of enclosure, we have

$$(1.21) \qquad E_\nu \, d\nu = \sum_{n=0}^{\infty} N(\epsilon_n) \cdot \epsilon_n.$$

Upon substituting from (1.14) and (1.16) into the right-hand member of (1.21) and making further elementary calculations, we obtain

$$(1.22) \qquad E_\nu \, d\nu = \frac{Ch\nu e^{-h\nu/kT} \, d\nu}{(1 - e^{-h\nu/kT})^2}.$$

We may eliminate the proportionality factor C from (1.22) by means of (1.20). When we then use the Rayleigh-Jeans expression (1.12) for $N_\nu \, d\nu$, we readily obtain Planck's radiation law (1.18).

Problem 1.6: Verify the calculations in obtaining (1.18), (1.20), and (1.22). Hint:

$$\sum_{n=0}^{\infty} x^n = \frac{1}{1-x}, \quad \sum_{n=0}^{\infty} nx^n = \frac{x}{(1-x)^2}, \quad |x| < 1.$$

Problem 1.7: Show that Planck's formula (1.18) is approximated by the Rayleigh-Jeans formula (1.13) when $h\nu/kT \ll 1$.

Problem 1.8: Show that Planck's formula (1.18) is approximated by Wien's formula (1.5) when $h\nu/kT \gg 1$. What values must be given to c_1 and c_2 in Wien's formula? Answer: $c_1 = 8\pi h/c^3$, $c_2 = h/k$.

Problem 1.9: Show that Planck's law (1.18) is consistent with the six experimentally observed properties of black body radiation (Section 1.2).

1.5. Determination of Planck's Constant from Radiation Data. Experimental determination of the proportionality factor a in Stefan's fourth power law (1.2), or of the factor b in Wien's displacement law (1.3), gives a means of obtaining the numerical value of the universal constant h in Planck's radiation law (1.18).

Upon substituting from Planck's radiation law (1.18) into Stefan's law (1.2), and changing the variable of integration from ν to $x = h\nu/kT$, we obtain

$$(1.23) \qquad \int_0^{\infty} E_\nu \, d\nu = \frac{8\pi k^4 T^4}{c^3 h^3} \int_0^{\infty} \frac{x^3 \, dx}{e^x - 1} = aT^4.$$

The integration to be performed is not elementary, but it may be shown that the integral over x is equal to $\pi^4/15$. Hence, from (1.23),

$$(1.24) \qquad h = \frac{2\pi k}{c}\, (\pi^2 k/15a)^{\frac{1}{3}}.$$

Using experimentally determined values of a, c, and k, we obtain $h = 6.55 \times 10^{-27}$ erg sec.

To obtain the numerical value of h from Wien's displacement law (1.3), we must find the value of ν at which E_ν reaches its maximum value. Writing Planck's law (1.18) in the form

$$(1.25) \qquad E_\nu = \frac{8\pi k^3 T^3 x^3}{h^2 c^3 (e^x - 1)},\ x = \frac{h\nu}{kT},$$

and differentiating logarithmically, we obtain

$$(1.26) \qquad \frac{\partial}{\partial \nu}\, (\ln E_\nu) = \left(\frac{3}{x} - \frac{e^x}{e^x - 1}\right) \cdot \frac{h}{kT}.$$

From (1.26) we find that E_ν reaches its maximum at a value $\nu_0 = kTx_0/h$ where x_0 satisfies

$$(1.27) \qquad 1 - e^{-x_0} = \tfrac{1}{3}x_0.$$

Numerical solution of (1.27) gives $x_0 = 2.82$. Hence $\nu_0 = 2.82kT/h$. Substituting into Wien's displacement law (1.3), we obtain

$$(1.28) \qquad h = \frac{2.82k}{b}.$$

Using experimentally determined values of b and k, we obtain $h = 6.63 \times 10^{-27}$ erg sec.

Planck's constant can also be determined by measurements of the photoelectric effect and from spectroscopic data. One of the best determinations, based on statistical analysis of spectroscopic measurements, is

$$(1.29) \qquad h = (6.62363 \pm .00016) \times 10^{-27} \text{ erg sec}.$$

Problem 1.10: It is customary to measure the energy density of black body radiation with respect to wavelength rather than frequency. Setting $E_\nu|d\nu| = E_\lambda|d\lambda|$, $\nu = c/\lambda$, in Planck's radiation law (1.18), obtain E_λ. Answer:

$$(1.30) \qquad E_\lambda = \frac{8\pi hc}{\lambda^5 (e^{hc/\lambda kT} - 1)}.$$

Problem 1.11: Let λ_m be the value of λ which maximizes E_λ, (1.30). Show that

$$(1.31) \qquad \lambda_m T = 0.2014hc/k.$$

Problem 1.12: Calculate h from (1.31) and the experimentally observed relation

(1.32) $$\lambda_m T = 0.288 \text{ cm } °C.$$

Answer: $h = 6.62 \times 10^{-27}$ erg sec.

1.6. The Photoelectric Effect. The photoelectric effect is a phenomenon in which radiative energy is transferred to bound electrons, liberat-

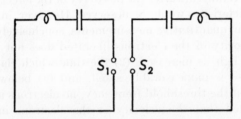

Fig. 1.4. Schema of Hertz's experiment.

ing them from atoms in a metallic surface. The effect was discovered by Heinrich Rudolf Hertz[8] (1857–1894) in 1888, in the same experiments in which he discovered radio waves. He was primarily interested in the radio waves, and did not study the secondary effect further. A schema of Hertz's momentous experiment is given in Fig. 1.4. Hertz observed that a spark across S_1 produced a spark across S_2 if either the two circuits are tuned or if light from S_1 falls upon the terminals of S_2. The photoelectric effect was rediscovered in 1888 by Wilhelm Hallwachs[9] (1859–1922) to whom credit for the initial discovery is frequently given, due to his careful study of the phenomenon.

A simplified diagram of a modern arrangement to illustrate the photoelectric effect is given in Fig. 1.5. It is observed that current flows

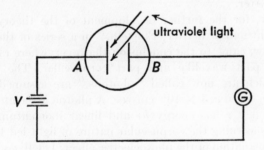

Fig. 1.5. The photoelectric effect.

[8] H. Hertz, *Ann. Physik,* **31,** 983 (1887).

[9] W. L. F. Hallwachs, *Ann. Physik,* **33,** 301 (1888); **37,** 666 (1889); *Lichtelektrizität,* Leipzig, 1914.

through G when terminal A is connected to the negative terminal of V, as illustrated, or when A is connected to the positive terminal, so long as V does not exceed a certain stopping potential V_0.

According to classical theory, (1) the velocity of the electrons liberated at A should increase as the intensity of the light is increased, (2) a measurable time should elapse after A is illuminated before a current is observed, and (3) the effect should be observed with light of any frequency. For several years after the discovery of the effect it was assumed that these characteristics would be observed. However, in 1902 Lenard,[10] by making careful quantitative measurements, conclusively demonstrated that (1) the velocity of the electrons liberated does not increase as the intensity of the light is increased, (2) the time which elapses before the effect is observed is immeasurably small, and (3) below a certain frequency, ν_0, called the threshhold frequency, no electrons are emitted. He also demonstrated that the velocity of the electrons increases as the frequency of the incident light is increased and that the current increases with increasing light intensity. Schaefer[11] gives calculations of the time expected, according to classical theory, before the effect should be observed. For a particular case he calculates 11.5 days.

The wave theory of light provides us with no explanation of the observed characteristics of the photoelectric effect. According to the wave theory, the energy of an incident wave increases with its intensity, and so a more intense wave should liberate electrons with greater velocities. Furthermore, according to this theory the energy is distributed continuously over the surface of the wave front, implying a delay time which should increase indefinitely as the intensity of the light is reduced. These conclusions from the wave theory are changed by Planck's introduction of energy quanta in his theory of black body radiation. Recall that Planck believed that radiation is continuous except in the immediate vicinity of matter.

Fortunately, for the further development of the theory of the dual natures of light and of matter, Einstein,[12] in a series of theoretical tests of Planck's law, came to the conclusion that everywhere radiation has a dual nature, part wavelike and part corpuscular. The corpuscles of radiation, which are now called "photons," are assumed to move *in vacuo* with the speed c, 3×10^{10} cm/sec. A photon associated with radiation of frequency ν has energy $h\nu$ and linear momentum $h\nu/c$. These conclusions concerning the corpuscular nature of light led Einstein to an immediate explanation of the photoelectric effect: Let W equal the energy

[10] P. Lenard, *Ann. Physik,* **2,** 359 (1900).

[11] C. Schaefer, *Einführung in die theoretische Physik,* Walter de Gruyter, 1937, Bd. 3, T. II, S. 7.

[12] A. Einstein, *Ann. Physik,* **17,** 132 (1905).

required to free an electron from a metallic surface. The energy $h\nu - W$ is available, when a photon "hits" the electron, to give it kinetic energy $mv^2/2$, where m is the mass of the electron and v is its speed. We then have

(1.33) $$\tfrac{1}{2}mv^2 = h\nu - W.$$

Electrons for which W is smallest are liberated with the greatest speed:

(1.34) $$\tfrac{1}{2}mv_{max}^2 = h\nu - W_{min} = h(\nu - \nu_0)$$

where $\nu_0 = W_{min}/h =$ the "threshold frequency." Let V_0 be the minimum retarding potential required to stop all electrons. Then

(1.35) $$eV_0 = \tfrac{1}{2}mv_{max}^2 = h(\nu - \nu_0).$$

From (1.35) we see that a plot of V_0 as a function of ν should be a straight line with slope h/e. This gives a direct experimental method for

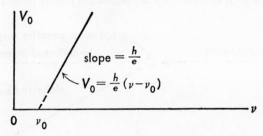

Fig. 1.6. Plot of stopping potential *vs.* frequency of incident light in the photoelectric effect.

determining h/e, from which h may be calculated, e already being known. In 1907 Joffé,[13] using several metals, obtained by this method values of h between 2.2×10^{-27} and 3.5×10^{-27}. In 1916, Robert Andrews Millikan[14] made very precise measurements, obtaining, with Li, $h/e = 1.379 \times 10^{-17}$ and, with Na, $h/e = 1.375 \times 10^{-27}$. Using $e = 4.774 \times 10^{-10}$, we obtain $h = 6.557 \times 10^{-27}$ erg sec.

Problem 1.13: Explain how Duane and Hunt[15] determined the value of h from spectroscopic data.

1.7. The Compton Effect. When a beam of X-rays strikes a carbon scatterer, such as a piece of graphite or paraffin, there may be observed two secondary beams, an undeflected beam of the frequency ν of the

[13] A. Joffé, *Ann. Physik*, **24**, 939 (1907).

[14] R. A. Millikan, *Phys. Rev.*, **4**, 73 (1914); **6**, 55 (1915); **7**, 355 (1916); *Autobiography*, Prentice-Hall, 1950, Ch. 9 and App. B.

[15] W. Duane and F. L. Hunt, *Phys. Rev.*, **6**, 166 (1915); F. C. Blake and W. Duane, *Phys. Rev.*, **10**, 624 (1927); see also: A. H. Compton and S. K. Allison, *X-Rays in Theory and Experiment*, second edition, Van Nostrand, 1935, pp. 39–40; G. L. Clark, *Applied X-Rays*, fourth edition, McGraw-Hill, 1955, pp. 109–10; H. Semat, *Introduction to Atomic and Nuclear Physics*, Rinehart, 1954, pp. 134–7.

incident X-ray beam and a deflected or scattered beam of frequency $\nu' < \nu$. In the Compton effect we are interested in the deflected beam for which it is observed that

$$(1.36) \qquad \frac{c}{\nu'} - \frac{c}{\nu} = .024(1 - \cos \varphi) \times 10^{-8} \text{ cms.}$$

where φ is the angle between the undeflected and the deflected beams (see Fig. 1.7). This effect was first satisfactorily explained by A. H. Compton[16] and by P. Debye[17] in 1923 by applying classical mechanics to the extreme quantum concept of radiant energy. The collision between a photon and an electron is governed by the two basic laws of classical mechanics: (1) conservation of energy and (2) conservation of momentum.

An electron which is struck by a photon is ejected from the nucleus to

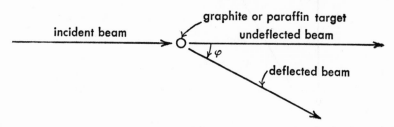

Fig. 1.7. The Compton effect.

which it is attached with such great velocity that we must use the relativistic energy-momentum relation

$$(1.37) \qquad E^2 = m_0^2 c^4 + p^2 c^2,$$

where m_0 is the "rest mass" of the electron and p is its momentum. We neglect the initial kinetic energy of the electron and the binding energy between the electron and the nucleus to which it is initially attached. For convenience we display the energies and momenta of a photon and an electron before and after collision in tabular form:

		Photon	*Electron*
Energy:			
	before collision................	$h\nu$	$m_0 c^2$
	after collision................	$h\nu'$	E
Momentum:			
	before collision................	$h\nu/c$	0
	after collision................	$h\nu'/c$	p

[16] A. H. Compton, *Phys. Rev.*, **21**, 483 (1923).
[17] P. Debye, *Physik. Z.*, **24**, 161 (1923).

Conservation of energy implies

(1.38) $$h\nu + m_0c^2 = h\nu' + E.$$

Conservation of momentum, when expressed in terms of components parallel and perpendicular to the direction of the incident beam, implies

(1.39)

(a) $$\frac{h\nu}{c} = \frac{h\nu'}{c}\cos\varphi + p\cos\theta,$$

(b) $$0 = -\frac{h\nu'}{c}\sin\varphi + p\sin\theta,$$

where θ is the angle through which the electron is deflected from the direction of the undeflected beam and φ is the angle between the deflected and the undeflected beams (see Fig. 1.8).

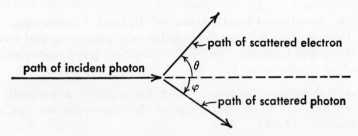

Fig. 1.8. Geometry of the Compton effect.

Eliminating θ from the momentum conservation equations (1.39) by means of the trigonometric identity $\cos^2\theta + \sin^2\theta = 1$, we find that

(1.40) $$\left(\frac{h}{c}\right)^2(\nu - \nu'\cos\varphi)^2 + \left(\frac{h}{c}\right)^2(\nu'\sin\varphi)^2 = p^2.$$

We now substitute for E from (1.38) and for p^2 from (1.40) into the relativistic energy-momentum relation (1.37), obtaining

(1.41) $$(h\nu - h\nu' + m_0c^2)^2 = m_0^2c^4 + h^2(\nu - \nu'\cos\varphi)^2 + h^2(\nu'\sin\varphi)^2.$$

This is reduced by a little algebra to

(1.42) $$m_0c^2(\nu - \nu') = h\nu\nu'(1 - \cos\varphi).$$

This is readily seen to agree with (1.36), even to the numerical factor. The relation (1.42) is usually written in the form

(1.43) $$\lambda' - \lambda = \lambda_0(1 - \cos\varphi)$$

where

(1.44) $$\lambda_0 = \frac{h}{m_0c} = 2.426 \times 10^{-10}\ \text{cm}$$

is called the *Compton wavelength*.

The Compton effect is often regarded as providing the most direct possible evidence for the existence of light quanta. Paradoxically, this effect has been observed in conjunction with other phenomena, such as Bragg reflection, which can be explained only by the wave theory of light. This is another example of the wave-particle duality, one of the basic principles of quantum mechanics.

In 1925 Compton and Simon,[18] using a Wilson cloud chamber, revealed the existence of the knock-on electron photographically. They verified that it is projected in the direction predicted by Compton's formulas.

Problem 1.14:   Compare and contrast the roles of conservation of energy and momentum in the photoelectric and the Compton effects. Prove that photon and electron alone cannot conserve momentum when the photon is entirely absorbed by the electron, giving up all of its energy to the electron.[19]

1.8. de Broglie's Classification of Optical Phenomena. Professor Louis de Broglie[20] (b. 1892) in his very interesting and readable book *Matter and Light, the New Physics* classifies optical phenomena into five leading groups, namely:

1. Neutral phenomena (those which are more or less equally well explained by either the wave concept or the corpuscular concept, or by a combination of both):
    (a) motion of light in a straight line, e.g. luminous rays and reflection by mirrors,
    (b) refraction,
    (c) radiation pressure,
    (d) various Doppler effects,
    (e) black body radiation;
2. Scalar wave phenomena (those which are specifically undulatory):
    (a) interference and diffraction;
3. Vectorial luminous phenomena (those which are undulatory):
    (a) polarization, double refraction;
4. Electro-optic phenomena (all optical phenomena which reveal the electromagnetic character of light):
    (a) Faraday, Zeeman, Kerr, Cotton, Mouton, and other effects;
5. Purely corpuscular phenomena:
    (a) photoelectric effect,
    (b) Compton and Raman effects.

Maxwell's electromagnetic wave theory completely fails in leading to an

---

[18] A. H. Compton and A. W. Simon, *Phys., Rev.*, **26,** 289 (1925).

[19] See C. D. Peaslee and H. Mueller, *Elements of Modern Physics*, Prentice-Hall, 1955, p. 205.

[20] L. de Broglie, *Matter and Light*, Dover, 1955, pp. 147–57.

explanation of phenomena in the fifth group and must be combined with the particle concept to explain satisfactorily black body radiation (see Fig. 1.9).

From the derivations of the Planck radiation law (1.18) and its limiting forms, the Rayleigh-Jeans formula (1.13) and Wien's formula (5.5), we reach the conclusions that the wave nature of light predominates when $h\nu \ll kT$, the corpuscular nature predominates when $h\nu \gg kT$. However, it can never be said that "light is entirely wavelike" or that "light is entirely corpuscular." It is better to regard these psychologically conflicting aspects as potentialities whose realization depends upon the experimental arrangement.

Even with circumstances under which only Maxwell's wave theory is adequate the photon density, that is, the number of photons per cc associ-

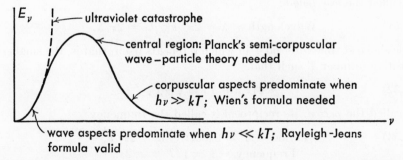

Fig. 1.9. Regions of validity of the wave, wave-particle, and the particle theories of black-body radiation.

ated with an electromagnetic wave, can be calculated. According to the wave theory, the energy density is $(E^2 + H^2)/8\pi$, where **E** and **H** are the electric and magnetic fields. We may therefore write, for a monochromatic field of frequency ν,

$$(1.45) \qquad N h\nu = \frac{1}{8\pi} \overline{(E^2 + H^2)}^t$$

where N is the number of photons per cc and the time average is taken over one period, for example.

Problem 1.15: Calculate the number of photons emitted per second by a 10 watt lamp which emits monochromatic light (green) of wavelength 6000 Å. Answer: 0.3×10^{20}.

1.9. Basic Wave Relations. It is easily verified that

$$(1.46) \quad \psi = C \cos (kx - \omega t + \delta),\ C \sin (kx - \omega t + \delta),\ C e^{\pm i(kx - \omega t + \delta)}$$

satisfy the classical wave equation

(1.47)
$$\frac{\partial^2 \psi}{\partial t^2} = c^2 \frac{\partial^2 \psi}{\partial x^2}$$

if

(1.48)
$$\omega^2 = c^2 k^2.$$

The argument $(kx - \omega t + \delta)$ in (1.46) is called the *phase* of the wave:

(1.49)
$$\text{Phase} = \varphi = kx - \omega t + \delta.$$

The shortest distance λ in which ψ repeats itself, that is, the smallest positive number λ such that

(1.50)
$$\psi(x + \lambda, t) \equiv \psi(x, t)$$

is called the *wavelength:*

(1.51)
$$\text{Wavelength} = \lambda = 2\pi/|k|; \; |k| = 2\pi/\lambda.$$

The shortest time interval T in which ψ repeats itself, that is, the smallest positive number T such that

(1.52)
$$\psi(x, t + T) \equiv \psi(x, t),$$

is called the *period;* its reciprocal is called the frequency:

(1.53)
$$\text{Period} = T = 2\pi/\omega, \qquad \omega = 2\pi/T,$$
$$\text{Frequency} = \nu = 1/T = \omega/2\pi.$$

The *circular frequency* $\omega = 2\pi\nu$ may be called the "frequency" without confusion. We adopt the sign convention that ω is always positive. This is not restrictive since we allow k, the *wave number*, to be either positive or negative.

Any one of the functions (1.46) represents a *monochromatic* wave: a wave composed of a single frequency. When k is positive, (1.46) represents a monochromatic wave traveling in the positive x direction; when k is negative, (1.46) represents a monochromatic wave traveling in the negative x direction. The phase velocity, defined by the equation

(1.54)
$$V_p = \left(\frac{dx}{dt}\right)_{\varphi=\text{constant}},$$

is the velocity of an object which "rides the wave." From (1.49) and (1.54) we find that

(1.55)
$$V_p = \frac{\omega}{k}.$$

If the phase velocity depends on the frequency, waves of different frequencies travel with different velocities. In this case there is *dispersion.*

A medium is *dispersive* or *nondispersive* to waves according to whether the phase velocity of the waves in the medium depends or does not depend on the frequency. The *dispersion relation*, the functional relation between ω and k, for a particular kind of wave in a particular medium, is very important in any study of wave motion.

Problem 1.16: Obtain the dispersion relation for transverse vibrations of a bar, for which the partial differential equation is

$$\frac{\partial^2 \psi}{\partial t^2} + a^4 \frac{\partial^4 \psi}{\partial x^4} = 0. \qquad \text{Answer: } \omega^2 = a^4 k^4.$$

Problem 1.17: In some applications it is convenient to permit k or ω to be complex-valued. Using the exponential form in (1.46), obtain the dispersion relation for waves along a frictionally damped string, for which the partial differential equation is

$$S \frac{\partial^2 \psi}{\partial x^2} = \rho \frac{\partial^2 \psi}{\partial t^2} + r \frac{\partial \psi}{\partial t}.$$

Observe from the dispersion relation that ω and k cannot both be real valued. Answer: $Sk^2 = \rho \omega^2 + ir\omega$.

1.10. Basic Photon Relations. We have seen that it is necessary to consider both the wavelike and the corpuscular natures of light in order to explain certain electromagnetic phenomena. With monochromatic waves of frequency ν and wavelength λ we associate photons of definite energy E and momentum p by the relations

$$(1.56) \qquad \text{Photon energy} = E = h\nu = \hbar\omega,$$

$$(1.57) \qquad \text{Photon momentum} = p = h/\lambda = \hbar|k|,$$

where $\hbar = h/2\pi$. These relations are readily seen to be consistent with the relations

$$(1.58) \qquad \lambda\nu = c, \qquad E = cp,$$

in the first of which wave properties λ and ν appear and in the second of which corpuscular properties E and p appear.

The relativistic relations between energy, momentum, mass, and velocity of a free particle are

$$(1.59) \qquad E^2 = m_0^2 c^4 + p^2 c^2,$$

$$(1.60) \qquad E = mc^2,$$

$$(1.61) \qquad p = mv,$$

where m_0, the "rest mass," is the mass measured by an observer moving with the particle, that is, in a reference frame in which v, the velocity of the particle, is zero. Comparison of the energy-momentum relation for photons, $E = cp$, with the energy-momentum relation (1.59) for free particles, leads us to consider a photon as being a free particle with zero rest mass: $m_0 = 0$ for a photon, although there is no physical reference frame in which a photon is at rest. The "equivalent" mass of a photon is $h\nu/c^2$.

In particle mechanics, energies are additive. The purely corpuscular theory of light requires additivity of energy, as implied by the equation $E = h\nu$. In the wave theory, the energy densities associated with two electromagnetic fields are

$$(1.62) \qquad \mathcal{E}_1 = \frac{1}{8\pi}(E_1^2 + H_1^2), \qquad \mathcal{E}_2 = \frac{1}{8\pi}(E_2^2 + H_2^2).$$

The fields are additive:

$$(1.63) \qquad \mathbf{E} = \mathbf{E}_1 + \mathbf{E}_2, \qquad \mathbf{H} = \mathbf{H}_1 + \mathbf{H}_2,$$

but, generally speaking, the energy densities are not additive:

$$(1.64) \qquad \mathcal{E} = \frac{1}{8\pi}(E^2 + H^2) \neq \mathcal{E}_1 + \mathcal{E}_2.$$

This deviation from additivity of energy densities is known as *interference*. With special laboratory arrangements, interference between two light sources may be inappreciable. Then the energy densities are additive, and we say that the sources are *incoherent*. More frequently, laboratory arrangements are specially designed with *coherent* sources to study interference phenomena.

Since the corpuscular theory implies additivity of energy, this theory of light is applicable only in case of noninteracting photons, as in the Compton and photoelectric effects, and in the case of incoherent sources, as in black body radiation. Interference phenomena cannot be explained by a purely corpuscular theory, nor can some phenomena in which there is no interference be explained by a purely wave theory.

1.11. Superposition of Waves To Form Wave Packets. In order to gain some insight into the compatibility of the wave and corpuscular theories of light it is necessary to examine in some detail the superposition of waves. We inquire first as to whether a monochromatic wave exhibits any corpuscular properties. Let us consider such a wave, for which the wave number k and the frequency ω have specified values, k_0 and ω_0. From our knowledge of the function

$$(1.65) \qquad \psi = C \cos(k_0 x - \omega_0 t + \delta_0), \ C > 0,$$

which may be taken as a *prototype* for all monochromatic waves, we see (Fig. 1.10) that a monochromatic wave is in space (at a fixed time) and in time (at a fixed place) infinitely and monotonously extended. On the other hand a corpuscle (for the present considerations, a photon) according to ordinary concepts is highly localized in space and in time. We thus observe: a monochromatic wave has none of the properties ordinarily associated with corpuscles.

By superposing two or more waves we can get away from the extreme

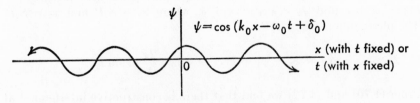

$$\psi = \cos (k_0 x - \omega_0 t + \delta_0)$$

x (with *t* fixed) or
t (with *x* fixed)

Fig. 1.10. A monochromatic wave.

monotony of a single wave. Let us begin by considering two monochromatic prototype waves with different phases and amplitudes:

$$(1.66) \qquad \begin{aligned} \psi_1 &= C_1 \cos \varphi_1, \ \varphi_1 = k_1 x - \omega_1 t + \delta_1, \ C_1 > 0, \\ \psi_2 &= C_2 \cos \varphi_2, \ \varphi_2 = k_2 x - \omega_2 t + \delta_2, \ C_2 > 0. \end{aligned}$$

Superposed, these give

$$(1.67) \qquad \psi = \psi_1 + \psi_2 = C_1 \cos \varphi_1 + C_2 \cos \varphi_2.$$

Cases of special interest are those in which $\varphi_2 = \varphi_1 \pm m\pi$ where m is an integer. If m is an even integer, $2n$, $\cos \varphi_2 = \cos \varphi_1$ and

$$(1.68) \qquad \psi = (C_1 + C_2) \cos \varphi_1.$$

In this case, the amplitudes add, the waves being *in phase*. On the other hand, if m is an odd integer, $m = 2n + 1$, $\cos \varphi_2 = - \cos \varphi_1$ and

$$(1.69) \qquad \psi = (C_1 - C_2) \cos \varphi_1.$$

In this case the amplitudes subtract, the waves being *out of phase*. Summarizing, there is *constructive interference* with the amplitudes' adding when the phase difference

$$(1.70) \qquad \Delta\varphi \equiv \varphi_2 - \varphi_1 = 2n\pi,$$

and there is *destructive interference* with the amplitudes' subtracting when the phase difference

$$(1.71) \qquad \Delta\varphi \equiv \varphi_2 - \varphi_1 = (2n + 1)\pi.$$

An observation of interference in agreement with the above results is quite reasonably construed as evidence of the wave nature of light. One of the first such experiments was performed by Thomas Young who, at the beginning of the nineteenth century, discovered that in certain circumstances two beams of light can enfeeble each other. Young's discovery temporarily resolved the conflict between the disciples of Newton, who espoused the corpuscular concept, and the adherents of Huyghens, who espoused the wave theory of light. In Young's experiment (see Fig. 1.11) coherent beams from a common source S pass through slits S_1 and S_2 and arrive at a point P on a photographic plate with phases $\varphi_1 = kx_1 - \omega t + \delta$ and $\varphi_2 = kx_2 - \omega t + \delta$, where $x_1 = S_1P$ and $x_2 = S_2P$. The phase difference at P is

$$(1.72) \qquad \Delta\varphi \equiv \varphi_2 - \varphi_1 = k(x_2 - x_1) = \frac{2\pi}{\lambda}(d \sin \theta).$$

From (1.70) and (1.72) we find that there is constructive interference at

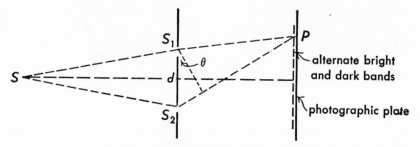

Fig. 1.11. Schema of Young's experiment.

P if $d \sin \theta = n\lambda$. Hence centers of bright bands are expected to be located on the photographic plate at angles θ_n determined by

$$(1.73) \qquad d \sin \theta_n = n\lambda.$$

Similarly centers of dark bands are expected at angles θ_n determined by

$$(1.74) \qquad d \sin \theta_n = (n + \tfrac{1}{2})\lambda.$$

Let us now consider the result of superposing two monochromatic waves which differ in wave numbers k and frequencies ω, but, for simplicity, have the same amplitudes. From (1.66), with $C_1 = C_2 = C$, and from the trigonometric identity

$$(1.75) \qquad \cos \varphi_1 + \cos \varphi_2 = 2 \cos \tfrac{1}{2}(\varphi_2 - \varphi_1) \cos \tfrac{1}{2}(\varphi_2 + \varphi_1),$$

we obtain

$$(1.76) \qquad \psi \equiv \psi_1 + \psi_2 = 2C \cos (k_g x - \omega_g t + \delta_g) \cos (k_w x - \omega_w t + \delta_w),$$

where

$$(1.77) \quad \begin{array}{llll} \text{(a)} & k_g = \tfrac{1}{2}(k_2 - k_1), & k_w = \tfrac{1}{2}(k_2 + k_1), \\ \text{(b)} & \omega_g = \tfrac{1}{2}(\omega_2 - \omega_1), & \omega_w = \tfrac{1}{2}(\omega_2 + \omega_1), \\ \text{(c)} & \delta_g = \tfrac{1}{2}(\delta_2 - \delta_1), & \delta_w = \tfrac{1}{2}(\delta_2 + \delta_1). \end{array}$$

The first cosine factor in (1.76) contains phase number and frequency differences k_g and ω_g, hence it varies slowly in space (at a given time) and slowly in time (at a given place). The second cosine factor in (1.76) contains phase number and frequency sums k_w and ω_w, hence it varies rapidly in space (at a given time) and rapidly in time (at a given place). A graph (Fig. 1.12) of the composite wave may be obtained by the method of multiplication of ordinates. The slowly variable cosine curve with amplitude $2C$ is drawn. Then a rapdily variable cosinelike curve is inscribed in it and its image on the horizontal axis as envelope. Thus there

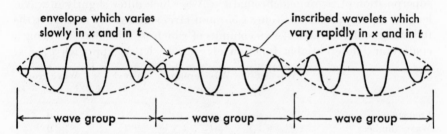

Fig. 1.12. Wave groups formed by the superposition of two waves with equal amplitudes but different in wave numbers and frequencies.

appear *groups of wavelets*. To a certain degree we may associate corpuscular aspects with the groups of wavelets.

By continuing thus, superposing more and more waves with properly chosen frequencies, wave numbers, initial phases, and amplitudes, we may ultimately obtain wave groups of almost any desired shape. The groups tend to be repetitiously, even periodically, distributed in space and in time, as long as we restrict ourselves to the superposition of a discrete set of waves (Fourier series and almost periodic functions). In order to represent a single corpuscle, we need a wave which is highly localized in a definite region of space (at a given time) and in a definite interval of time (at a given place). To obtain such, it is necessary to superpose a continuous set of waves rather than a discrete set. Then we may obtain a *wave packet:* a group of waves of different wave numbers and frequencies, with phases and amplitudes so adjusted that they interfere constructively over only a small region of space (at a given time) and over a short interval of time (at a given place), outside of which they interfere destructively. The Fourier integral theorem provides the requisite tool for the mathematical representation of such groups of waves. The possibility of representing highly localized wave packets as super-positions of monochromatic waves makes compatible not only the corpuscular and the wave theories of light, but also the corpuscular and the wave theories of matter.

Problem 1.18: Describe the interference pattern obtained when light passes through a single slit.[21]

1.12. Group and Phase Velocities. In general, the waves in a group do not all travel with the same velocity. At the present we are interested in the concept of *group velocity*. It is to be realized that this concept loses its significance when a group loses its identity due to dispersion. There is dispersion unless, as in the case of light *in vacuo*, all waves travel with the same velocity.

A formula for the group velocity may be obtained by considering the superposition of two monochromatic waves which differ slightly in wavelengths and frequencies. From (1.55) and (1.77) we readily construct the following table, in the last two columns of which we consider ω as being a continuous, differentiable function of k as we let k_2 approach $k_1 = k$:

	Wavelet $k_2 \neq k_1$	Wave group $k_2 \neq k_1$	Wavelet $k_2 \to k_1 = k$	Wave group $k_2 \to k_1 = k$
Frequency	$\frac{1}{2}(\omega_2 + \omega_1)$	$\frac{1}{2}(\omega_2 - \omega_1)$	ω	0
Wave number	$\frac{1}{2}(k_2 + k_1)$	$\frac{1}{2}(k_2 - k_1)$	k	0
Velocity	$\dfrac{\omega_2 + \omega_1}{k_2 + k_1}$	$\dfrac{\omega_2 - \omega_1}{k_2 - k_1}$	ω/k	$d\omega/dk$

The last two entries in the table serve to define the *phase velocity* V_p and the *group velocity* V_g:

$$(1.78) \qquad V_p = \frac{\omega}{k}; \qquad V_g = \frac{d\omega}{dk}.$$

For light waves *in vacuo*, $\omega^2 = c^2 k^2$ and $V_p = V_g = \pm c$. Light waves travel *in vacuo* without dispersion, all waves traveling with the same velocity and the velocity of a group being equal to the velocity of a single wave.

Problem 1.19: Show that

$$(1.79) \qquad V_g = -\lambda^2 \frac{d(V_p/\lambda)}{d\lambda} = V_p - \lambda \frac{dV_p}{d\lambda}.$$

Problem 1.20: For transverse vibrations of a bar, $\omega^2 = a^4 k^4$ (see Problem 1.16). Show that $V_g = 2V_p$.

Problem 1.21: For gravity controlled water waves, $V_p = \sqrt{\dfrac{g\lambda}{2\pi}}$.

---

[21] See M. Born, *Atomic Physics*, sixth edition, Hafner, 1957, p. 87.

Show that $V_p = 2V_g$.

Problem 1.22: For surface tension controlled water waves, $V_p = \sqrt{\dfrac{2\pi T}{\lambda \rho}}$ (approximately). Show that $V_g = 3V_p/2$.

1.13. Incomplete Determinism of Both Position and Momentum.

Adopting for the present the corpuscular theory of light, we may consider Young's experiment as an attempt to measure the y coordinate (Fig. 1.13) of a photon. We do not know which of the two slits any particular photon passes through, whence the indeterminacy in y is $\Delta y = d$, where d is the distance between the slits. Furthermore, we do not know at what angle the photon emerges from the slit through which it passes, since we do not know where it appears in the diffraction pattern. Whatever the angle of emergence, $p_y = p \sin \theta$. Assuming for simplicity

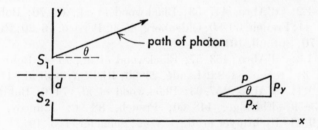

Fig. 1.13. Photon interpretation of Young's experiment.

that the wavelength λ and hence the momentum $p = h/\lambda$ are accurately known, we then have

(1.80) $$\Delta p_y = p \Delta \sin \theta.$$

The photon may have emerged at any angle θ, but there is a high probability that it emerged near a maximum of intensity, $\theta = \theta_n$, where, according to (1.73), $\sin \theta_n = n\lambda/d$. Since we do not know near which maximum of intensity it emerged, we see that

(1.81) $$\Delta \sin \theta \geq \sin \theta_{n+1} - \sin \theta_n = \lambda/d.$$

From (1.80) and (1.81) we find that

(1.82) $$\Delta p_y \geq p\lambda/d.$$

Hence, since $p = h/\lambda$ and $d = \Delta y$,

(1.83) $$\Delta y \, \Delta p_y \geq h.$$

The result (1.83) serves to illustrate the very important *Heisenberg Uncertainty Principle*:[22] In any measurement of a position coordinate of a particle there is an uncertainty in the momentum transferred to the particle by its interaction with the measuring apparatus such that the

[22] W. Heisenberg, *Z. Physik*, **43**, 172 (1927).

product of the uncertainties in the position coordinate and in its conjugate momentum component has a positive lower bound.

The numerical value of this positive lower bound depends upon the statistical definition of uncertainties in measurements. When the uncertainty in an observation is defined as the root mean square deviation of a set of observations from their mean, it may be shown that

$$(1.84) \qquad \Delta x \, \Delta p_x \geq \tfrac{1}{2}\hbar, \; \Delta y \, \Delta p_y \geq \tfrac{1}{2}\hbar, \; \Delta z \, \Delta p_z \geq \tfrac{1}{2}\hbar.$$

These are the famous *Heisenberg Uncertainty Relations*.

1.14. References for Supplementary Reading.

Section 1.1: d'Abro, 1–13; Blackwood et al., 1–4; Dushman, 1–19; French, 28–30; Jauncey, 1–29; Oldenberg, 1–12, 83–4; Richtmyer et al., 5–48; Shankland, 1–3.

Section 1.2: d'Abro, 447–53; Blackwood et al., 66–70; Bohm, 5–7; Born, 238–41; French, 69–80; Oldenberg, 85–9; Persico, 16–20; Richtmyer et al., 66–70; Sproull, 101–6.

Section 1.3: d'Abro, 453–57; Blackwood et al., 71–4; Bohm, 15–18; Born, 241–3; French, 84–88; Landé, 23–30; Richtmyer et al., 117–24.

Section 1.4: d'Abro, 457–63; Blackwood et al., 74–6; Bohm 18–22; Born, 243–59; Eldridge, 148–60; French, 88–96; Jauncey, 174–79; Houston, 9–11; Richtmyer et al., 124–32; Schaefer, 1–5, 19–23.

Section 1.5: Blackwood et al., 76–77; French, 88–95; Jauncey, 174–9.

Section 1.6: d'Abro, 467–69; Blackwood et al., 77–90; Bohm, 23–6; Born, 81–4; Dushman, 106–10; French, 45–6; Houston, 11–12; Jauncey, 203–12; Oldenberg, 79–83; Persico, 20–23; Schaefer, 6–12; Shankland, 238–40; Sproull, 73–81.

Section 1.7: d'Abro, 469–71; Blackwood et al., 143–9; Bohm, 33–7; Born, 87–9; 334–6; Dushman, 117–20; Finkelnburg, 192–7; French, 131–5; Houston, 12–14; Jauncey, 323–8; Oldenberg, 213–17; Peaslee and Mueller, 203–6; Persico, 23–31; Schaefer, 12–19; Shankland, 204–13; Sproull, 98–101.

Section 1.8: de Broglie, 123–61.

Section 1.9: d'Abro, 269–93, 674–86; Shortley and Williams, 375–92.

Section 1.10: Peaslee and Mueller, 198–203.

Section 1.11: d'Abro, 293–308; Bohm, 59–65; Born, 78–81; March, 14–17.

Section 1.12: Born, 336–7; French, 174–9; Jauncey, 67–9; Landé, 36–8; Semat, 187–9, 201.

Section 1.13: d'Abro, 45–57; Bohm, 103–14; Dushman, 166–71; Eldridge, 348–50; Finkelnburg, 198–202; French, 191–5; Houston, 24–30; Landé, 38–42; March, 3–11; Schiff, 1–16; Shankland, 48–50, 115–16, 213–14; Sproull, 112–20.

CHAPTER 2

THE DUAL NATURE OF MATTER

2.1. de Broglie's Imaginative Researches. In 1924, in his doctoral thesis, Louis de Broglie[1] observed that on the left-hand sides of the equations

$$(2.1) \qquad\qquad E = h\nu, \qquad p = h/\lambda,$$

appear properties associated with corpuscles, on the right-hand sides appear properties associated with waves. He then reasoned that if these relations are valid, as explanations of the photoelectric and Compton effects certainly indicated, then all failures to obtain a purely wave or a purely corpuscular theory of light must be due to its impossibility: a purely wave or a purely corpuscular theory would imply the absence of any relations between wave and corpuscular properties. Further, he argued, if the corpuscular and wave concepts of light are inseparable, it may be that corpuscular and wave concepts of matter are inseparable. That is, in order to explain some phenomena exhibited by matter, it may be necessary to consider the wave aspect of matter, just as it is necessary to consider the corpuscular aspect of light to explain some phenomena exhibited by radiation.

The following statements by de Broglie are very interesting and instructive:

"When I began to consider these difficulties I was chiefly struck by two facts. On the one hand the Quantum Theory of Light cannot be considered satisfactory, since it defines the energy of a light corpuscle by the equation $W = h\nu$ containing the frequency ν. Now a purely corpuscular theory contains nothing that enables us to define a frequency; for this reason alone, therefore, we are compelled, in the case of Light, to introduce the idea of a corpuscle and that of periodicity simultaneously.

"On the other hand, determination of the stable motion of electrons in the atom introduces integers; and up to this point the only phenomena involving integers in Physics were those of interference and of normal modes of vibration. This fact suggested to me the idea that electrons too

---

[1] L. de Broglie, *Thesis*, Paris, 1924; *Ann. Physik*, **3**, 22 (1925).

could not be regarded simply as corpuscles, but that periodicity must be assigned to them.

"In this way, then, I obtained the following idea, in accordance with which I pursued my investigations:—that it is necessary in the case of Matter, as well as of radiation generally and of Light in particular, to introduce the idea of the corpuscle and of the wave simultaneously; or in other words, in the one case as in the other, we must assume the existence of corpuscles accompanied by waves. But corpuscles and waves cannot be independent of each other; in Bohr's terms, they are two complementary aspects of Reality; and it must consequently be possible to establish a certain parallelism between the motion of a corpuscle and the propagation of its associated wave. The first object at which to aim, therefore, was to establish the existence of this parallelism.

"With this in view, I began by considering the simplest case: that of an

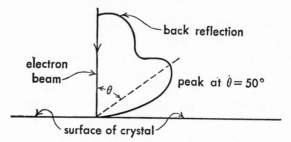

Fig. 2.1. Intensity of electron current measured as a function of θ.

isolated corpuscle, i.e., one removed from all external influence; with this we wish to associate a wave."[2]

2.2. The Davisson-Germer Experiment. Professor de Broglie's ideas provided the impetus needed for the development of the modern concept of the dual nature of matter. Soon after de Broglie's dissertation appeared, Elsasser[3] pointed out that, if de Broglie's ideas were correct, particles such as electrons should exhibit diffraction effects. In 1927, Davisson and Germer[4] succeeded in observing a diffraction pattern (Fig. 2.1) in low energy electrons reflected from a nickel crystal, thereby demonstrating the experimental significance of de Broglie's ideas. The presence of the reflected maximum which was observed at 50° to the normal when 54 ev electrons were incident normally on a nickel crystal cannot be explained except by attributing wavelike properties to electrons.

[2] From *Matter and Light* by L. de Broglie, reprinted by permission of Dover Publications, Inc., New York 14, New York, pp. 168–9.

[3] W. Elsasser, *Naturwissenschaften*, **13**, 711 (1925).

[4] C. J. Davisson and L. H. Germer, *Nature*, **119**, 558 (1927); *Phys. Rev.*, **30**, 706 (1927); C. J. Davisson, *J. Opt. Soc. Am.*, **18**, 193 (1929); for an interesting account see K. K. Darrow, *Bell System Tech. J.*, **30**, 786 (1951).

Since the low energy electrons used in the experiment do not penetrate the crystal appreciably, interference depends primarily on scattering by atoms in the two-dimensional surface layer of the crystal. For a simplified derivation of the relation involved, consider a row of atoms (Fig. 2.2) in the surface of the crystal, each of which according to Huyghens's principle acts as a secondary source of waves. Waves emanating from neighboring atoms A and B a distance d apart interfere constructively at P if the path difference $AP - BP = n\lambda$, where n is an integer and λ is the wavelength of the waves associated with the electrons. Hence a first-order maximum of intensity is to be expected at an angle θ given by

(2.2) $d \sin \theta = \lambda.$

For nickel, the line spacing d is known from X-ray data to be 2.15Å.

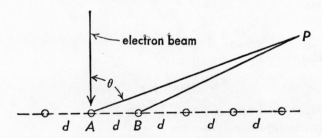

Fig. 2.2. Simplified explanation of diffraction maximum

Further, the wavelength λ of waves associated with particles of energy $E = p^2/2m$ is

(2.3) $\lambda = \dfrac{h}{p} = h(2mE)^{-\frac{1}{2}}$

where m is the particle mass. For V ev electrons this reduces to

(2.4) $\lambda = (150/V)^{\frac{1}{2}}$ Ängstroms.

From (2.4), we find that for 54 ev electrons, $\lambda = 1.67$ Å. Then from (2.2), using $d = 2.15$ Å, we find that a reflection peak should appear at $\theta = 51°$. This agrees extremely well with the location observed.

Problem 2.1: Obtain (2.4) from (2.3).

2.3. Basic Wave-Particle Relations. The relativistic energy-momentum relation for a free particle,

(2.5) $E^2 = p^2c^2 + m_0^2c^4,$

is accepted as correct not only for a particle of matter, for which the rest mass m_0 is positive, but also for a photon, when we consider a photon as being a particle of zero rest mass. With matter and with light we associate both corpuscular and wave properties, the corpuscular properties of energy E and momentum p being related to the wave properties of frequency ν and wavelength λ by the Einstein-de Broglie relations (2.1). However, instead of using the ordinary frequency ν and the wavelength λ, we often find it convenient to calculate in terms of the circular frequency $\omega = \nu/2\pi$ and the wave number $k = 2\pi/\lambda$; in terms of these the Einstein-de Broglie relations are

$$(2.6) \qquad\qquad E = \hbar\omega, \qquad p = \hbar k,$$

where $\hbar = h/2\pi$.

Much of the quantum mechanics of particles is based on the nonrelativistic approximation, in which the energy E of a free particle does not greatly exceed its rest energy m_0c^2. From (2.5) we obtain, by means of the formula

$$(2.7) \qquad\qquad (1 + x)^{\frac{1}{2}} \cong 1 + \tfrac{1}{2}x, \; |x| \ll 1,$$

the nonrelativistic approximation

$$(2.8) \qquad\qquad E \cong m_0c^2 + p^2/2m_0.$$

It is customary to drop the rest energy and write, for a free particle in the nonrelativistic approximation

$$(2.9) \qquad\qquad E = p^2/2m.$$

Problem 2.2:   Obtain the relativistic dispersion relation

$$(2.10) \qquad\qquad \omega^2 = k^2c^2 + m_0^2c^4/\hbar^2$$

for a free particle. Also obtain, in the nonrelativistic approximation

$$(2.11) \qquad\qquad \omega = \hbar k^2/2m.$$

2.4. Group and Phase Velocities of Matter Waves.   With waves of any nature, for which there exists a differentiable dispersion relation, there may be associated a phase velocity V_p and a group velocity V_g related to the frequency ω and the wave number k by the formulas (1.78). When the phase velocity depends on the frequency there is dispersion of waves of different frequencies.

According to ordinary concepts about corpuscles, we should expect that the de Broglie waves associated with particles of matter should travel without dispersion, inasmuch as spreading out of the particle would be associated with spreading of the associated wave. Let us investigate this by calculating, therefore, the phase and group velocities of matter waves associated with free particles. In the nonrelativistic approximation we find, using (1.78), (2.11) and the relations $p = \hbar k = mv$, that

(2.12) $\qquad V_p = p/2m = v/2, \qquad V_g = p/m = v.$

Hence the group velocity corresponds to the classical particle velocity, as we might have expected, but the phase velocity is only one-half of the classical particle velocity. This implies a rapid spreading of matter waves, incompatible with our expectation that they should remain highly localized. Calculations illustrating how rapid the spreading is will be given in Section 5.6.

Evidently, to retain the de Broglie wave-particle concept of matter we must modify classical concepts concerning the meaning of "position" and "velocity" of a corpuscle. An inconsistency may have already been observed, inasmuch as (2.6) associates a monochromatic wave with a particle of definite energy, whereas, according to Section 1.11, a monochromatic wave is too "monotonous" to represent a corpuscle.

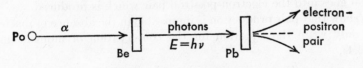

Fig. 2.3. Pair production.

Problem 2.3: Using the relativistic dispersion relation (2.10) for a free particle and the relations $p = \hbar k = mv$, show that

(2.13) $\qquad V_p = E/p = c^2/v, \qquad V_g = pc^2/E = p/m = v.$

From this, $V_p > c$ since $v < c$.

2.5. Pair Production and Annihilation. Since both light and matter exhibit both wavelike and corpuscular properties under appropriately designed experimental arrangements, it is natural to raise the questions as to whether light can be converted into matter and whether matter can be converted into light. In addition to the conservation of energy and momentum, there would be expected conservation of charge.

In 1932, Anderson[5] discovered the positron. Out of a group of 1300 photographs of cosmic ray tracks, 15 showed positive particles penetrating a lead plate, none of which could be attributed to particles with mass as large as that of a proton. Independently, Chadwick, Blackett and Occhialini[6] allowed α rays from polonium to fall on a sheet of beryllium, as shown in Fig. 2.3. The neutrons and high energy photons which were

[5] C. D. Anderson, *Science*, **76**, 238 (1932); *Phys. Rev.*, **43**, 491 (1933); **44**, 406 (1933); R. T. Beyer, *Foundations of Nuclear Physics* (reprints), Dover, 1949, pp. 1–4.

[6] P. M. S. Blackett and G. P. S. Occhialini, *Proc. Roy. Soc. (London)*, **139A**, 699 (1933); J. Chadwick, P. M. S. Blackett, and G. P. S. Occhialini, ibid. **144A**, 235 (1934); *Nature*, **131**, 473 (1933).

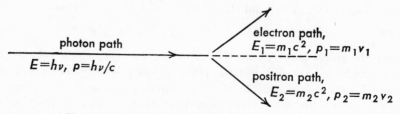

Fig. 2.4. Geometry for the analysis of pair production.

produced then passed through a sheet of lead. Pairs of tracks, one track of a pair curved upward and the other downward, were observed in the chamber, to which a magnetic field was applied. Blackett and Occhialini suggested that each pair of tracks was produced by an electron and a positron into which a photon had been transmuted. This pair production is possible only in the strong electric field of a nucleus (Pb atom) which takes part of the momentum, though practically all of the energy of the photon goes into the electron-positron pair which is produced.

To show that pair production is impossible in the absence of matter, we need only write the equation for the conservation of momentum (see Fig. 2.4),

$$(2.14) \qquad \frac{h\nu}{c} = m_1 v_1 \cos \theta_1 + m_2 v_2 \cos \theta_2$$

in the form

$$(2.15) \qquad h\nu = m_1 c^2 \left(\frac{v_1}{c} \cos \theta_1 \right) + m_2 c^2 \left(\frac{v_2}{c} \cos \theta_2 \right)$$

and observe an inconsistency with the energy conservation equation

$$(2.16) \qquad h\nu = m_1 c^2 + m_2 c^2$$

since $\frac{v_1}{c} \cos \theta_1 < 1$ and $\frac{v_2}{c} \cos \theta_2 < c$.

Pair annihilation (Fig. 2.5) has also been observed, the mean lifetime of a slow positron in water being 3.5×10^{-10} sec.

Problem 2.4: Show that only photons for which the associated wavelength is less than one-half of the Compton wavelength (1.44) have sufficient energy to produce an electron-positron pair.

Problem 2.5: Show that the principles of conservation of energy and of momentum can be satisfied by the production of one photon when a

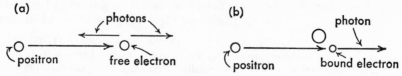

Fig. 2.5. Pair annihilation: (a) Two photons produced in the case of a free electron; (b) One photon produced in the case of a bound electron.

bound electron is annihilated with the positron, but that the production of at least two photons is required when a free electron is annihilated with the positron.

2.6. References for Supplementary Reading.

Section 2.1: d'Abro, 604–17; Blackwood et al., 155–8; Born, 89–92; Finkelnburg, 202–6; French, 175–9; Jauncey, 373–5; Kramers, 8–13; March, 11–14; McConnell, 30–32; Richtmyer et al., 177–80; Schaefer, 243–50; Semat, 169–70; Shankland, 36–8.

Section 2.2: d'Abro, 630–36; Blackwood et al., 158–61; Bohm, 71; Born, 92–4; French, 179–83; Houston, 14–16; Jauncey, 375–6; Oldenberg, 377–82; Peaslee and Mueller, 206–8; Richtmyer et al., 180–85; Schaefer, 266–70; Semat, 171–85; Shankland, 38–45, 366–74; Sherwin, 1–7; Sproull, 106–12.

Section 2.3: Blackwood et al., 168–9; Born, 94–102; Dushman, 162–5; Eldridge, 352–6; Finkelnburg, 61–5; Mott and Sneddon, 1–9; Schiff, 17–18.

Section 2.4: Eldridge, 340–42; Jauncey, 373–5; Semat, 185–9.

Section 2.5: Blackwood et al., 309–16; Born, 44–7; Jauncey, 479–83; Semat, 434–8.

CHAPTER 3

DEVELOPMENT OF A PICTORIAL DESCRIPTION OF THE ATOM[1] (PRIOR TO 1925)

3.1. Pictures of the Atom Prior to 1900. In their attempts to explain the behavior of matter in terms of deterministic natural laws, the Greeks originated the idea that material bodies are composed of enormous numbers of atoms. According to the Greeks, atoms differ from each other in shape, size, position, and arrangement, and are in continuous motion in a void. The atoms of Leucippius, Democritus, and Plato were regular bodies without structure and were incapable of change.

For centuries the Greek concept of atoms remained dormant and without further development. Some textbooks of the late nineteenth century pictured atoms as being connected by hooks and eyes, which were probably meant to explain chemical affinities. There was no explanation of the inconsistency between these diagrams and the concept that atoms are the smallest indivisible blocks of matter. However, before criticizing too harshly those who drew these pictures, we might inquire, "What do we mean by a picture of an atom?" Dirac[2] (b. 1902) says that a picture is *"any way of looking at the fundamental laws which makes their self-consistency obvious."* Thus, "one may gradually acquire a picture of atomic phenomena by becoming familiar with the laws of quantum mechanics." These statements by Dirac should be kept in mind throughout our attempts to understand physical laws by drawing pictures and by constructing models.

During the nineteenth century, the statistical mechanics of gases was initiated and the foundations of chemistry were laid, yet no internal structure was attributed to atoms. There was lacking a willingness to reject the concept that atoms are the smallest indivisible blocks of matter.

The initial experimental steps in determining the structure of atoms were taken by Joseph John Thomson (1865–1940) at the Cavendish

---

[1] For a detailed and interesting account of the development of a model of the atom, from the inelastic atom and Lord Kelvin's *vortex atom* to the introduction of Schroedinger's theory, see F. Cajori, *A History of Physics*, Macmillan, revised edition, 1929.

[2] P. A. M. Dirac, *The Principles of Quantum Mechanics*, fourth edition, Oxford, 1958, p. 10.

physical laboratory at Cambridge. In studying the deflection of cathode rays, which had commanded the attention of Julius Plücker, William Crookes, Heinrich R. Hertz, P. Lenard, and others, Thomson arrived at the conclusion, in 1897, that these "rays" were not ether waves but particles of matter smaller than atoms. Thomson called these particles "corpuscles." The name "electron" had been introduced by G. Johnstone Stoney (1826–1911) in 1891, not as the name of Thomson's particles but as the name of the fundamental unit of electricity, namely, the electric charge on a hydrogen ion in electrolysis. The word "electron" ultimately came to be applied to Thomson's "corpuscles," and the discovery of the electron is usually attributed to Thomson.[3]

3.2. Thomson's Model of the Hydrogen Atom. In 1902, Thomson[4] proposed a model of the atom in which electrons are imbedded in a cloud of positive charge uniformly distributed in a sphere. In the case of

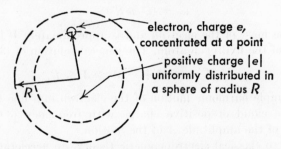

Fig. 3.1. J. J. Thomson's model of the hydrogen atom.

hydrogen, a single electron is imbedded in a uniform cloud of positive charge of some radius R (Fig. 3.1). The motion of the electron within this cloud is determined by the Coulomb inverse square law of attraction between positive and negative charges.

As a consequence of the inverse square law, the attraction between the electron and the cloud of positive charge is the same as that between two point charges. The effective positive charge is that within a sphere of radius r, when the electron is at a distance r from the center of the cloud. The density of the positive charge is

$$(3.1) \qquad \rho = |e|/(\tfrac{4}{3}\pi R^3), \ r \leq R,$$

and the effective positive charge is

$$(3.2) \qquad q = |e|, \ r \geq R,$$
$$= \tfrac{4}{3}\pi r^3 \rho = |e|r^3/R^3, \ r \leq R.$$

[3] See F. Cajori, op. cit. pp. 357–9.

[4] J. J. Thomson, *Nature*, **67**, 601 (1903); *Phil. Mag.*, **7**, 237 (1904); *Recollections and Reflections*, G. Bell and Sons, 1936; the Thomson atom has recently been quantized by H. Zatzkis, *Am. J. Phys.*, **26**, 635 (1958).

From this, the centrally directed attractive force is

$$(3.3) \qquad \begin{aligned} F_r &= e^2/r^2, \ r \geq R, \\ &= e^2r/R^3, \ r \leq R. \end{aligned}$$

Considering for simplicity only the case of rectilinear motion within and through the center of the cloud of positive charge, we have as equation of motion of the electron

$$(3.4) \qquad m\ddot{r} = -e^2r/R^3,$$

or

$$(3.5) \qquad \ddot{r} + \omega_0^2 r = 0,$$

where

$$(3.6) \qquad \omega_0 = (e^2/mR^3)^{\frac{1}{2}}.$$

Here m is the mass of the electron and is approximately 1/1840'th that of the mass of the hydrogen atom. The general solution of (3.5),

$$(3.7) \qquad r = A \cos(\omega_0 t + \epsilon), \ 0 < A \leq R,$$

represents simple harmonic motion of the electron in a line through the center of the cloud of positive charge with frequency (3.6) which is independent of the amplitude A of the motion.

According to classical electromagnetic theory, an accelerated electron radiates electromagnetic energy (light). A harmonic motion yields radiation of a single frequency—monochromatic radiation. More complicated periodic motions which are obtained when the path of the electron is not rectilinear yield, according to Fourier analysis, light with components of frequencies $\omega_0, 2\omega_0, 3\omega_0, 4\omega_0, \ldots$. As energy is lost by radiation, the electron in Thomson's model should rapidly settle toward a static position at the center of the cloud of positive charge and the radiation cease.

Does Thomson's model of the atom make the self-consistency of any fundamental laws more obvious? The emission and absorption spectra of hydrogen, which will be described in Section 3.4, are much more complicated than predicted by Thomson's model. Further, Thomson's model was shown by Rutherford (1871–1937) in 1911 to be inconsistent with observed large angle scattering of α particles. It had been observed that about 1 in 20,000 of incident α particles were deflected through an average angle of 90° in passing through a layer of gold foil .00004 cm thick. On the other hand, a simple calculation showed that the chance of an α particle being deflected through 90° by a Thomson atom is vanishingly small. It was also shown that the observed distribution of α particles deflected through large angles is not explainable by multiple deflections by a large number of Thomson atoms. In brief, atoms are much harder and less easily penetrable than implied by Thomson's model.

Although Thomson's picture of the atom helps little if at all in making the self-consistency of fundamental laws obvious, his idea of a cloud of charge distributed in space has been retained in one of the interpretations of modern quantum mechanics (see Section 8.2).

3.3. Lord Rutherford's Model of the Atom.[5] Certain natural sources, such as polonium, emit α particles, which are just He^{++} ions, with speeds up to 10^9 cm/sec. The path of an α particle is scarcely affected by an electron, which is about 7500 times lighter than an α particle. However, large angle scattering of α particles by atoms is frequently observed. To account for this, Rutherford in 1911 put forward the hypothesis that the massive positive charge of the atom is concentrated in a very small volume. Rutherford treated the scattering in terms of the relative motion of

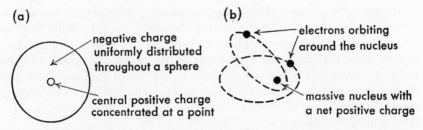

Fig. 3.2. Rutherford's models of the atom: (a) Hard core of positive charge with surrounding cloud of negative charge; (b) Miniature solar system.

two point charges under their mutual repulsion through the Coulomb law of force. Rutherford at first supposed that the negative charge, of negligible mass, is distributed uniformly throughout a sphere (Fig. 3.2a).

The final picture of the atom as suggested by Rutherford is very similar to a miniature solar system. The massive nucleus with a net positive charge plays the part of the sun. The electrons orbit around this central mass, behaving like planets (Fig. 3.2b). The hydrogen atom was pictured as having only one electron orbiting around a massive pointlike positive charge. Due to the attraction between the electron and the nucleus, the system will be in equilibrium only if the electron revolves around the nucleus. Let us calculate the velocity, radius, and frequency for the electron in the hydrogen atom, assuming a circular orbit.

From the energy equation

$$(3.8) \qquad E = \frac{1}{2} mv^2 - \frac{e^2}{r},$$

[5] Lord Rutherford, *Phil. Mag.*, **21**, 669 (1911); **37**, 581 (1919); R. T. Beyer, *Foundations of Nuclear Physics* (reprints), Dover, 1949, pp. 111–37.

the equality between centripetal force (circular path) and Coulombic attraction,

$$(3.9) \qquad \frac{mv^2}{r} = \frac{e^2}{r^2},$$

and the relation between velocity and frequency of traversing a circular orbit,

$$(3.10) \qquad v = 2\pi r v_0,$$

we may express r, v, and v_0 in terms of the energy E, electron charge e, and electron mass m:

$$(3.11) \quad r = \frac{e^2}{-2E}, \qquad v = \left(\frac{-2E}{m}\right)^{\frac{1}{2}}, \qquad v_0 = \frac{1}{2\pi e^2}\left(\frac{-8E^3}{m}\right)^{\frac{1}{2}}.$$

According to classical electromagnetic theory, the electron, being continuously attracted toward the core of the atom, should radiate electromagnetic energy of frequency equal to the frequency of revolution. Calculations show that it should radiate all of its energy and spiral into the nucleus in about 10^{-10} seconds. As E decreases, r also decreases but v and v_0 increase continuously, as shown by (3.11). This continuously varying spectral frequency is in complete disagreement with the observed discrete spectrum of hydrogen.

More generally, the electron in Rutherford's model of the hydrogen atom executes an elliptical orbit around the nucleus. Since the motion is periodic, there exist Fourier series representing the coordinates x, y, and z of the electron as functions of the time:

$$(3.12) \qquad x = \sum_{n=0}^{\infty} \{a_n \cos(n\omega t) + b_n \sin(n\omega t)\},$$

with similar series for y and z. Then, according to classical electromagnetic theory, the atom should emit lines of all frequencies of the form $n\omega/2\pi$, except for any terms $\cos(n\omega t)$ and $\sin(n\omega t)$ which do not happen to appear in the Fourier series (3.12). Thus the spectrum should consist of lines uniformly spaced on a frequency scale. This is not at all true of the observed spectrum except that the lines of high frequency are approximately uniformly spaced on a frequency scale. Thus, Rutherford's model gives approximately the correct results for lines of high frequency.

Quite evidently, Rutherford's model, although superior to Thomson's model according to Dirac's criterion, is still not adequate.

3.4. Description of the Spectrum of Hydrogen. Spectroscopic analysis of the light emitted by a Plucker tube containing hydrogen reveals many lines easily classified into two categories:

(1) Background of numerous, closely spaced lines of low intensity, the *many line spectrum*, emitted by hydrogen molecules;

(2) Less numerous but more intense lines emitted by hydrogen atoms, clustered into groups or series:

    (a) Lyman series, in the ultraviolet,

    (b) Balmer series, in the visible and ultraviolet,

    (c) Paschen series, in the infrared,

    (d) Bracket series, in the far infrared,

    (e) Pfund series, in the far infrared.

The wavelengths and the corresponding wave numbers $\bar{\nu} = \nu/c = \dfrac{1}{\lambda}$ of the α, β, γ, and δ lines, the first four lines, of the Lyman, Balmer, and Paschen series are given in Table 3.1. Each series of lines approaches a series limit (l).

TABLE 3.1. SOME WAVE LENGTHS AND WAVE NUMBERS FOR LINES IN THE SPECTRUM OF HYDROGEN, WITH CORRESPONDING QUANTUM NUMBERS

Line	λ, Å	$\bar{\nu}$, cm^{-1}	m	n
Lyman				
α	1,215.7	85,258	1	2
β	1,025.8	97,491	1	3
γ	972.5	102,823	1	4
δ	949.5	105,291	1	5
(l)		109,678	1	∞
Balmer				
α	6,562.8	15,233	2	3
β	4,861.3	20,565	2	4
γ	4,340.5	23,032	2	5
δ	4,101.7	24,373	2	6
(l)		27,420	2	∞
Paschen				
α	18,756	5,331	3	4
β	12,821	7,799	3	5
γ	10,939	9,139	3	6
δ	10,052	9,948	3	7
(l)		12,186	3	∞

Intensive efforts were made to obtain a theoretical explanation of the series. The first promising step was made in 1885 by the Swiss spectroscopist Johann Jakob Balmer[6] (1825–1898) who discovered that the wavelengths and wave numbers of the nine then known lines in the spectrum of hydrogen (first nine lines of the Balmer series) could be calculated very

[6] J. J. Balmer, *Ann. Physik*, **25**, 80 (1885).

closely by a formula which in its modern form is

$$(3.13) \qquad \frac{1}{\lambda} = \bar{\nu} = R\left(\frac{1}{m^2} - \frac{1}{n^2}\right), \qquad R = 109{,}678 \text{ cm}^{-1}.$$

For the Balmer lines, $m = 2$ and $n = 3, 4, 5, \ldots$. The coefficient R, called the *Rydberg constant*, is the same for all lines.

Formula (3.13) is found to be very accurate for computing the wave number of any line in the spectrum of hydrogen, values of m and n being taken as indicated in Table 3.1. Among many significant features in the spectrum of hydrogen and formula (3.13) are: (1) the wave number of each line can be conveniently represented as the difference between two numbers, called *terms*, whose general form is R/n^2, and (2) the lines in a series can be represented as the difference between a fixed term and a variable term.

Problem 3.1: Calculate from (3.13) the wave numbers of the α lines and of the series limits in the Lyman, Balmer, and Paschen series.

3.5. Bohr's Model of the Hydrogen Atom. In 1913 Niels Bohr[7] (b. 1885), borrowing from Rutherford's model of the hydrogen atom, namely, a central positively charged proton around which a single electron revolves, introduced the following four basic assumptions which led to a successful interpretation of the spectrum of hydrogen:

(a) The electron moves only in certain "privileged" orbits which are characterized by the condition that, over one of them, the angular momentum is an integral multiple of $\hbar = h/2\pi$;

(b) The privileged orbits are *stationary* or *stable states* in the sense that no radiation occurs as long as the electron remains in one of them;

(c) An electron in a stationary state of high energy, an *excited state*, may drop spontaneously into a stationary state of lower energy;

(d) The energy liberated when an electron drops from an excited state to a less excited state contributes to a spectral line of definite frequency ν given by the *frequency condition*

$$(3.14) \qquad \nu = \frac{E - E'}{h},$$

where E and E' are the energies in the initial and final states, respectively.

Assuming Coulomb's law of force and Newton's law of motion to be applicable, the path of the electron around the nucleus should be a conic section. Considering for the sake of simiplicity a circular path, Bohr's first assumption, called the *quantizing condition*, gives

$$(3.15) \qquad mrv = n\hbar,$$

where m is the mass of the electron, v its velocity, r is the radius of the

---

[7] N. Bohr, *Phil. Mag.*, **26**, 1, 476, 485 (1913).

circular path, and n is a positive integer. Elimination of r from (3.9) and (3.15) gives the velocity in the n'th Bohr circle:

$$(3.16) \qquad v_n = e^2/n\hbar.$$

From (3.15) and (3.16) we find that the radius of the n'th Bohr circle is

$$(3.17) \qquad r_n = n^2 r_1$$

where

$$(3.18) \qquad r_1 = \hbar^2/me^2$$

is the radius of the first Bohr circle. Finally, from (3.8), (3.16) and (3.18) we find that the energy in the n'th circle is

$$(3.19) \qquad E_n = -Rch/n^2$$

where

$$(3.20) \qquad R = \frac{me^4}{4\pi\hbar^3 c} = \frac{2\pi^2 me^4}{h^3 c}.$$

The state for which $n = 1$ is called the *ground state*. When the electron is in the corresponding Bohr orbit, the atom is said to be *unexcited*. States for which $n > 1$ are called *excited states*. According to Bohr's frequency condition (3.14), when the electron drops from the n'th state to the m'th state, $n > m \geq 1$, radiation of frequency

$$(3.21) \qquad \nu_{n \to m} = \frac{E_n - E_m}{h} = Rc\left(\frac{1}{m^2} - \frac{1}{n^2}\right)$$

is emitted. Comparing (3.21) and (3.13), we see that Bohr's assumptions lead to Balmer's formula (3.13) when R as given in (3.20) is identified with the Rydberg constant. A Grotrian diagram (Fig. 3.3) provides a convenient graphical representation of the Bohr energy levels, of the energy jumps, and of the corresponding spectral lines.

It has been previously noted (Section 3.3) that classical electromagnetic theory leads us to expect spectra with uniformly spaced lines when the orbital motion of the electron in the Rutherford model is periodic. In (3.21), let us replace m by n and n by $n + \Delta n$ and take $\Delta n \ll n$. We obtain

$$(3.22) \qquad \nu_{n+\Delta n \to n} = \frac{Rc\,\Delta n(2n + \Delta n)}{n^2(n + \Delta n)^2} \simeq 2\,\frac{Rc\,\Delta n}{n^3}.$$

From this we conclude that, for large values of n and small values of Δn (large energies and small energy jumps), the spectral lines should be approximately uniformly spaced. This is a simple illustration of the *Correspondence Principle:*[8] In the limit of large quantum numbers and low

[8] N. Bohr, *Z. Physik*, **13**, 117 (1923); *Theory of Spectra and Atomic Constitution*, second edition, Cambridge, 1924.

quantum jumps, quantum theory agrees with classical theory. This principle was formulated by Bohr in 1923 and played a very significant and helpful role in the early development of the quantum theory.

Problem 3.2: Calculate r_1, v_1 and R. Answers:

$$(3.23) \qquad r_1 = 0.527 \text{ Å}, \qquad v_1 = c/137, \qquad R = 109{,}720 \text{ cm}^{-1}.$$

Problem 3.3: How did de Broglie account for Bohr's quantum condition in terms of waves?[9]

Problem 3.4: A natural refinement of the calculations of this section is removal of the restriction that the nucleus (charge Ze) remain fixed at the

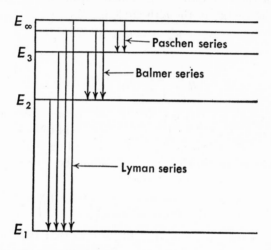

Fig. 3.3. Grotrian diagram showing the energy levels of hydrogen and energy jumps.

center of the circular orbit of the electron (charge $-e$). For masses m_a and m_b rotating with speeds v_a and v_b in circular orbits of radii r_a and r_b around their center of mass, Bohr's quantum condition is

$$(3.24) \qquad m_a r_a v_a + m_b r_b v_b = n\hbar,$$

where n is a positive integer. By definition of the center of mass,

$$(3.25) \qquad m_a r_a = m_b r_b.$$

Newton's law of motion and the Coulombic inverse square law are best expressed by equality between the centripetal forces $m_a v_a^2/r_a$ and $m_b v_b^2/r_b$

[9] See M. Born, *Atomic Physics*, sixth edition, Hafner, 1957, p. 131; A. d'Abro, *The Rise of the New Physics*, Dover, 1951, Vol. II, p. 624; A. P. French, *Principles of Modern Physics*, Wiley, 1958, p. 184; or H. Semat, *Introduction to Atomic and Nuclear Physics*, Rinehart, 1954, p. 228.

and the Coulombic attraction Ze^2/r^2 and by the energy equation, viz.:

(3.26) $$m_a v_a^2/r_a = Ze^2/r^2, \qquad m_b v_b^2/r_b = Ze^2/r^2,$$

where $r = r_a + r_b$, and

(3.27) $$E = \tfrac{1}{2} m_a v_a^2 + \tfrac{1}{2} m_b v_b^2 - Ze^2/r.$$

Let $M = m_a + m_b$ and define the "reduced mass" by $\mu = m_a m_b/M$. Show that

(3.28) $$r_a = \frac{n^2 \hbar^2}{Ze^2 m_a}, \qquad r_b = \frac{n^2 \hbar^2}{Ze^2 m_b}, \qquad r = \frac{n^2 \hbar^2}{Ze^2 \mu},$$

that

(3.29) $$v_a = \frac{Ze^2 m_b}{M n \hbar}, \qquad v_b = \frac{Ze^2 m_a}{M n \hbar},$$

and that

(3.30) $$E = -\frac{R_\mu ch}{n^2}$$

where

(3.31) $$R_\mu = 2\pi^2 Z^2 e^4 \mu / h^3 c.$$

Problem 3.5: Describe the Franck-Hertz experiment,[10] and explain how it confirms Bohr's view that spectral lines are due to transitions between discrete stationary states of atoms.[11]

3.6. References for Supplementary Reading.

Section 3.1: Blackwood et al., 23–38.

Section 3 2: d'Abro, 473; Dushman, 85; French, 105–7; Jauncey, 358.

Section 3.3: d'Abro, 472–76; Blackwood et al., 46–8; Dushman, 121–4; Jauncey, 358–9; Oldenberg, 99–107; Persico, 7–10; Richtmyer et al., 142–5; Schaefer, 36–47; Semat, 83–9; Shankland, 59–69; Sproull, 46–54.

Section 3.4: d'Abro, 481–7; Blackwood et al., 51–65, 93–6; Dushman, 124–7; Eldridge, 164–7; Finkelnburg, 67–83; French, 103–5; Jauncey, 350–59; McConnell, 24–7; Oldenberg, 108–12; Persico, 32–6; Richtmyer et al., 133–42; Schaefer, 32–6; Semat, 205–6; Shankland, 91–3.

Section 3.5: d'Abro, 488–509; Blackwood et al., 96–105, 164–7; Born, 84–6, 103–13, 131–2; Dushman, 127–39; Eldridge, 178–92; Finkelnburg, 84–103, 164–6; French, 107–14, 119–22, 184; Green, 7–10; Jauncey, 359–69, 383–9; Landé, 31–5; Oldenberg, 113–29, 145–9, 383–92; Pauling and Wilson, 25–30; Peaslee and Mueller, 208–23; Persico, 37–54, 265–8; Richtmyer et al., 148–61; Schaefer, 75–8; Semat, 206–18; Shankland, 87–8, 90–91; White, 23–36.

[10] J. Franck and G. Hertz, *Verhandl. deut. physik. Ges.*, **16**, 12 (1914).

[11] See M. Born, op. cit. p. 85; A. d'Abro, op. cit. p. 585; S. Dushman, *Fundamentals of Atomic Physics*, McGraw-Hill, 1951, pp. 141–4; J. A. Eldridge, *The Physical Basis of Things*, McGraw-Hill, 1934, pp. 214–18; C. D. Peaslee and H. Mueller, *Elements of Modern Physics*, Prentice-Hall, 1955, pp. 158–60; or E. Persico, *Fundamentals of Quantum Mechanics*, Prentice-Hall, 1950, pp. 47–53.

CHAPTER 4

THE OLD QUANTUM THEORY

4.1. Some Principles of Classical Mechanics. Let q represent any set of independent position coordinates of a conservative mechanical system. The Lagrangian function $L(q,\dot{q})$ is defined in terms of the kinetic energy $T(q,\dot{q})$, which is a positive definite quadratic form in the $\dot{q} \equiv \dfrac{dq}{dt}$ and the potential energy $V(q)$ by

$$(4.1) \qquad\qquad L = T - V.$$

The Lagrangian equations of motion

$$(4.2) \qquad\qquad \frac{d}{dt}\left(\frac{\partial L}{\partial \dot{q}_i}\right) - \frac{\partial L}{\partial q_i} = 0,$$

provide a complete system of second-order, ordinary differential equations for the q as functions of t. When these functions are substituted into

$$(4.3) \qquad\qquad E \equiv T(q,\dot{q}) + V(q),$$

it is found that E is independent of t. This is what is meant by the statement that E, called the *energy*, is a *constant of the motion*.

Generalized momentum coordinates p_i are defined by

$$(4.4) \qquad\qquad p_i = \frac{\partial L}{\partial \dot{q}_i}.$$

Since L is quadratic in the $\dot{q}$'s, the p's are linear functions of the $\dot{q}$'s. The equations (4.4) may be solved for the $\dot{q}$'s as functions of the q's and p's. Then the Hamiltonian function

$$(4.5) \qquad\qquad H \equiv H(q,p) = \sum_i \dot{q}_i p_i - L,$$

in which L is to be expressed as a function of the q's and p's, may be formed. Hamilton's equations of motion

$$(4.6) \qquad\qquad \dot{q}_i = \frac{\partial H}{\partial p_i}, \qquad \dot{p}_i = -\frac{\partial H}{\partial q_i},$$

constitute a complete system of first-order, ordinary differential equations for the q's and p's, replacing the second-order Lagrangian equations (4.2). Alternatively to (4.5), it is found that

$$(4.7) \qquad H = T + V$$

expressed as a function of the q's *and* p's.   Thus $H(q,p) = E = $ a constant of the motion, in the sense stated above.

A position coordinate q_i and the corresponding momentum coordinate p_i are called *conjugate variables*.

Problem 4.1:   Obtain the Hamiltonian function for a free particle, using rectangular coordinates. Solve Hamilton's equations of motion, and verify that H is a constant of the motion. Answer:

$$(4.8) \qquad H = (p_x^2 + p_y^2 + p_z^2)/2m.$$

Problem 4.2:   Obtain the Hamiltonian function for a nonisotropic linear oscillator in three space dimensions, using rectangular coordinates. Solve Hamilton's equations of motion and verify that H is a constant of the motion. Answer:

$$(4.9) \qquad H = (p_x^2 + p_y^2 + p_z^2)/2m + (\tfrac{1}{2})(ax^2 + by^2 + cz^2).$$

Problem 4.3:   Obtain the Hamiltonian function for an isotropic linear oscillator in three space dimensions, using spherical coordinates. Answer:

$$(4.10) \qquad H = \frac{1}{2m}\left(p_r^2 + \frac{p_\theta^2}{r^2} + \frac{p_\varphi^2}{r^2 \sin^2 \theta} \right) + \tfrac{1}{2}kr^2.$$

Problem 4.4:   Obtain the Hamiltonian function for a particle in a gravitational field, using cylindrical coordinates with polar axis parallel to the field. Answer:

$$(4.11) \qquad H = \frac{1}{2m}\left(p_\rho^2 + p_z^2 + \frac{p_\varphi^2}{\rho^2} \right) + mgz.$$

Problem 4.5:   The nonrelativistic Hamiltonian function for a charged particle in a static electromagnetic field

$$(4.12) \qquad \mathbf{E} = -\operatorname{grad} \Phi, \qquad \mathbf{H} = \operatorname{Curl} \mathbf{A},$$

is

$$(4.13) \qquad H = \frac{1}{2m}\left(\mathbf{p} - \frac{e}{c}\mathbf{A} \right)^2 + e\Phi.$$

Starting with this and the Hamiltonian equations of motion (4.6), obtain the Lorentzian equations of motion

$$(4.14) \qquad m\ddot{\mathbf{q}} = e\mathbf{E} + \frac{e}{c}\dot{\mathbf{q}} \times \mathbf{H}$$

where the q's are rectangular coordinates.[1]

---

[1] See N. F. Mott and I. N. Sneddon, *Wave Mechanics and Its Applications*, Oxford, 1948, p. 39; or C. Schaefer, *Einführung in die theoretische Physik*, Walter de Gruyter, 1937, p. 294.

4.2. Classical Solution for the Orbital Motion of an Electron.

An electron of mass m is attracted toward the origin with force Ze^2/r^2.

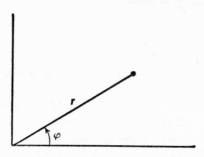

Fig. 4.1. Polar coordinates in the plane of the motion.

Proof that the motion is in a plane, we omit. Taking polar coordinates r, φ (see Fig. 4.1) in the plane of the motion, we have

(4.15)
$$\text{(a)} \quad T = mv^2/2 = \tfrac{1}{2}m(\dot{r}^2 + r^2\dot{\varphi}^2),$$
$$\text{(b)} \quad V = -Ze^2/r.$$

Hence

(4.16)
$$L \equiv T - V = \tfrac{1}{2}m(\dot{r}^2 + r^2\dot{\varphi}^2) + Ze^2/r.$$

From (4.4) and (4.16) we obtain

(4.17)
$$\text{(a)} \quad p_r \equiv \frac{\partial L}{\partial \dot{r}} = m\dot{r},$$
$$\text{(b)} \quad p_\varphi \equiv \frac{\partial L}{\partial \dot{\varphi}} = mr^2\dot{\varphi}.$$

Using (4.15) and (4.17), we express $H = T + V$ as a function of r, φ, p_r, and p_φ, obtaining

(4.18)
$$H = \frac{1}{2m}\left(p_r^2 + \frac{p_\varphi^2}{r^2}\right) - \frac{Ze^2}{r}.$$

From (4.6) and (4.18) we obtain the Hamiltonian equations of motion:

(4.19)
$$\text{(a)} \quad \dot{r} \equiv \frac{\partial H}{\partial p_r} = \frac{1}{m}p_r, \qquad \text{(b)} \quad \dot{\varphi} \equiv \frac{\partial H}{\partial p_\varphi} = p_\varphi/mr^2,$$
$$\text{(c)} \quad \dot{p}_r \equiv -\frac{\partial H}{\partial r} = \frac{p_\varphi^2}{mr^3} - \frac{Ze^2}{r^2}, \qquad \text{(d)} \quad \dot{p}_\varphi \equiv -\frac{\partial H}{\partial \varphi} = 0.$$

We might proceed with the solution, but it suffices for present purposes to note from (4.19d) that

(4.20)
$$p_\varphi = P = \text{a constant},$$

to recall that

(4.21) $$H = E = \frac{1}{2m}\left(p_r{}^2 + \frac{P^2}{r^2}\right) - \frac{Ze^2}{r} = \text{a constant,}$$

and to recall that the orbits are conic sections with one focus at the origin. The three types of conic sections are (a) hyperbola, when $E > 0$, (b) parabola, when $E = 0$, and (c) ellipse, when $E < 0$.

We desire, for the elliptic case, to express the semi-axes a and b of the ellipse (see Fig. 4.2) as functions of the energy E and the angular momentum P. Letting $AF = r_{\min} = a - c$, $FA' = r_{\max} = a + c$, we have

(4.22)
(a) $r_{\min} + r_{\max} = 2a,$
(b) $r_{\min} \cdot r_{\max} = (a - c)(a + c) = a^2 - c^2 = b^2.$

At A and at A', $r = r_{\min}$ and $r = r_{\max}$, respectively. Hence at these two

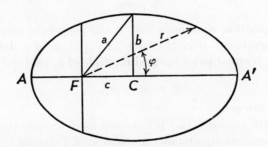

Fig. 4.2. Geometry for an elliptical orbit.

points, $\dot{r} = 0$, or $\dot{p}_r = 0$ since $p_r = m\dot{r}$. From (4.21) we see then that $r_{\min}$ and $r_{\max}$ are the roots of the equation

(4.23) $$E = \frac{P^2}{2mr^2} - \frac{Ze^2}{r}.$$

Writing (4.23) in the form

(4.24) $$r^2 + \frac{Ze^2}{E}r - \frac{P^2}{2mE} = 0$$

we see that

(4.25)
(a) sum of roots $= -Ze^2/E = r_{\min} + r_{\max},$
(b) product of roots $= -P^2/2mE = r_{\min} \cdot r_{\max}.$

Hence, using (4.22), we finally obtain

(4.26)   (a) $a = -Ze^2/2E,$ (b) $b = P/\sqrt{-2mE}.$

These expressions are important in the Wilson-Sommerfeld quantization of elliptic orbits (Section 4.3).

4.3. The Wilson-Sommerfeld Quantum Conditions. Let us recall Bohr's quantization rule (a), Section 3.5: The angular momentum for a circular orbit is an integral multiple of $\hbar = h/2\pi$. Letting

$$p_\varphi = mrv = \text{angular momentum,}$$

we have $p_\varphi = nh/2\pi$, or $p_\varphi \cdot 2\pi = nh$. Now $p_\varphi = $ a constant for a circular orbit, or, in fact, for any system with a central force only. We may therefore write Bohr's quantization condition in the form

$$(4.27) \qquad \int_0^{2\pi} p_\varphi \, d\varphi = nh.$$

W. Wilson[2] and A. Sommerfeld[3] independently generalized this, obtaining the *Wilson-Sommerfeld quantization rule:* Any periodic motion is quantized in such a way that the *action integral,*

$$\oint p_i \, dq_i,$$

where q_i is a position coordinate and p_i the conjugate momentum, and where the integration is over the range of variation of q_i during a period of the motion, is equal to an integral multiple of h, that is,

$$(4.28) \qquad \oint p_i \, dq_i = n_i h,$$

where n_i is an integer.

Let us briefly consider the Wilson-Sommerfeld quantum conditions from a more rigorous standpoint: A theorem of Poincaré states that the action integral

$$(4.29) \qquad J = \iint_S \sum_i dp_i \, dq_i$$

is invariant under canonical transformations.[4] In (4.29), S is any arbitrary two-dimensional surface in phase space. When the motion is periodic, S may be taken to be bounded by a closed trajectory C, since closed trajectories remain closed trajectories under canonical transformations. Then

$$(4.30) \qquad J = \sum_i J_i,$$

where

$$(4.31) \qquad J_i = \iint_S dp_i \, dq_i = \oint_C p_i \, dq_i.$$

Hence the invariance of J is assured by (4.28).

---

[2] W. Wilson, *Phil. Mag.,* **29,** 795 (1915).

[3] A. Sommerfeld, *Ann. Physik,* **51,** 1 (1916); *Atomic Structure and Spectral Lines,* Dutton, 1922.

[4] See H. Goldstein, *Classical Mechanics,* Addison-Wesley, 1950.

4.4. Application to the Hydrogen Atom.[3] An important immediate application of the Wilson-Sommerfeld conditions (4.28) is to the
hydrogen atom. Picture the electron as performing an elliptic orbit around
the nucleus (see Fig. 4.3). Substituting from (4.20) into the Wilson-
Sommerfeld quantum condition (4.28), we obtain

$$(4.32) \qquad J_\varphi = \oint p_\varphi \, d\varphi = \int_0^{2\pi} P \, d\varphi = 2\pi P = kh,$$

where k is an integer. The choice $k = 0$ may be disallowed since $k = 0$
implies $P = 0$, or straight line motion into the nucleus. Further, negative
values of k need not be considered, since the motion corresponding to a
negative value differs from that corresponding to a positive value only
by reversal of the direction of travel around the nucleus.

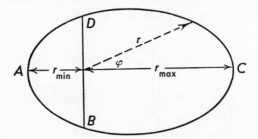

Fig. 4.3. Geometry for Sommerfeld's treatment of the hydrogen atom.

The phase integral J_r, in terms of points designated in Fig. 4.3, is

$$(4.33) \qquad J_r = \oint p_r \, dr = \int_{ABC} p_r \, dr + \int_{CDA} p_r \, dr.$$

From the energy equation (4.21) we obtain

$$(4.34) \qquad p_r = \pm \sqrt{2m \left(E + \frac{Ze^2}{r} - \frac{P^2}{2mr^2} \right)} = \pm \sqrt{}.$$

Now r increases along ABC, decreases along CDA. Hence, since, by
(4.19a), $p_r = m\dot{r}$, $p_r = + \sqrt{}$ along ABC, $p_r = - \sqrt{}$ along CDA.
Hence

$$(4.35) \qquad \begin{aligned} J_r &= \int_{r_{min}}^{r_{max}} (+ \sqrt{}) \, dr + \int_{r_{max}}^{r_{min}} (- \sqrt{}) \, dr \\ &= 2 \int_{r_{min}}^{r_{max}} (+ \sqrt{}) \, dr. \end{aligned}$$

Sommerfeld evaluated this integral, obtaining, when (4.28) is imposed,

$$(4.36) \qquad J_r = -2\pi P + 2\pi Ze^2 \sqrt{\frac{m}{-2E}} = sh$$

where $s = $ "radial quantum number" $= 0, 1, 2, 3, \ldots .$

Eliminating P from (4.36) by means of (4.32) we find that

$$(4.37) \qquad 2\pi Z e^2 \sqrt{\frac{m}{-2E}} = (s + k)h.$$

Now setting $n = s + k =$ "principal quantum number," and solving for E, we obtain the energy levels

$$(4.38) \qquad E_n = -\frac{2\pi^2 m Z^2 e^4}{h^2 n^2} = -\frac{RZ^2 ch}{n^2},$$

where R is the Rydberg constant (3.20).

Comparing (4.38) with (3.19), we see that the Wilson-Sommerfeld conditions give the same energy levels for the hydrogen atom as the simpler Bohr theory gave. The gain is that we are no longer restricted to circular

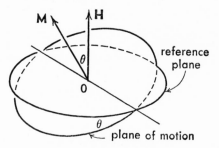

Fig. 4.4. Spatial quantization.

orbits. However, we cannot yet consider nonperiodic motions, nor can we predict transition probabilities, that is, line intensities.

Using (4.26), (4.32), and (4.38), we find the semi-axes of the "Sommerfeld ellipses" to be

$$(4.39) \qquad \text{(a)} \quad a_n = n^2 a_1, \qquad \text{(b)} \quad b_{n.k} = n k a_1,$$

where

$$(4.40) \qquad a_1 = h^2 / m Z e^2$$

is the radius of the first Bohr orbit (see (3.18)), and where $1 \leq k \leq n$.

The motion in space may be considered more generally. According to classical mechanics, the elliptic path lies in some plane containing the nucleus. Let θ be the angle between the plane of the motion and some reference plane (see Fig. 4.4). The angle between the perpendiculars OM and OH to the two planes is also θ. Let $p_\varphi =$ the total angular momentum, $p_\chi =$ the projection of p_φ onto OH. Applying the Wilson-Sommerfeld quantization rules (4.28), we obtain, since both p_φ and p_χ are constant,

$$\text{(4.41)} \quad \begin{aligned} &\text{(a)} \quad \oint p_\varphi \, d\varphi = 2\pi p_\varphi = kh, \\ &\text{(b)} \quad \oint p_\chi \, d\chi = 2\pi p_\chi = mh, \end{aligned}$$

where m and k are integers. Evidently $|m| \leq k$ since $|p_\chi| \leq p_\varphi$. We take $-k < m < k$ to obtain agreement with experiment. This exclusion, of $m = \pm k$, for which the Sommerfeld theory gives no very satisfactory explanation, may be justified today by means of a comparison with the results of wave mechanics.

From (4.41) we obtain

$$\text{(4.42)} \qquad \cos \theta = \frac{p_\chi}{p_\varphi} = \frac{m}{k}, \; -k < m < k.$$

This equation determines a discrete set of values of θ. It provides an example of *spatial quantization*, which can be directly observed when a magnetic field is present. Because of its significance there, m is called the "magnetic quantum number." It need never be confused with the symbol m for mass.

The energy levels E_n, given by (4.38), depend on the principal quantum number n but not on the azimuthal quantum number k nor on the magnetic quantum number m. For fixed n, there are n different Sommerfeld ellipses of different eccentricities, obtained by substituting $k = 1, 2, \ldots , n$ in (4.39). Thus, except for $n = 1$, there is a multiplicity of states corresponding to the same energy level. This is an example of the very important phenomenon known as *degeneracy*. We also have here an example of a general rule: *The ground state is nondegenerate.*

Problem 4.6: Plot to scale, on the same sheet of paper and with a common focus, the three Sommerfeld ellipses for $n = 3$.

Problem 4.7: Determine the Wilson-Sommerfeld energy levels of a particle bouncing in a gravitational field of strength g, off a level and perfectly elastic floor. Given that $E = p^2/2m + mgz$. Answer:

$$\text{(4.43)} \qquad E_n = (3m^2 ngh)^{\frac{2}{3}}/2m.$$

Problem 4.8: Determine the Wilson-Sommerfeld energy levels of a plane, rigid rotator of moment of inertia I about a fixed axis. The classical energy is

$$\text{(4.44)} \qquad E = \tfrac{1}{2} I \dot\varphi^2 = \frac{1}{2I} p_\varphi^2.$$

Answer:

$$\text{(4.45)} \qquad E_n = n^2 \hbar^2/2I.$$

Problem 4.9: Determine the Wilson-Sommerfeld energy levels of a one-dimensional harmonic oscillator. The classical energy is

$$(4.46) \qquad E = p^2/2m + kx^2/2.$$

Answer:

$$(4.47) \qquad E_n = nh\nu$$

where

$$(4.48) \qquad \nu = \frac{1}{2\pi} \sqrt{k/m}$$

is the classical frequency of vibration.

Problem 4.10: Determine the Wilson-Sommerfeld energy levels of a particle constrained to move along the x axis in the region $0 \le x \le L$. Answer:

$$(4.49) \qquad E_n = h^2 n^2/8mL^2.$$

Problem 4.11: Determine the Wilson-Sommerfeld energy levels of a particle of mass M, constrained to move in a box with edges of lengths a, b, and c. For the case $a = b = c$, find the number of states corresponding to each of the first four energy levels. Answer:

$$(4.50) \qquad E_{l,m,n} = \frac{h^2}{8M}\left(\frac{l^2}{a^2} + \frac{m^2}{b^2} + \frac{n^2}{c^2}\right).$$

4.5. Sommerfeld's Relativistic Treatment of the Hydrogen Atom. Coincident with his promulgation of the quantum conditions (4.28), Sommerfeld pointed out that, according to the Bohr formula (3.16) for the velocity of an electron in a circular orbit, $v_n = e^2/n\hbar$, the speed of the electron is so great that the relativistic variation of the mass of the electron with its speed should not be disregarded. For example, taking $n = 1$, we find

$$(4.51) \qquad \alpha \equiv \frac{v_1}{c} = \frac{e^2}{\hbar c} \cong \frac{1}{137}.$$

A Bohr electron in the ground state has a velocity almost equal to .01 c. In an elliptical orbit around the nucleus, the velocity of the electron varies, and the corresponding relativistic variation of the mass of the electron may be expected to affect the energy levels, resulting perhaps in detectable shifts in spectral lines.

Sommerfeld therefore calculated the phase integrals J_φ and J_r taking into consideration the relativistic variation of mass with speed as given by the formula

$$(4.52) \qquad m = m_0\left(1 - \frac{v^2}{c^2}\right)^{-\frac{1}{2}}.$$

Setting $J_\varphi = kh$, $J_r = sh$, as required by the Wilson-Sommerfeld quantum condition (4.28), and solving the relations obtained for E, he derived the formula

$$(4.53) \qquad E = m_0 c^2 \left\{ -1 + \left(1 + \frac{\alpha^2}{(s + \sqrt{k^2 - \alpha^2})^2} \right)^{-\frac{1}{2}} \right\}.$$

A sufficiently accurate approximation to (4.53) is given by the formula

$$(4.54) \qquad E_{n,k} = -\frac{Rch}{n^2} - \frac{Rch\alpha^2}{n^4} \left(\frac{n}{k} - \frac{3}{4} \right),$$

where $n = s + k$.

The Sommerfeld energy levels (4.53) or (4.54), depend on both n and k and not only on n, as with the Bohr energy levels (3.19). This result provides an example of a general rule: *The introduction of a perturbation tends to decrease the degeneracy of the energy levels.* In this example, the variation of mass with velocity may be considered as a perturbation. The degeneracy is not completely removed since the energy levels do not depend on the magnetic quantum number m. When a magnetic field is present, it is found that the levels do depend on m as well as on n and k. The degeneracy is then completely removed, unless we consider *electron spin*, a property which was attributed to electrons by Uhlenbeck and Goudsmit[5] and by Bichowsky and Urey[6] in 1925 in order fully to account for observed degeneracies of energy levels.

Problem 4.12: Verify the correctness of (4.54) by obtaining the first two terms in the series expansion of the right-hand member of (4.53) in powers of α^2. (Hint: In (4.53), use the approximation

$$(1 + x)^{-\frac{1}{2}} \cong 1 - \frac{1}{2}x + \frac{3}{8}x^2.$$

Also use (4.51) and (3.20) to introduce the Rydberg constant.)

4.6. References for Supplementary Reading.

Section 4.1: Atkin, 133–7, 142–6; Houston, 18–24; Mandl, 58–60; Mott and Sneddon, 37–9; Pauling and Wilson, 1–20; Schaefer, 47–66.

Section 4.2: Schaefer, 79–84.

Section 4.3: Born, 113–18; French, 114–18; McConnell, 27–30; Pauling and Wilson, 28–36; Persico, 227–40; White, 38–40.

Section 4.4: Born, 119–21; Pauling and Wilson, 36–49; Persico, 240–52; Schaefer, 66–75, 84–91; White, 42–51.

Section 4.5: Persico, 256–8; Schaefer, 91–9; White, 132–9.

[5] G. E. Uhlenbeck and S. Goudsmit, *Nature*, **117**, 264 (1926); *Physica*, **5**, 266 (1925); *Z. Physik*, **35**, 8, 618 (1926).

[6] F. R. Bichowsky and H. C. Urey, *Proc. Natl. Acad. Sci. U. S.*, **12**, 80 (1926).

CHAPTER 5

WAVE EQUATIONS AND WAVE PACKETS

5.1. Origin and Basic Properties of Wave Equations. By application of relevant basic principles of physics and suitable simplifying assumptions, theoreticians derive differential equations which are satisfied by functions representing wave fields. For example, the equation (1.47), which governs the motion of waves along a stretched string, is derived by application of Newton's second law and assumptions of transverse motion in a plane, small displacements, absence of friction, etc.

For many types of waves, the *principle of superposition* is found to be applicable. Mathematically, this means that if ψ_1 and ψ_2 are functions representing possible waves, then $c_1\psi_1 + c_2\psi_2$ represents a possible wave. The principle of superposition implies that the partial differential equation governing the waves must be *linear*. To define this important concept more explicitly, let us write the partial differential governing the waves in the general form

$$(5.1) \qquad\qquad L\psi = 0$$

and consider L as being an *operator* which annihilates ψ. The principle of superposition implies that if $L\psi_1 = 0$ and $L\psi_2 = 0$, then $L(c_1\psi_1 + c_2\psi_2) = 0$, for any constants c_1 and c_2.

The partial differential equation $L\psi = 0$ involves both space and time derivatives. For waves in homogeneous, isotropic media, the equation has constant coefficients. In this case we may make the notation more precise by writing

$$(5.2) \qquad\qquad L\left(\frac{\partial}{\partial x}, \frac{\partial}{\partial t}\right)\psi = 0.$$

For waves in three-space dimensions we would write

$$(5.3) \qquad\qquad L\left(\frac{\partial}{\partial x}, \frac{\partial}{\partial y}, \frac{\partial}{\partial z}, \frac{\partial}{\partial t}\right)\psi = 0$$

or, more briefly,

$$(5.4) \qquad\qquad L\left(\text{grad}, \frac{\partial}{\partial t}\right)\psi = 0.$$

5.2. Prototype Wave Functions and Dispersion Relations. Of particular importance in the solution of wave equations (5.2) for waves in one-space dimension are prototype wave functions of the form

$$(5.5) \qquad \psi = Ce^{i(kx-\omega t)}$$

These have the property that, for any nonnegative integer n,

$$(5.6) \qquad \text{(a)} \quad \left(\frac{\partial}{\partial x}\right)^n \psi = (ik)^n \psi,$$

$$\text{(b)} \quad \left(\frac{\partial}{\partial t}\right)^n \psi = (-i\omega)^n \psi.$$

In ordinary cases, the operator L involves a finite number of differentiations with respect to x and t. Equations (5.6) then indicate that

$$(5.7) \qquad L\left(\frac{\partial}{\partial x}, \frac{\partial}{\partial t}\right) Ce^{i(kx-\omega t)} = L(ik, -i\omega)Ce^{i(kx-\omega t)}$$

From (5.7) we see that L annihilates the prototype wave function (5.5) if and only if ω and k satisfy the relation

$$(5.8) \qquad L(ik, -i\omega) = 0.$$

From (5.8) we formulate a rule for obtaining the dispersion relation for waves which satisfy the wave equation (5.2): Replace $\frac{\partial}{\partial x}$ by ik and $\frac{\partial}{\partial t}$ by $-i\omega$ in the operator $L\left(\frac{\partial}{\partial x}, \frac{\partial}{\partial t}\right)$ which annihilates the wave function and set the result equal to zero. This substitution may be indicated by the correspondences

$$(5.9) \qquad \text{(a)} \quad \frac{\partial}{\partial x} \leftrightarrow ik, \qquad \text{(b)} \quad \frac{\partial}{\partial t} \leftrightarrow -i\omega.$$

To formulate a rule for obtaining the partial differential equation governing waves which satisfy a given integral, algebraic dispersion relation

$$(5.10) \qquad \Omega(\omega, k) = 0,$$

we invert the correspondences (5.9), writing

$$(5.11) \qquad \text{(a)} \quad k \leftrightarrow -i\frac{\partial}{\partial x}, \qquad \text{(b)} \quad \omega \leftrightarrow i\frac{\partial}{\partial t}.$$

Then, from (5.10) and (5.11), the wave equation may be written

$$(5.12) \qquad \Omega\left(i\frac{\partial}{\partial t}, -i\frac{\partial}{\partial x}\right)\psi = 0.$$

The prototype wave function in three-space dimensions,

$$(5.13) \qquad \psi = \psi(\mathbf{r}, t) = Ce^{i(\mathbf{k}\cdot\mathbf{r}-\omega t)}$$

where $\mathbf{r} = (x,y,z)$ and $\mathbf{k} = (k_1,k_2,k_3)$, changes most rapidly in the direction of the *propagation vector* $\mathbf{k}$ since, from (5.13),

$$(5.14) \qquad \text{grad } \psi = i\psi\mathbf{k}.$$

Letting $\hat{k}$ be the unit vector parallel to $\mathbf{k}$, we can find λ so that for the prototype wave function (5.13) we have

$$(5.15) \qquad \psi(\mathbf{r} + \lambda\hat{k},t) = \psi(\mathbf{r},t)$$

for all $\mathbf{r}$ and t. For this we need

$$(5.16) \qquad e^{i\mathbf{k}\cdot(\mathbf{r}+\lambda\hat{k})-i\omega t} \equiv e^{i\mathbf{k}\cdot\mathbf{r}-i\omega t},$$

or

$$(5.17) \qquad e^{i\lambda k} = 1$$

where

$$(5.18) \qquad k = |\mathbf{k}| = \mathbf{k} \cdot \hat{k} = \sqrt{k_1^2 + k_2^2 + k_3^2}$$

$=$ the *magnitude* of $\mathbf{k}$ $=$ the *wave number*. The smallest positive λ, namely,

$$(5.19) \qquad \lambda = 2\pi/k,$$

satisfying (5.17) is called the *wavelength*.

Let $\mathbf{s}$ be any vector perpendicular to $\mathbf{k}$. Then $\mathbf{k} \cdot \mathbf{s} = 0$ and

$$(5.20) \qquad e^{i\mathbf{k}\cdot(\mathbf{r}+\mathbf{s})-i\omega t} = e^{i(\mathbf{k}\cdot\mathbf{r}-\omega t)}.$$

Hence the prototype wave function (5.13) has the same value at all points P' on a plane through a given point P and perpendicular to $\mathbf{k}$. We say that (5.13) represents a *plane wave* with *wave vector* $\mathbf{k}$, the vector $\mathbf{k}$ serving to specify the direction of propagation of the wave and the wavelength.

Problem 5.1: Show that (5.13) represents a wave of frequency $\nu = \dfrac{\omega}{2\pi}$ and that a person traveling with velocity

$$(5.21) \qquad V_p = \frac{\omega}{k} = \omega/\sqrt{k_1^2 + k_2^2 + k_3^2}$$

in the direction of $\mathbf{k}$ "rides the wave."

Problem 5.2: Let λ_1, λ_2, and λ_3 be the smallest positive numbers for which the prototype wave function (5.13) satisfies

$$(5.22) \qquad \psi(x + \lambda_1, y + \lambda_2, z + \lambda_3, t) = \psi(x,y,z,t)$$

for all x, y, z, and t. Show that

$$(5.23) \qquad \lambda_1 = \frac{2\pi}{|k_1|}, \qquad \lambda_2 = \frac{2\pi}{|k_2|}, \qquad \lambda_3 = \frac{2\pi}{|k_3|}.$$

From (5.18), (5.19), and (5.23) show further that

(5.24)
$$\frac{1}{\lambda_2} = \frac{1}{\lambda_1{}^2} + \frac{1}{\lambda_2{}^2} + \frac{1}{\lambda_3{}^2}.$$

Problem 5.3: Using (5.23) and (5.24), show that the assignments

(5.25)   (a) $\mathbf{p} = \hbar\mathbf{k}$,   (b) $p = |\mathbf{p}| = \hbar k$,

are consistent with the de Broglie relation $p = h/\lambda$.

Problem 5.4: The partial differential equation for transverse vibrations of a stretched string imbedded in an elastic medium is

$$\frac{\partial^2\psi}{\partial t^2} = c^2\frac{\partial^2\psi}{\partial x^2} - b^2\psi.$$

Obtain the dispersion relation. Then, from the dispersion relation, obtain the partial differential equation. Answer: $\omega^2 = c^2k^2 + b^2$.

Problem 5.5: Let the partial differential equation for waves in a homogeneous medium be written in the form (5.3). Show that the prototype wave function (5.13) satisfies this equation provided ω and $\mathbf{k}$ satisfy the dispersion relation

(5.26) $$L(ik_1, ik_2, ik_3, -i\omega) = 0.$$

More briefly, write (5.4) and

(5.27) $$L(i\mathbf{k}, -i\omega) = 0.$$

Thus obtain the correspondences

(5.28)   (a) grad $\leftrightarrow i\mathbf{k}$,   (b) $\dfrac{\partial}{\partial t} \leftrightarrow -i\omega$,

and inversely

(5.29)   (a) $\mathbf{k} \leftrightarrow -i$ grad,   (b) $\omega \leftrightarrow i\dfrac{\partial}{\partial t}$.

Waves for which the dispersion relation is

(5.30) $$\Omega(\omega, \mathbf{k}) = 0$$

satisfy the partial differential equation

(5.31) $$\Omega\left(i\frac{\partial}{\partial t}, -i\,\text{grad}\right)\psi = 0.$$

Problem 5.6: *In vacuo,* components of the electromagnetic field satisfy the wave equation

(5.32) $$\frac{\partial^2\psi}{\partial t^2} = c^2\,\text{Lap }\psi,$$

where, in Cartesian coordinates

(5.33) $$\text{Lap} = \frac{\partial^2}{\partial x^2} + \frac{\partial^2}{\partial y^2} + \frac{\partial^2}{\partial z^2}.$$

Obtain the dispersion relation for electromagnetic waves. Answer:

(5.34) $$\omega^2 = c^2(k_1{}^2 + k_2{}^2 + k_3{}^2)$$

or, briefly, $\omega^2 = c^2 k^2$.

5.3. The Schroedinger[1] and the Klein-Gordon Equations.[2] The correspondences (5.11) when applied to the nonrelativistic dispersion relation (2.11) for de Broglie waves associated with free particles in one-space dimension lead immediately to the partial differential equation

(5.35) $$i\frac{\partial \psi}{\partial t} = -\frac{\hbar}{2m}\frac{\partial^2 \psi}{\partial x^2}.$$

This is the *Schroedinger time dependent wave equation* (STDWE) for a free particle in one-space dimension. Similarly, application of (5.11) to the relativistic dispersion relation (2.10) for de Broglie waves associated with free particles in one-space dimension leads to the equation

(5.36) $$\frac{\partial^2 \psi}{\partial t^2} = c^2\frac{\partial^2 \psi}{\partial x^2} - \frac{m_0{}^2 c^4}{\hbar^2}\psi,$$

the *Klein-Gordon equation* for a free particle in one-space dimension. The Klein-Gordon equation is frequently called the *Schroedinger relativistic wave equation.*[2]

In obtaining the above wave equations, we proceeded from the energy-momentum relations (2.9) and (2.5), first to the dispersion relations (2.11) and (2.10) via the Einstein-de Broglie relations (2.6), and finally to a wave equation by means of the correspondence (5.11). The intermediate steps, that is, writing down the dispersion relations (2.11) and (2.10), can conveniently and easily be eliminated since the Einstein-de Broglie relations (2.6) and the correspondences (5.11) imply the correspondences

(5.37)   (a) $p \leftrightarrow -i\hbar\frac{\partial}{\partial x}$,   (b) $E \leftrightarrow i\hbar\frac{\partial}{\partial t}$,

for free particles in one-space dimension. More generally, (5.25), (2.6), and (5.28) imply the correspondences

(5.38)   (a) $\mathbf{p} \leftrightarrow -i\hbar\,\text{grad}$,   (b) $E \leftrightarrow i\hbar\frac{\partial}{\partial t}$,

[1] E. Schroedinger, *Ann. Physik,* **79,** 361, 489 (1926); **80,** 437 (1926); **81,** 109 (1926).
[2] O. Klein, *Z. Physik,* **37,** 895 (1926); W. Gordon, *Z. Physik,* **40,** 117 (1926); the Klein-Gordon equation was also proposed by V. Fock, *Z. Physik,* **38,** 242 (1926) and **39,** 226 (1926); by J. Kudar, *Ann. Physik,* **81,** 632 (1926); by Th. de Donder and H. van Dungen, *Compt. rend.,* **183,** 22 (1926); and by Schroedinger at the time when he developed his nonrelativistic wave equation: *Ann. Physik,* **81,** 109 (1926), Sec. 6.

and

(5.39) $$p^2 \leftrightarrow -\hbar^2 \text{ div grad} = -\hbar^2 \text{ Lap},$$

for free particles in three-space dimensions.

We shall assume that (5.37), (5.38), and (5.39), which have been justified only for de Broglie waves associated with free particles, retain their validity when applied to particles in potential fields. The wave equations in such cases have spatially dependent coefficients.

Problem 5.7: From the nonrelativistic energy-momentum relation

(5.40) $$E = \frac{p^2}{2m} + V(\mathbf{r})$$

for a particle in a potential field $V(\mathbf{r})$, obtain the Schroedinger time dependent wave equation

(5.41) $$-\frac{\hbar^2}{2m} \text{ Lap } \psi + V\psi = i\hbar \frac{\partial \psi}{\partial t}.$$

Problem 5.8: From the relativistic energy-momentum relation

(5.42) $$(E - e\Phi)^2 = (c\mathbf{p} - e\mathbf{A})^2 + m_0^2 c^4$$

for a particle of charge e in an electromagnetic field (see (4.12)), obtain the *Klein-Gordon* equation

(5.43) $$\left(-\hbar^2 \frac{\partial^2}{\partial t^2} - 2ie\hbar\Phi \frac{\partial}{\partial t} - ie\hbar \frac{\partial \Phi}{\partial t} + e^2\Phi^2 \right) \psi$$
$$= (-\hbar^2 c^2 \text{ Lap} + 2ie\hbar c\mathbf{A} \cdot \text{grad} + ie\hbar c(\text{div } \mathbf{A}) + e^2 A^2 + m_0^2 c^4)\psi.$$

5.4. de Broglie Wave Packets for Free Particles. In the prototype wave function (5.5) let us take $\omega = \hbar k^2/2m$ and replace C by $\frac{1}{\sqrt{2\pi}} \varphi(k) \, dk$, where $\varphi(k)$ is a real or complex valued function of k. Integrating over-all real values of k, we obtain a *wave packet* (see Section 1.11)

(5.44) $$\psi(x,t) = \frac{1}{\sqrt{2\pi}} \int_{-\infty}^{\infty} \varphi(k) e^{i\left(kx - \frac{\hbar k^2 t}{2m}\right)} \, dk,$$

provided $\varphi(k)$ is so chosen that the continuum of prototype waves thus superposed interfere constructively over only a small region.

The restriction on $\varphi(k)$ for the existence of the integral in (5.44) is well known from the theory of the *Fourier integral:* If $\varphi(k)$ is *square integrable* over $(-\infty, \infty)$, that is, if $\int_{-\infty}^{\infty} |\varphi(k)|^2 \, dk$ exists, then the integral in (5.44) exists. The Fourier integral theorem states further that if $\varphi(k)$ is square integrable, then the function

(5.45) $$\psi(x) = \frac{1}{\sqrt{2\pi}} \int_{-\infty}^{\infty} \varphi(k) e^{ikx} \, dk$$

is square integrable over $(-\infty, \infty)$, that is, $\int_{-\infty}^{\infty} |\psi(x)|^2 \, dx$ exists, and

$$(5.46) \qquad \varphi(k) = \frac{1}{\sqrt{2\pi}} \int_{-\infty}^{\infty} \psi(x) e^{-ikx} \, dx.$$

Equations (5.44), (5.45), and (5.46) solve the initial value problem: Given a square integrable function $\psi(x)$ which represents a de Broglie wave packet for a nonrelativistic free particle at $t = 0$. Find the wave packet $\psi(x,t)$ at any time $t \neq 0$. We simply calculate $\varphi(k)$ from the given $\psi(x)$ using (5.46) and then calculate $\psi(x,t)$ from $\varphi(k)$ using (5.44). Incidentally, (5.44) and (5.45) readily give for a free particle

$$(5.47) \qquad \varphi(k,t) = \varphi(k) e^{-i\hbar k^2 t / 2m}.$$

It is almost superfluous to point out that the terms "wave packet" and "square integrable function" are used synonymously in this text.

Since ψ uniquely determines φ and φ uniquely determines ψ, we shall frequently use the notation

$$(5.48) \qquad \psi \leftrightarrow \varphi.$$

For example, from (5.44) and (5.55) we see that, when

$$(5.49) \qquad \psi(x) \leftrightarrow \varphi(k)$$

for a free particle, then

$$(5.50) \qquad \psi(x,t) \leftrightarrow \varphi(k) e^{-i\hbar k^2 t / 2m}.$$

However, the abbreviated symbols ψ and φ may be used indiscriminately, as in (5.48), when distinction between $\psi(x,t)$ and $\psi(x)$, or between $\varphi(k,t)$ and $\varphi(k)$, is not needed.

The equivalents of (5.44), (5.45), and (5.46) for a free particle in three-space dimensions are

$$(5.51) \qquad \psi(\mathbf{r},t) = (2\pi)^{-3/2} \int_{\infty} \varphi(\mathbf{k}) e^{i(\mathbf{k}\cdot\mathbf{r} - \hbar k^2 t / 2m)} \, d\mathbf{k},$$

$$(5.52) \qquad \psi(\mathbf{r}) = (2\pi)^{-3/2} \int_{\infty} \varphi(\mathbf{k}) e^{i\mathbf{k}\cdot\mathbf{r}} \, d\mathbf{k},$$

and

$$(5.53) \qquad \varphi(\mathbf{k}) = (2\pi)^{-3/2} \int_{\infty} \psi(\mathbf{r}) e^{-i\mathbf{k}\cdot\mathbf{r}} \, d\mathbf{r},$$

respectively, where

$$(5.54) \quad \begin{array}{l} \text{(a)} \quad \int_{\infty} (\quad) \, d\mathbf{k} = \int_{-\infty}^{\infty} \int_{-\infty}^{\infty} \int_{-\infty}^{\infty} (\quad) \, dk_1 \, dk_2 \, dk_3, \\ \text{(b)} \quad \int_{\infty} (\quad) \, d\mathbf{r} = \int_{-\infty}^{\infty} \int_{-\infty}^{\infty} \int_{-\infty}^{\infty} (\quad) \, dx \, dy \, dz, \end{array}$$

and

$$(5.55) \qquad \begin{array}{l} \mathbf{k} \cdot \mathbf{r} = k_1 x + k_2 y + k_3 z, \\ k^2 = k_1{}^2 + k_2{}^2 + k_3{}^2. \end{array}$$

Problem 5.9: For what electromagnetic fields is the total energy finite? (Hint: See (1.62).)

Problem 5.10: Find $\psi(x)$, given $\varphi(k) = 1$ when $-a \leq k \leq a$, $\varphi(k) = 0$ for all other values of k. Answer: $\psi(x) = \sqrt{\dfrac{2}{\pi}} \dfrac{\sin ax}{x}$.

Problem 5.11: Find $\varphi(k)$, given $\psi(x) = \exp(-|x|)$.

Answer: $$\varphi(k) = \sqrt{\frac{2}{\pi}} \left(\frac{1}{1 + k^2}\right).$$

Problem 5.11: Find $\varphi(k)$, given the Gaussian wave packet

$$(5.56) \qquad \chi(x) = Ae^{-x^2/4\sigma^2}$$

and the definite integral

$$(5.57) \qquad \int_{-\infty}^{\infty} e^{-s^2/a^2}\, ds = a\sqrt{\pi}.$$

Answer:

$$(5.58) \qquad \varphi(k) = A\sigma\sqrt{2}\, e^{-\sigma^2 k^2}.$$

Problem 5.13: Find the wave function $\psi(x,t)$ for de Broglie matter waves for a free particle in the nonrelativistic approximation, given that at $t = 0$ the wave function is the Gaussian function (5.56). (Hint: Substitute from (5.58) into (5.44) and let

$$(5.59) \qquad b^2 = \sigma^2 + i\hbar t/2m.$$

Complete the square in the integrand for $\psi(x,t)$. Then let $k = s + ix/2b^2$, $dk = ds$, $a = 1/b$, and use (5.57).) Answer:

$$(5.60) \qquad \psi(x,t) = \frac{A\sigma}{b}\, e^{-x^2/4b^2}.$$

Problem 5.14: Let $\psi_1 \leftrightarrow \varphi_1$ and $\psi_2 \leftrightarrow \varphi_2$. Show that, for any constants c_1 and c_2, real or complex,

$$(5.61) \qquad c_1\psi_1 + c_2\psi_2 \leftrightarrow c_1\varphi_1 + c_2\varphi_2.$$

Problem 5.15: Let $\psi(x) \leftrightarrow \varphi(k)$. Show that $\psi(x + a) \leftrightarrow e^{iak}\varphi(k)$ and that $e^{-iax}\psi(x) \leftrightarrow \varphi(k + a)$, where a is real.

5.5. Statistical Properties of Wave Packets. Statistical parameters of special interest in the study of a wave packet are its *norm*, *centroid*, and *spread*. In order to simplify the notation in defining these parameters, and for purposes of later generalizations, we introduce the *inner products* of wave packets, defined by

$$(5.62) \quad \begin{aligned} &\text{(a)} \quad (\psi_1,\psi_2) = \int_{-\infty}^{\infty} \psi_1{}^*\psi_2\, dx, \\ &\text{(b)} \quad (\varphi_1,\varphi_2) = \int_{-\infty}^{\infty} \varphi_1{}^*\varphi_2\, dk. \end{aligned}$$

The *norms* $N(\psi)$ and $N(\varphi)$ are defined by

(5.63)   (a) $N(\psi) = (\psi,\psi)$,   (b) $N(\varphi) = (\varphi,\varphi)$.

An exceptionally important theorem is *Parseval's theorem:* Let $\psi_1 \leftrightarrow \varphi_1$ and $\psi_2 \leftrightarrow \varphi_2$. Then

(5.64) $(\psi_1,\psi_2) = (\varphi_1,\varphi_2)$.

As a special case of Parseval's theorem we obtain the useful theorem: Let $\psi \leftrightarrow \varphi$. Then

(5.65) $N(\psi) = N(\varphi)$.

The total energy in an electromagnetic field is proportional to the norm of the field.

Mean or *expectation values* of functions $f(x,t)$ and $g(k,t)$ at time t are defined to be

(5.66)   (a) $\langle f \rangle_t = \dfrac{(\psi,f\psi)}{(\psi,\psi)}$,   (b) $\langle g \rangle_t = \dfrac{(\varphi,g\varphi)}{(\varphi,\varphi)}$.

Observe that $\langle f \rangle_t$ is not a function of x although it may be a function of t even when f itself does not depend on t. Similarly, $\langle g \rangle_t$ is not a function of k although it may be a function of t even when g itself does not depend on t. When not needed for clarity, the subscript t need not be placed on the bracket "$\langle \ \rangle$" indicating expectation value.

The mean value of x for a wave packet is called its *centroid*. A de Broglie wave packet is highly localized in the neighborhood of its centroid since the waves which constitute the packet interfere destructively except in a limited region. Of great importance in connection with the Heisenberg uncertainty principle is the *width* Δx of a wave packet and the *propagation number spread* Δk of the waves composing the packet, defined precisely by

(5.67)   (a) $\Delta x = \sqrt{\langle (x - \langle x \rangle)^2 \rangle}$ (b) $\Delta k = \sqrt{\langle (k - \langle k \rangle)^2 \rangle}$.

It is frequently convenient to speak of $\langle x \rangle$ and Δx as the centroid and spread in "x space," and of $\langle k \rangle$ and Δk as the centroid and spread in "k space." We might be inclined to expect that Δk is small if Δx is small and large if Δx is large. However, a theorem of great importance in applications (e.g. to electric filters) and in quantum mechanics states the contrary: For any wave packet

(5.68) $(\Delta x)(\Delta k) \geq \tfrac{1}{2}$.

Problem 5.16: Show that for a free particle $N(\varphi)$ is constant, independent of t. (Hint: Use (5.47), (5.63b), and (5.62b).)

Problem 5.17: Show that for a free particle $N(\psi)$ is a constant, independent of t.

Problem 5.18: Show that

(5.69)

$$\text{(a)} \quad \frac{\partial}{\partial t}(\psi_1,\psi_2) = \left(\psi_1, \frac{\partial\psi_2}{\partial t}\right) + \left(\frac{\partial\psi_1}{\partial t}, \psi_2\right),$$

$$\text{(b)} \quad \frac{\partial}{\partial t}(\varphi_1,\varphi_2) = \left(\varphi_1, \frac{\partial\varphi_2}{\partial t}\right) + \left(\frac{\partial\varphi_2}{\partial t}, \varphi_2\right).$$

Problem 5.19: Show that

(5.70)

(a) $\langle c \rangle = c$,
(b) $\langle cf \rangle = c\langle f \rangle$,
(c) $\langle c_1 f_1 + c_2 f_2 \rangle = c_1\langle f_1 \rangle + c_2\langle f_2 \rangle$,
(d) $\langle f(t) \rangle = f(t)$.

Problem 5.20: Show that

(5.71)   (a) $(\Delta x)^2 = \langle x^2 \rangle - \langle x \rangle^2$,   (b) $(\Delta k)^2 = \langle k^2 \rangle - \langle k \rangle^2$.

Problem 5.21: Let $\psi = 1$ when $-a \leq x \leq a$, $\psi = 0$ for all other values of x. Calculate $\Delta x^n \equiv \sqrt{\langle x^{2n} \rangle - \langle x^n \rangle^2}$. Answer: $\Delta x^n = na^n/(n+1)\sqrt{2n+1}$, n even, $= a^n/\sqrt{2n+1}$, n odd.

Problem 5.22: Calculate $N(\psi)$ for the Gaussian wave packet (5.60). Observe that $N(\psi)$ does not depend on t in agreement with Problem 5.17. (Hint: Let $D = bb^* = |b^2| = (\sigma^4 + \hbar^2 t^2/4m^2)^{1/2}$ where b^2 is given by (5.59).) Then $\frac{1}{b^2} + \frac{1}{b^{*2}} = \frac{2\sigma^2}{D^2}$ and $\psi^*\psi = \frac{A^2\sigma^2}{D} e^{-\sigma^2 x^2/2D^2}$. Answer:

(5.72) $N(\psi) = A^2\sigma\sqrt{2\pi}$.

Problem 5.23: Calculate $N(\varphi)$ for the Gaussian wave packet (5.47), where $\varphi(k)$ is given by (5.58). Answer: See (5.72).

Problem 5.24: Calculate (a) $\langle x \rangle_t$, (b) $(\Delta x)_t$, (c) $\langle k \rangle_t$, and (d) $(\Delta k)_t$ for the Gaussian wave packet (5.60), given the definite integrals

(5.73)   (a) $\int_{-\infty}^{\infty} se^{-s^2/a^2} ds = 0$,   (b) $\int_{-\infty}^{\infty} s^2 e^{-s^2/a^2} ds = \frac{1}{2}a^3\sqrt{\pi}$.

Verify that (5.68) is satisfied. Answers:

(5.74)
(a) $\langle x \rangle_t = 0$,   (b) $(\Delta x)_t = \sigma(1 + \hbar^2 t^2/4m^2\sigma^4)^{1/2}$
(c) $\langle k \rangle_t = 0$,   (d) $(\Delta k)_t = 1/2\sigma$.

Problem 5.25: Generalize (5.62)–(5.71) to packets in three-space dimensions.

Problem 5.26: By means of the assignment (5.25), show that the generalization of (5.68) to wave packets in three-space dimensions implies the Heisenberg uncertainty relations (1.84).

5.6. The Spreading of de Broglie Wave Packets. Dispersion occurs when the group velocity V_g is not equal to the phase velocity V_p. Since these velocities are not equal for de Broglie matter waves associated with free particles (see (2.12) or (2.13)), the de Broglie wave packet associated with a particle of mass m should spread. If the rate of spreading is appreciable, we encounter a conflict with ordinary concepts in which we visualize a particle as remaining highly localized in space.

A statistical measure of the amount of spreading is the ratio $(\Delta x)_t/(\Delta x)_0$. Kemble[3] has given a general formula from which this ratio may be computed for any wave packet:

$$(5.75) \quad (\Delta x)_t^2 = (\Delta x)_0^2 + \hbar(\langle xk \rangle_0 + \langle kx \rangle_0 - 2\langle x \rangle_0 \langle k \rangle_0) \frac{t}{m}$$
$$+ \hbar^2 (\Delta k)_0^2 t^2 / m^2.$$

However, we have not yet defined expressions such as $\langle xk \rangle$ and $\langle kx \rangle$. Let us therefore limit present considerations to the Gaussian wave packet, for which all needed quadratures have already been performed. To facilitate calculations, we solve (5.74b) for t, obtaining

$$(5.76) \quad t = \frac{2m(\Delta x)_0^2}{\hbar} \sqrt{\frac{(\Delta x)_t^2}{(\Delta x)_0^2} - 1}.$$

In Table 5.1 are shown the times required for Gaussian wave packets representing a gram mass, a microgram mass, a proton mass, and an electron mass to double their widths, and for the packets representing a proton mass and an electron mass to increase in width by a factor of 10^8, for various initial widths, as calculated from (5.76). As readily seen from the table, spreading is inappreciable except for atomic and smaller masses. This is contrary to ordinary concepts if we think in terms of particles remaining localized in space. However, the results of the calculations are fully justifiable, provided they are properly interpreted.

TABLE 5.1. SPREADING OF GAUSSIAN WAVE PACKETS, CALCULATED FOR SELECTED MASSES AND INITIAL WIDTHS

Mass, gms	$(\Delta x)_0$, cms	t when $(\Delta x)_t/(\Delta x)_0 = 2$	t when $(\Delta x)_t/(\Delta x)_0 = 10^8$
1	1	10^{21} yrs	
1	10^{-3}	10^{15} yrs	
10^{-6}	1	10^{15} yrs	
10^{-6}	10^{-3}	10^9 yrs	
1.67×10^{-24}	1	1.5 hrs	1 yr
1.67×10^{-24}	10^{-3}	.005 secs	32 secs
9.11×10^{-28}	1	3 secs	4.7 days
9.11×10^{-28}	10^{-3}	3×10^{-6} secs	.017 secs
9.11×10^{-28}	10^{-8}	3×10^{-16} secs	1.7×10^{-12} secs

[3] E. C. Kemble, *Fundamental Principles of Quantum Mechanics*, Dover, 1958, p. 223.

For values of t so large that

(5.77) $$\hbar t/2m(\Delta x)_0{}^2 \gg 1,$$

we may neglect the 1 under the radical in (5.74b) and then obtain

(5.78) $$(\Delta x)_t \cong \hbar t/2m(\Delta x)_0.$$

For the Gaussian wave packet (5.56), from which our equations are derived,

(5.79) $$(\Delta x)_0 \, \Delta k = \tfrac{1}{2}.$$

But the momentum of a corpuscle is proportional to the propagation number of its de Broglie wave:

(5.80) $$p = \hbar k, \qquad \Delta p = \hbar \, \Delta k.$$

Hence, from (5.79) and (5.80), for the Gaussian wave packet (5.60),

(5.81) $$(\Delta x)_0 (\Delta p)_0 = \hbar/2.$$

Eliminating $(\Delta x)_0$ first from (5.78), then partially from (5.77), by means of (5.81), we find that

(5.82) $$(\Delta x)_t \cong \frac{t(\Delta p)_0}{m}$$

for

(5.83) $$t(\Delta v)_0 \gg (\Delta x)_0.$$

The same conclusion can be obtained from classical physics. For a free particle, $x = x_0 + v_0 t$. Assuming that the time t is accurately measurable but that x_0 and v_0 are inaccurately known, $(\Delta x) = (\Delta x)_0 + t(\Delta v)_0$. For times t so great that (5.83), we again have (5.82). Both classical and quantum mechanics imply (5.82) when $t(\Delta v)_0 \gg (x)_0$, but only quantum mechanics gives (5.78). The smaller $(\Delta x)_0$, the more rapidly $(\Delta x)_t$ increases with time.

5.7. References for Supplementary Reading.

Section 5.1:   Schiff, 18–20.
Section 5.3:   French, 185–8; McConnell, 33–6; White, 54–6.
Section 5.4: Bohm, 77–80; Kemble, 10–14, 35–7; Kramers, 13–25; Mott and Massey, 14–18; Persico, 106–10; Sproull, 468–72.
Section 5.5:   Persico, 110–19.
Section 5.6:   Bohm, 65–9, 99–102; Shankland, 50–57.

CHAPTER 6

OBSERVABLES AND LINEAR OPERATORS

6.1. Observables, Variables, and Operators. An *observable* is any quantity that can be measured. In classical mechanics, observables of principal interest are *position, linear momentum, angular momentum,* and *energy.* Quantum mechanics has added *parity* and *electron spin* to this list.

According to classical mechanics, observables can be simultaneously measured with any desired degree of precision, at least in principle, by sufficient refinement of the measuring apparatus. According to quantum mechanics, such is not the case, even in theory. For example, in any measurement of the position coordinates of a particle, there is an uncertainty in the momentum transferred to the particle, by its interaction with the measuring apparatus, such that the Heisenberg uncertainty relations (1.84) are satisfied.

In classical mechanics, observables are *represented* by ordinary mathematical variables, such as x, y, z, p_x, etc. In quantum mechanics, *observables* are also *associated* with *operators.* One must now carefully distinguish between the three concepts: the *observable A*, the *variable A*, and the *operator A*. Distinguishing symbols such as A_{obs}, A_{var}, and A_{op} could be used but in practice there is seldom justification for confusion if the same symbol is used throughout, the concept being determined by the context.

6.2. Linear Operators and Linear Manifolds. The concept of a *linear operator* is important both for the mathematical development and for the interpretation of quantum mechanics. An operator is a law (i.e. a process) by which we associate with each member of a certain set of objects a member of the same set or of another set of objects. For the present, the objects considered will be functions with all necessary mathematical properties such as continuity, differentiability, etc. For example, the first set of objects may be the set of all square integrable functions $\psi(x)$ and the second set of objects may be the set of their Fourier transforms. We may write $\mathcal{O}\psi(x) = \varphi(k)$ where $\mathcal{O}$ is the operator defined by (5.46). An operator is defined by a correspondence between members of two sets of objects, or between members of a single set of objects. For example, a translation operator T_c is defined by $T_c f(x) = f(x + c)$. When $Af = g$, we frequently write $f \leftrightarrow g$. and say that "A transforms f into g."

66

The operator A defined by $Af = c \cdot f$ is an example of *multiplicative* operators in which the operation consists of a multiplication. Another multiplicative operator is defined by $Bf = x \cdot f$. An important property of multiplicative operators is their *commutativity:* When A and B are multiplicative operators, $A(Bf) = B(Af)$. Of great importance in quantum mechanics are relations between noncommuting operators.

The wave functions on which the operators of quantum mechanics operate form *linear manifolds:* A set of functions $\{f\}$ is said to form a *linear manifold M* if, f_1 and f_2 being any two members of M, $c_1 f_1 + c_2 f_2$ is also a member of M, for any real or complex constants c_1 and c_2.

In Problem 6.8 it is to be proved that the set of all square integrable functions, that is, of all wave packets, forms a linear manifold.

An operator A is said to be *linear over a linear manifold M* if, for every f and g of M and for all real and complex numbers c and d,

(6.1a) Af is defined

and

(6.1b) $A(cf + dg) = c \cdot Af + d \cdot Ag.$

This definition does not require that Af belong to M for every f of M. For example, let M be the linear manifold of square integrable functions and let $Af = x \cdot f$. The function $f = 1/\sqrt{1 + x^2}$ belongs to M but Af does not belong to M. To eliminate this possibility, we may replace condition (6.1a) by a stronger condition:

(6.1a)'   for every f of M, Af is defined and belongs to M.

We then may say that A is *strongly linear over M.*

In other cases the same objective may be attained by limiting considerations to a more restricted linear manifold. For example, when interested in the operator $A = x\cdot$, we might limit our considerations to functions f such that $x^n f$ is square integrable for every nonnegative integer n.

When A and B are linear over a linear manifold M, linear operators cA and $A \pm B$ are defined over M by

(6.2) $(cA)f = c(Af),$

(6.3) $(A \pm B)f = Af \pm Bf.$

When, further, A and B are strongly linear over M, operators AB and A^n are defined over M by

(6.4) $(AB)f = A(Bf),$

(6.5) $A^n f = A(A^{n-1}f), n = 2, 3, \ldots.$

We say that $A = 0$ over M if $Af = 0$ for all f in M.

Examples of nonlinear operators are the operators A and B defined by $Af = f + c$, $c \neq 0$, and $Bf = f^2$.

Problem 6.1:   Show that the following equations define linear operators:

(1) $Af(x) = f(-x)$,
(2) $Af(x) = f(x) + f(-x)$,
(3) $Af(x) = f(x) - f(-x)$,
(4) $Af(x) = f(x + c)$,
(5) $Af(x) = p \dfrac{d^2f(x)}{dx^2} + q \dfrac{df(x)}{dx} + rf(x)$,

where p, q, and r may be functions of x.

Problem 6.2:   Let $A = \dfrac{4d^2}{dx^2}$, $B = -\dfrac{d^4}{dx^4}$, $C = \dfrac{d^2}{dx^2} + 4$. Show that

$A = B$ and that $C = 0$ over the linear manifold of all linear combinations of $f_1 = \sin 2x$ and $f_2 = \cos 2x$.

6.3. Inner Products and Norms.   Many problems in quantum mechanics require modification of the definitions of inner products and norms given in (5.62) and (5.63). To avoid repetition with individual cases, we give here abstract definitions which are generally applicable.

A complex number (f,g) associated with each pair of functions f and g belonging to a linear manifold M having the properties

(6.6)
  (a) $(f,g) = (g,f)^*$,
  (b) $(f,f) \geq 0$, and $(f,f) = 0$ if and only $f = 0$,
  (c) $(f,cg + dh) = c(f,g) + d(f,h)$

for every f, g, and h belonging to M and for all constants c and d, is called an *inner product*. A linear manifold M for which an inner product is defined is called an *inner product space*. From (6.6a) there follows that (f,f) is a real number, justifying (6.6b). The inner product $N(f) \equiv (f,f)$ is called the *norm of f*. A function whose norm equals one is said to be *normalized*.

Problem 6.3:   Show that:

(6.7)
  (a) $(cf,g) = c^*(f,g)$,
  (b) $(cf + dg, c'f' + d'g')$
          $= c^*c'(f,f') + c^*d'(f,g') + d^*c'(g,f') + d^*d'(g,g')$,
  (c) $N(cf + dg) = c^*c(f,f) + c^*d(f,g) + cd^*(g,f) + dd^*(g,g)$,
  (e) $(f,g) + (g,f) = $ a real number,
  (f) $i(f,g) - i(g,f) = $ a real number,
  (g) $(f,g)(g,f) = |(f,g)|^2 = |(g,f)|^2 = $ a real number.

Problem 6.4: Find a constant c so that $N(cf) = 1$, where $f \neq 0$. Answer:

$$(6.8) \qquad\qquad c = e^{i\delta}/\sqrt{N(f)}$$

where δ is an arbitrary real number.

Problem 6.5: Show that if $(Af,g) = 0$, or if $(f,Ag) = 0$, for every f and g, then $Af = 0$ for every f. (Hint: Let $g = Af$, or $f = Ag$, and use (6.6b).)

Problem 6.6: Show that if $(f,Ag) = (f,Bg)$ for all f, and g in a linear manifold M, then $A = B$ over M.

Problem 6.7: Show that (5.62) defines inner products satisfying (6.6) and, consequently, (6.7).

6.4. The Schwartz Inequality.

Of great usefulness is the *Schwartz inequality:*

$$(6.9) \qquad\qquad 0 \leq (f,g)(g,f) \leq (f,f)(g,g),$$

where the second equality occurs only if $f = 0$, or $g = 0$, or there exists a constant c such that $f = cg$. *Proof:* By (6.6b), $(f + qg, f + qg) \geq 0$ for all real and complex values of q, the inequality holding unless $f + qg = 0$. In that case, taking $c = -q$, we have $f = cg$. More generally we have, using (6.7b), $(f + qg, f + qg) = (f,f) + q^*(g,f) + q(f,g) + qq^*(g,g) \geq 0$ for all q. Letting $q = r + is$, $q^* = r - is$ this gives $(f,f) + Pr + Qs + (g,g)(r^2 + s^2) \geq 0$ for all r and all s, where $P = (f,g) + (g,f)$ and $Q = i(f,g) - i(g,f)$ are real numbers. The values of r and s for which this nonnegative expression has its minimum value are readily found by differentiation to be given by the equations $P + 2r(g,g) = 0$, $Q + 2s(g,g) = 0$. Eliminating r and s, we obtain (6.9).

Problem 6.8: Show that if $N(f)$ and $N(g)$ are finite, then $N(cf + dg)$, where c and d are constants, is finite. Hence show that the set of all square integrable functions form a linear manifold. (Hint: The hypothesis and the Schwartz inequality (6.9) imply that (f,g) and (g,f) are finite. Now use (6.7c).)

Problem 6.9: Show that

$$(6.10) \qquad\qquad \sqrt{N(f + g)} \leq \sqrt{N(f)} + \sqrt{N(g)},$$

the equality holding only in case $f = 0$ or $g = 0$ or $f = cg$ for some c. (Hint: Write $N(f + g) = (f + g, f + g) = (f, f + g) + (g, f + g)$ and use the Schwartz inequality.)

6.5. Expectation Values and Uncertainties.

In classical mechanics, the state of a system of particles is described at any instant of time by giving the positions and velocities of each particle in the system. Moreover, the classical observables can be measured to any desired degree of precision, at least in theory, by sufficient refinement of the measuring apparatus.

According to one of the basic principles of quantum mechanics, all the information that can be obtained about the quantum mechanical state of a system is contained in the specification of a wave function ψ. From this function can be calculated, for example, the expectation values of observables and the expected uncertainties in their measurement. Postponing motivation until later, we give here two very basic definitions:

1. The *expectation value* $\langle A \rangle$ of an observable A, when the state of a system is described by a wave function ψ, is

$$(6.11) \qquad \langle A \rangle = (\psi, A\psi)/(\psi, \psi)$$

where (f, g) is an appropriately defined inner product.

2. The *expectation value of the uncertainty* in a measurement of an observable A, ΔA, is

$$(6.12) \qquad \Delta A = \sqrt{\langle (A - \langle A \rangle)^2 \rangle}.$$

It is to be noted that $\langle A \rangle$ is defined only for wave functions ψ such that (ψ, ψ) and $(\psi, A\psi)$ are finite. Also, since

$$(6.13) \qquad (\Delta A)^2 = \langle A^2 \rangle - \langle A \rangle^2,$$

ΔA is defined only for wave functions ψ such that (ψ, ψ), $(\psi, A\psi)$ and $(\psi, A^2\psi)$ are finite. The set of all wave functions ψ such that $\langle A \rangle$ and ΔA are defined form a linear manifold which we shall denote by M_A.

Problem 6.10:   Obtain (6.13) from (6.12).

6.6. Real Observables and Hermitean Operators.   In agreement with the fact that the only possible results of measurements of real observables, such as position coordinates and components of momentum, are real numbers, we wish to impose the condition that the expectation value $\langle A \rangle$ of a real observable A be real for all wave functions belonging to M_A. Since a number z is real if and only if $z = z^*$, we readily see from (6.6a) and (6.11) that $\langle A \rangle$ is real when calculated for a given wave function ψ if and only if $(\psi, A\psi) = (A\psi, \psi)$. This equality for all wave functions belonging to M_A imposes a stringent condition on the operator A which may be associated with the real observable A and leads to the so-called *Hermitean property* of linear operators. Two definitions are given, then these definitions are shown to be equivalent.

First Definition of Hermiticity: A linear operator A is said to be Hermitean over an inner product space M if and only if

$$(6.14) \qquad (f, Af) = (Af, f)$$

for every f in M.

Second Definition of Hermiticity: A linear operator A is said to be Hermitean over an inner product space M if and only if

(6.15) $$(f,Ag) = (Af,g)$$

for every f and g in M.

Quite evidently, the second definition implies the first, since (6.15) becomes (6.14) when $g = f$. To show that the first definition implies the second, replace f in (6.14) by $f + cg$. Then, by hypothesis, $(f + cg, Af + cAg) = (Af + cAg, f + cg)$, or, by (6.7b), $(f,Af) + c(f,Ag) + c^*(g,Af) + cc^*(g,Ag) = (Af,f) + c(Af,g) + c^*(Ag,f) + cc^*(Ag,g)$. But $(f,Af) = (Af,f)$ and $(g,Ag) = (Ag,f)$ by hypothesis. Hence $c\{(f,Ag) - (Af,g)\} = c^*\{(Ag,f) - (g,Af)\}$. By (6.6a) this is an equation of the form $cX = c^*X^*$ which, by hypothesis, is to be true for all values of c. Taking $c = 1$, $c^* = 1$, we find that $X = X^*$. But by taking $c = i$, $c^* = -i$, we find that $X = -X^*$. Hence $X = 0$, or (6.15).

A linear operator A associated with a real observable A must satisfy (6.14) and (6.15) for all f and g belonging to M_A. We have shown that (6.14) and (6.15) are equivalent, (6.14) is as strong as (6.15).

Problem 6.11: Show that the operator $A = c\cdot$ is Hermitean if and only if c is real.

Problem 6.12: Let A be Hermitean. Show that cA is Hermitean if and only if c is real.

Problem 6.13: Show that A^n is Hermitean if A is Hermitean.

Problem 6.14: Let A and B be Hermitean. Show that $A^mB^n + B^nA^m$ is Hermitean. In particular, $AB + BA$ is Hermitean.

Problem 6.15: Let A be a Hermitean operator. Prove that $\langle A^2 \rangle \geq 0$ for all ψ and that $\langle A^2 \rangle = 0$ for a certain ψ if and only if $A\psi = 0$.

Problem 6.16: Prove that if $Af = cf$ for a certain f with finite norm, where A is Hermitean, then c is real, (f,Af) and (Af,Af) are finite, $\langle A \rangle = c$, $\langle A^n \rangle = c^n$, and $\Delta A = 0$.

Problem 6.17: Prove that if $Af = cf$ and $Ag = dg$ for certain f and g with finite norms and certain constants c and d, where A is Hermitean and $c \neq d$, then f and g are orthogonal. Show also that $(f,Ag) = 0$ and $(g,Af) = 0$.

Problem 6.18: Let a wave function f with finite norm satisfy the equation $i\hbar \frac{\partial f}{\partial t} = Hf$. Show that, if H is Hermitean, then $\frac{\partial N(f)}{\partial t} = 0$.

Problem 6.19: Prove that, for given g, there exists no function f such that $Hf = g$, where H is Hermitean, unless g is orthogonal to every function f_0 which satisfies the homogeneous equation $Hf_0 = 0$.

Problem 6.20: A *projection* operator P which projects functions f onto a given function g, which has unit norm, may be defined by $Pf = (g,f)g$. Show that P is Hermitean and that $P^2 = P$.

6.7. Anti-Hermitean Operators.   Later we shall encounter certain very useful operators for which (6.11) is always a pure imaginary number. Now a complex number z is pure imaginary if and only if $z = -z^*$. Hence from (6.6a) we see that (6.11) gives a pure imaginary number if and only if $(\psi, A\psi) = -(A\psi, \psi)$. This motivates the

First Definition of Anti-Hermiticity: A linear operator A is said to be anti-Hermitean over an inner product space $M(A \neq 0$ over $M)$ if and only if

$$(6.16) \qquad\qquad (f, Af) = -(Af, f)$$

for every f in M.

Frequently it is convenient to use a *Second Definition of Anti-Hermiticity:* A linear operator A is said to be anti-Hermitean over an inner product space $M(A \neq 0$ over $M)$ if and only if

$$(6.17) \qquad\qquad (f, Ag) = -(Af, g)$$

for every f and g in M.

Problem 6.21:   Prove the equivalence of the two definitions of anti-Hermiticity.

Problem 6.22:   Show that the operator $A = c\cdot$ is anti-Hermitean if and only if c is pure imaginary.

Problem 6.23:   Let A be Hermitean, $A \neq 0$. Show that iA is anti-Hermitean.

Problem 6.24:   Let A be anti-Hermitean. Show that iA is Hermitean.

Problem 6.25:   Let $A = \dfrac{d}{dx}$ and $B = i\dfrac{d}{dx}$ over the linear manifold of differentiable, square integrable wave functions. Show that A is anti-Hermitean and that B is Hermitean.

6.8. Adjoint Operators.   A general theorem from the theory of linear operators states that if A is any linear operator defined over a linear manifold M, then there exists a linear operator B over M such that $(f, Ag) = (Bf, g)$ for all f and g in M. Quite trivially, if A is Hermitean, $B = A$, if A is anti-Hermitean, $B = -A$. In these and in more general cases we call B the *adjoint* of A and for convenience introduce the symbol $A\dagger$. As with Hermiticity and anti-Hermiticity, we have a choice of two equivalent definitions:

First Definition of $A\dagger$: $A\dagger$ is called the *adjoint* of A over an inner product space M if and only if

$$(6.18) \qquad\qquad (A\dagger f, f) = (f, Af)$$

for every f in M.

Second Definition of $A\dagger$: $A\dagger$ is called the *adjoint* of A over an inner product space M if and only if

(6.19) $$(A\dagger f,g) = (f,Ag)$$

for every f and g in M.

Problem 6.26: Prove that the two definitions of the adjoint of a linear operator are equivalent.

Problem 6.27: Let $A = c\cdot$. Show that $A\dagger = c^*$.

Problem 6.28: Prove that if $B = A\dagger$, then $A = B\dagger$, that is, if $A\dagger$ is the adjoint of A, then A is the adjoint of $A\dagger$, or, symbolically, $(A\dagger)\dagger = A$.

Problem 6.29: Show that $A\dagger = A$ if and only if A is Hermitean, and that $A\dagger = -A$ if and only if $A \neq 0$ is anti-Hermitean.

Problem 6.30: Show that $(AB)\dagger = B\dagger A\dagger$, and that $(cA)\dagger = c^*A\dagger$.

Problem 6.31: Show that, if A and B are Hermitean, then $(A^mB^n)\dagger = B^nA^m$. In particular, $(AB)\dagger = BA$.

Problem 6.32: Let $C = (A + A\dagger)/2$, $D = (A - A\dagger)/2$. Show that C is Hermitean and that D is anti-Hermitean. Express A and $A\dagger$ in terms of C and D.

Problem 6.33: Let A and B be Hermitean and let a and b be real numbers. Show that $(aA \pm ibB)\dagger = aA \mp ibB$. In particular, show that $L_+ \equiv A + iB$ and $L_- \equiv A - iB$ are adjoint operators.

Problem 6.34: Prove that $\langle A\dagger A \rangle \geq 0$ for every f belong to M_A and that $\langle A\dagger A \rangle = 0$ for a certain f if and only if $Af = 0$.

6.9. Commutators. Two linear operators A and B over a linear manifold M are said to *commute* over M if,

(6.20) $$A(Bf) = B(Af)$$

for every f in M. For brevity, we frequently say "A and B commute" and write "$AB = BA$," implying recognition of the linear manifold over which (6.20) is satisfied. Two linear operators A and B over a linear manifold M are said to *anti-commute* over M if $A(Bf) = -B(Af)$ for every f in M. For brevity, we write $AB = -BA$ over M.

Due to the extreme importance of the commutation relation, we associate with any two operators A and B over a linear manifold M a third operator (A,B) called *the commutator of A and B*, defined by

(6.21) $$(A,B) = AB - BA$$

over M. A and B commute over M if and only if $(A,B) = 0$ over M.

Quantities (operators) which commute with all other quantities are called *c numbers*. Quantities which do not commute with all other quantities are called *q numbers*.

Problem 6.35: Demonstrate the following basic properties of the commutator:

(6.22)

(a) $(A,B) = -(B,A)$,
(b) $(A,B + C) = (A,B) + (A,C)$,
(c) $(A,BC) = B(A,C) + (A,B)C$,
(d) $(AB,C) = A(B,C) + (A,C)B$

Problem 6.36: Show that if two operators do not commute at least one of them is not multiplicative.

Problem 6.37: Show that, if A and B are noncommuting Hermitean operators, then (A,B) is anti-Hermitean and $i(A,B)$ is Hermitean.

Problem 6.38: Prove that the product of two Hermitean operators is Hermitean if and only if they commute.

Problem 6.39: Show that $(f,ABg) = (BAf,g)$ for any two Hermitean operators A and B and for all f and g. Does this imply that A and B commute? Explain.

Problem 6.40: Show that

$$(6.23) \qquad \left(f(x), \frac{d}{dx}\right) = -\frac{df}{dx}.$$

Problem 6.41: Let

$$(6.24) \qquad \text{(a)} \quad L_+ = x + \frac{d}{dx}, \qquad \text{(b)} \quad L_- = x - \frac{d}{dx}.$$

Show that

$$(6.25) \qquad (L_+,L_-) = 2.$$

6.10. Born's Proof[1] of the General Uncertainty Relation. The Heisenberg uncertainty relations (1.84) are special cases of the following basic theorem which provides the mathematical foundation for all quantum mechanical uncertainty relations:

THEOREM: Let $C = i(A,B)$, where A and B are Hermitean. Then, for all wave functions belonging to $M_{A,B}$,

$$(6.26) \qquad (\Delta A)^2(\Delta B)^2 \geq \tfrac{1}{4} \langle C \rangle^2.$$

Proof: Let $a = \langle A \rangle$, $b = \langle B \rangle$. Since A and B are Hermitean, a and b are real. Define Hermitean operators S and T by $S = A - a$, $T = B - b$. Then by (6.12), $\langle S^2 \rangle = (\Delta A)^2$ and $\langle T^2 \rangle = (\Delta B)^2$. Further, $(S,T) = ST - TS = (A - a)(B - b) - (B - b)(A - a) = AB - BA = -iC$. Now define an operator L by $L = S + i\lambda T$ where λ is real. Then by Problem 6.33, $L\dagger = S - i\lambda T$. From Problem 6.34 we know that $\langle L\dagger L \rangle \geq 0$ for all wave functions. But then $\langle L\dagger L \rangle = \langle (S - i\lambda T)(S + i\lambda T) \rangle = \langle S^2 \rangle + i\lambda \langle (ST - TS) \rangle + \lambda^2 \langle T^2 \rangle = (\Delta A)^2 + \lambda \langle C \rangle + \lambda^2 (\Delta B)^2$. The mini-

---

[1] M. Born, *Atomic Physics*, sixth edition, Hafner, 1957, p. 387.

mum value of this nonnegative expression is given by taking $\lambda = -\langle C \rangle / 2(\Delta B)^2$. From this value of λ we obtain (6.26).

6.11. References for Supplementary Reading.

Section 6.1:   Persico, 314–17, 331–40; Schiff, 41–2.

Section 6.2:   Persico, 283–8.

Section 6.3:   Kemble, 114–19.

Section 6.5:   Persico, 344–6.

Section 6.8:   Kemble, 278–9; Mandl, 71–4.

Section 6.9:   Bohm, 182; Frenkel, 56–8; Kramers, 100–110; McConnell, 44–51; Persico, 342–4.

Section 6.10:   Bohm, 205–7; Born, 387–9; Mandl, 82–8; Pauling and Wilson, 428–32; Peaslee and Mueller, 242–3; Persico, 132–45.

CHAPTER 7

QUANTUM MECHANICAL OPERATORS

7.1. Classical and Quantum Mechanical Poisson Brackets.
The Hermitean operators associated with real observables must satisfy
relations which emerge naturally from the Poisson brackets of central
importance in classical mechanics. The Poisson bracket $[u,v]$ of two
differentiable functions u and v of the position coordinates q_i and conjugate momenta p_i is defined by

$$(7.1) \qquad [u,v] = \sum_i \left(\frac{\partial u}{\partial q_i} \frac{\partial v}{\partial p_i} - \frac{\partial v}{\partial q_i} \frac{\partial u}{\partial p_i} \right).$$

From (7.1) it may be shown (Problem 7.1) that

$$(7.2) \qquad \begin{array}{ll} \text{(a)} & [u,v] = -[v,u], \\ \text{(b)} & [u,v+w] = [u,v] + [u,w], \\ \text{(c)} & [u,vw] = v[u,w] + [u,v]w, \\ \text{(d)} & [uv,w] = u[v,w] + [u,w]v. \end{array}$$

The similarity in form of (6.22) and (7.2) suggests an intimate relation
between commutators and Poisson brackets. To obtain this relation,
Dirac[1] evaluated the Poisson bracket $[u_1u_2,v_1v_2]$ in two different ways,
assuming that u_1 and v_1 do not commute, and that u_2 and v_2 do not commute. Let $D = [u_1u_2,v_1v_2]$. Using (7.2c) first,

$$(7.3) \qquad D = v_1[u_1u_2,v_2] + [u_1u_2,v_1]v_2.$$

Now using (7.2d),

$$(7.4) \qquad D = v_1u_1[u_2,v_2] + v_1[u_1,v_2]u_2 + u_1[u_2,v_1]v_2 + [u_1,v_1]u_2v_2.$$

Starting over, this time using (7.2d) first,

$$(7.5) \qquad D = u_1[u_2,v_1v_2] + [u_1,v_1v_2]u_2.$$

Now using (7.2c),

$$(7.6) \qquad D = u_1v_1[u_2,v_2] + u_1[u_2,v_1]v_2 + v_1[u_1,v_2]u_2 + [u_1,v_1]v_2u_2.$$

[1] P. A. M. Dirac, *Principles of Quantum Mechanics*, fourth edition, Oxford, 1958,
pp. 84–7.

Equality of the expressions (7.4) and (7.6) for D gives

$$(7.7) \qquad v_1 u_1 [u_2, v_2] + [u_1, v_1] u_2 v_2 = u_1 v_1 [u_2, v_2] + [u_1, v_1] v_2 u_2$$

or

$$(7.8) \qquad [u_1, v_1](u_2 v_2 - v_2 u_2) = (u_1 v_1 - v_1 u_1)[u_2, v_2].$$

From this, using the commutation notation (6.21),

$$(7.9) \qquad [u_1, v_1](u_2, v_2) = (u_1, v_1)[u_2, v_2].$$

Since the pairs u_1, v_1 and u_2, v_2 are arbitrary, (7.9) implies that, for any u, v,

$$(7.10) \qquad (u, v) = \text{(a constant)} \times [u, v].$$

Classically, the constant factor in (7.10) vanishes for all u and v. Quantum mechanically, operators u_{op} and v_{op} which do not necessarily commute are associated with observables u_{obs} and v_{obs}. Hence the correspondence between classical and quantum mechanics implies that there is a nonzero, universal constant such that

$$(7.11) \qquad (u_{op}, v_{op}) = \text{(a constant)}[u_{obs}, v_{obs}]_{op}.$$

What is the constant? For real observables u_{obs} and v_{obs}, the Poisson bracket $[u_{obs}, v_{obs}]$ is a real observable. Consequently u_{op}, v_{op}, and $[u_{obs}, v_{obs}]_{op}$ must be Hermitean operators. However, for Hermitean u_{op} and v_{op} the commutator (u_{op}, v_{op}) is anti-Hermitean. We conclude that the constant factor in (7.11) is a pure imaginary number and that

$$(7.12) \qquad (u_{op}, v_{op}) = i \times \text{(a real constant)} \times [u_{obs}, v_{obs}]_{op}.$$

The real constant in (7.12) cannot be determined by theory alone. Recourse must be had to experiment. It is found that agreement with experiment is obtained by taking as this constant factor Planck's constant $\hbar = h/2\pi$. Hence the *general commutation relation*

$$(7.13) \qquad (u_{op}, v_{op}) = i\hbar [u_{obs}, v_{obs}]_{op}.$$

In applying (7.13) it is assumed that the quantum mechanical Poisson brackets, or at least the simpler of them, such as the brackets which reduce to constants, have the same values as the corresponding classical Poisson brackets.

Problem 7.1: Verify (7.2).

Problem 7.2: Verify that, for $i, j = 1, 2, 3$,

$$(7.14) \quad \text{(a)} \quad [x_i, x_j] = 0, \qquad \text{(b)} \quad [p_i, p_j] = 0, \qquad \text{(c)} \quad [x_i, p_j] = \delta_{ij}.$$

From (7.13) and (7.14) obtain the *Heisenberg Commutation Relations*[2]

(7.15)   (a) $(x_i,x_j) = 0,$ (b) $(p_i,p_j) = 0,$ (c) $(x_i,p_j) = i\hbar\delta_{ij}.$

7.2. Representations of Wave Functions and of Operators. In obtaining operators satisfying the Heisenberg commutation relations (7.15) we at first restrict our considerations, for simplicity of presentation, to one-space dimension. It will later be seen that the problem at hand has many solutions. In this section three solutions which are especially convenient for application of elementary mathematical methods are obtained.

Any particular entity which completely determines the wave function will be called a *representation* of it. For example, representations of cos x are (a) "adjacent side/hypotenuse," (b) a certain power series, (c) the Euler formula $(e^{ix} + e^{-ix})/2$, (d) the Laplace transform $s/(1 + s^2)$, etc., etc.

Two representations of the wave function, $\psi(x,t)$ and $\varphi(k,t)$, called the "position representation" and the "k representation," respectively, have already been introduced. Since $p = \hbar k$, the k representation, $\varphi(k,t)$, determines a third representation, the momentum representation $\Phi(p,t)$. We could set $\Phi(p,t) = \varphi(p/\hbar,t)$, but it is better to set $\Phi(p,t) = c\cdot\varphi(p/\hbar,t)$ and determine c to retain equality of norms and of inner products. Define inner products and norms in the momentum representation by

(7.16) $$(\Phi_1,\Phi_2) = \int_{-\infty}^{\infty} \Phi_1^*\Phi_2 \, dp,$$

and

(7.17) $$N(\Phi) = (\Phi,\Phi),$$

respectively. From (5.62)–(5.65), (7.16), and (7.17), we find that by taking $c = \hbar^{-\frac{1}{2}}$ we have

(7.18) $$(\psi_i,\psi_j) = (\Phi_i,\Phi_j) = (\varphi_i,\varphi_j),$$

and

(7.19) $$N(\psi_i) = N(\Phi_i) = N(\varphi_i),$$

when, in an obvious extension of (5.48),

(7.20) $$\psi_i \leftrightarrow \Phi_i \leftrightarrow \varphi_i.$$

---

[2] W. Heisenberg, *The Physical Principles of the Quantum Theory*, Dover, 1930, p. 118.

Any one of the three representations of the wave function determines the other two by the relations

(7.21)

$$\text{(a)} \quad \psi(x) = \frac{1}{\sqrt{2\pi}} \int_{-\infty}^{\infty} \varphi(k)e^{ikx}\, dk,$$

$$\text{(b)} \quad \varphi(k) = \frac{1}{\sqrt{2\pi}} \int_{-\infty}^{\infty} \psi(x)e^{-ikx}\, dx,$$

$$\text{(c)} \quad \Phi(p) = \frac{1}{\sqrt{\hbar}} \varphi(p/\hbar).$$

Turning now to representations of operators, it is quite natural to write

(7.22)

$$\text{(a)} \quad x_{\text{op}}\psi = x \cdot \psi,$$
$$\text{(b)} \quad p_{\text{op}}\Phi = p \cdot \Phi,$$
$$\text{(c)} \quad k_{\text{op}}\varphi = k \cdot \varphi,$$

making x_{op} multiplicative in the position representation, p_{op} multiplicative in the momentum representation, and k multiplicative in the k representation. From the Heisenberg commutation relation (7.15c) for $i = j$ we see that both x and p cannot be multiplicative in the same representation, since x and p do not commute. The assignments (7.22) suggest the definition: A representation in which a given operator A is multiplicative is called the "A representation."

Let A_x, A_p, and A_k be the three representations of a certain linear operator A. Since the correspondence (7.20) is determined uniquely and completely for all wave packets by the transformation equations (7.21), we must have

(7.23) $$A_x\psi \leftrightarrow A_p\Phi \leftrightarrow A_k\varphi$$

whenever $\psi \leftrightarrow \Phi \leftrightarrow \varphi$. Then we will be justified in writing

(7.24) $$A_x \leftrightarrow A_p \leftrightarrow A_k.$$

The program is to use the above principles and equations to determine two of the three representations of various operators A, B, . . . from chosen representations, then verify that the general commutation relation (7.13) is satisfied. In particular, the Heisenberg commutation relations (7.15) must be satisfied.

Consider first the operator $A = x_{\text{op}}$. According to (7.22a), $A_x = x\cdot$. We want to determine A_p and A_k so that for $A = x$, (7.23) is satisfied whenever $\psi \leftrightarrow \Phi \leftrightarrow \varphi$. From (7.21b) we see that

(7.25) $$i\frac{\partial}{\partial k}\varphi = \frac{1}{\sqrt{2\pi}} \int_{-\infty}^{\infty} x \cdot \psi e^{-ikx}\, dx$$

whence

(7.26)
$$i\frac{\partial}{\partial k}\varphi \leftrightarrow x \cdot \psi$$

whenever $\varphi \leftrightarrow x$. This implies that $A_k = i\frac{\partial}{\partial k}$ when $A_x = x\cdot$. Since $p = \hbar k$, $\frac{\partial}{\partial k} = \frac{\partial p}{\partial k}\frac{\partial}{\partial p} = \hbar\frac{\partial}{\partial p}$, or $A_p = i\hbar\frac{\partial}{\partial p}$. We now have

(7.27)
$$x \cdot \leftrightarrow i\hbar\frac{\partial}{\partial p} \leftrightarrow i\frac{\partial}{\partial k}.$$

Second, consider $A = p$. According to (7.22b), $A_p = p\cdot$. Again from $p = \hbar k$, $A_k = \hbar k\cdot$. From (7.21a) we see that

(7.28)
$$-i\frac{\partial}{\partial x}\psi = \frac{1}{\sqrt{2\pi}}\int_{-\infty}^{\infty} k \cdot \varphi e^{ikx}\, dk,$$

whence

(7.29)
$$-i\frac{\partial}{\partial x}\psi \leftrightarrow k\varphi$$

whenever $\psi \leftrightarrow \varphi$. Thus we have

(7.30)
$$-i\hbar\frac{\partial}{\partial x} \leftrightarrow p \leftrightarrow \hbar k.$$

Problem 7.3: Let $A = c\cdot$. What are A_x, A_p, and A_k? In particular, what operators should be associated with m (electron mass) and e (electron charge) in the three representations?

Problem 7.4: Obtain, for any nonnegative integer n,

(7.31)
$$\text{(a)} \quad x^n \cdot \leftrightarrow \left(i\hbar\frac{\partial}{\partial p}\right)^n \leftrightarrow \left(i\frac{\partial}{\partial k}\right)^n,$$
$$\text{(b)} \quad \left(-i\hbar\frac{\partial}{\partial x}\right)^n \leftrightarrow p^n \leftrightarrow \hbar^n k^n,$$

and for any polynomials $f(x)$ and $g(p)$

(7.32)
$$\text{(a)} \quad f(x) \leftrightarrow f\left(i\hbar\frac{\partial}{\partial p}\right) \leftrightarrow f\left(i\frac{\partial}{\partial k}\right),$$
$$\text{(b)} \quad g\left(-i\hbar\frac{\partial}{\partial x}\right) \leftrightarrow g(p) \leftrightarrow g(\hbar k).$$

Problem 7.5: Apply the results of Problem 7.4 to the Hamiltonian

(7.33)
$$H = p^2/2m + V(x).$$

for a particle in one-space dimension. For what types of potential functions $V(x)$ are the momentum and the k representations readily applicable? Answers:

$$\text{(a)} \quad H_x = -\frac{\hbar^2}{2m}\frac{d^2}{dx^2} + V(x),$$

(7.34) $$\text{(b)} \quad H_p = \frac{p^2}{2m} + V\left(i\hbar\frac{d}{dp}\right),$$

$$\text{(c)} \quad H_k = \frac{\hbar^2 k^2}{2m} + V\left(i\frac{d}{dk}\right).$$

Problem 7.6: Generalize (7.16)–(7.34) to particles in three-space dimensions. (Refer to Problem 5.25.)

Problem 7.7: The position representation of an operator T is defined by $T_x f(x) = f(x + c)$, $c = a$ constant. What is T_k? Answer: $T_k = e^{ikc}$.

7.3. The Energy Operator. Specification of the total energy of a system is a statement that the energy has a certain value E which, for a conservative system, is a constant. It is therefore natural that, in any representation, the linear operator associated with a *specified* total energy is simply the multiplicative operator

(7.35) $$E_{op} = E\cdot.$$

Classically, the total energy may have any value above some arbitrary zero. Quantum mechanically, bound systems are restricted to quantized energy levels. A major problem in quantum mechanics is the determination of energy levels of bound systems. We do not know the energy quantum levels until the problem is solved. Thus E in (7.35), although regarded as specified, is actually an unknown.

The selection of the energy operator is not so trivial when the total energy is not regarded as being specified. Then we have two choices, one emphasizing corpuscular properties and the other emphasizing wavelike properties. Emphasizing corpuscular properties, we naturally take

(7.36) $$E_{op} = H_{op}$$

where H_{op} is a selected representation of the Hamiltonian operator formed from the Hamiltonian function for the system according to rules formulated in Section (7.2).

Transition from corpuscular to wavelike concepts is given by the equation $E = \hbar\omega$. For unspecified energy, we need a linear operator which emphasizes the wavelike property ω but which does not refer to any specific value of ω. To obtain such an operator, we may start by considering the wave function (5.5) associated with a free particle having specified energy $E = \hbar\omega$. For this wave function we readily find that

(7.37) $$i\hbar\frac{\partial}{\partial t}\psi = \hbar\omega\psi = E\psi.$$

This suggests

$$(7.38) \qquad\qquad E_{op} = i\hbar \frac{\partial}{\partial t}$$

for the energy operator when wavelike aspects are emphasized, the energy itself being unspecified.

Problem 7.8: Give the position, the momentum, and the **k** representations of the Hamiltonian operator for a particle in three-space dimensions, for which the classical Hamiltonian function is

$$(7.39) \qquad\qquad H = p^2/2m + V(\mathbf{r}).$$

Answers:

$$(7.40) \qquad
\begin{aligned}
&\text{(a)} \quad H_r = -\frac{\hbar^2}{2m} \text{ Lap} + V(\mathbf{r}), \\
&\text{(b)} \quad H_p = p^2/2m + V(i\hbar \text{ grad}_p), \\
&\text{(c)} \quad H_k = \frac{\hbar^2 k^2}{2m} + V(i \text{ grad}_k).
\end{aligned}$$

7.4. Symmetrization of Operators. Let A and B be two real observables with which Hermitean operators A and B are associated. Then the expectation values $\langle A \rangle$ and $\langle B \rangle$ are real for all wave functions. Further, AB is a real observable and necessarily the expectation value $\langle AB \rangle$ should be real for all wave functions. However, the operator AB is not Hermitean unless the operators A and B commute (see Problem 6.38). To obtain a real expectation value $\langle AB \rangle$, we must associate a Hermitean operator with the observable AB. Since cases in which the operators A and B do not commute are of frequent occurrence, we need a general method for associating a Hermitean operator C with an observable AB having the property that, when the operators A and B commute, the operator C is equal to the product of the operators A and B. From Problem 6.14 we see that these conditions are satisfied by

$$(7.41) \qquad\qquad C_{op} = (A_{op}B_{op} + B_{op}A_{op})/2$$

when $C_{obs} = A_{obs}B_{obs}$.

Problem 7.9: Obtain the position representation of a Hermitean-Hamiltonian operator for a particle in an electromagnetic field, for which the classical Hamiltonian function is (4.13). Answer:

$$(7.42) \quad H = \frac{1}{2m}\left(-\hbar^2 \text{ Lap} + \frac{2i\hbar e}{c} \mathbf{A} \cdot \text{grad} + \frac{i\hbar e}{c} \text{ div } \mathbf{A} + \frac{e^2 A^2}{c^2}\right) + e\Phi.$$

7.5. Calculation of Expectation Values. Recalling (7.18) and (7.19), as well as (7.23) and (7.24), we see that the expectation value $\langle A \rangle$

of an observable A may be calculated in either the position, the momentum, or the k representation:

$$(7.43) \qquad \langle A \rangle = \frac{(\psi, A_r \psi)}{(\psi, \psi)} = \frac{(\Phi, A_p \Phi)}{(\Phi, \Phi)} = \frac{(\varphi, A_k \varphi)}{(\varphi, \varphi)}.$$

Parseval's theorem implies the finiteness of all three denominators in (7.43) if any one denominator is finite, and of all three numerators if any one numerator is finite. Frequently we limit our considerations to a linear manifold of functions for which $\langle r \rangle$, $\langle p \rangle$, $\langle M \rangle$ and $\langle H \rangle$ are finite (M = angular momentum). Wave functions for which these expectation values exist will be called *proper* wave functions. Wave functions for which not all of these expectation values exist will be called *improper* wave functions. Proper wave functions in the infinite region must be bounded and must approach zero at infinity.

The availability of operators associated with functions of r and p enables us to compute the expectation values of products of components of r and p. Problem 7.12 illustrates the importance of symmetrization.

Problem 7.10: Show that, for a free particle,

$$(7.44) \qquad \begin{array}{ll} \text{(a)} & \langle x \rangle_t = \langle x \rangle_0 + \langle p \rangle_0\, t/m, \\ \text{(b)} & \langle p \rangle_t = \langle p \rangle_0. \end{array}$$

(Hint: Calculate in the k representation, using (5.47).)

Problem 7.11: Writing

$$(7.45) \qquad \psi = |\psi| e^{i\Delta},$$

where $|\psi|$ and Δ are real valued functions of r and t, show that

$$(7.46) \qquad \langle p \rangle = \hbar \int_\infty |\psi|^2 \operatorname{grad} \Delta\, dr \Big/ \int_\infty |\psi|^2\, dr.$$

Problem 7.12: Calculate $\langle xp \rangle$ and $\langle px \rangle$ for the Gaussian wave packet (5.56), first without symmetrizing and then with symmetrizing. (Hint: See (5.72) and (5.73b).)

7.6. References for Supplementary Reading.

Section 7.1: Dirac, 84–9; Mott and Sneddon, 356–62; Schiff, 133–5.
Section 7.4: Bohm, 182–91.
Section 7.5: Kemble, 219–24; Sherwin, 108–43.

CHAPTER 8

THE SCHROEDINGER WAVE EQUATION

8.1. Operator Derivation of Schroedinger Wave Equations.
Classically, the Hamiltonian function for a particle in a conservative field is equal to the total energy:

(8.1) $$H(\mathbf{r},\mathbf{p}) = p^2/2m + V(\mathbf{r}) = E.$$

This equality between observables implies not that $H_{op} = E_{op}$ but that

(8.2) $$H_{op}\psi = E_{op}\psi.$$

The use of any convenient representation is implied by (8.2), the symbol ψ not necessarily implying the position representation.

For unspecified energy, $E_{op} = i\hbar \dfrac{\partial}{\partial t}$ and (8.2) becomes the *Schroedinger time dependent wave equation* (STDWE):

(8.3) $$H\psi = i\hbar \frac{\partial\psi}{\partial t}.$$

For specified energy, $E_{op} = E\cdot$ and (8.2) becomes the *Schroedinger time independent wave equation* (STIWE):

(8.4) $$H\psi = E\psi$$

Frequently (8.3) is written in the form (8.4) with the understanding from the context that $E = i\hbar \dfrac{\partial}{\partial t}$ just as $H = H_{op}$.

Equations (8.3) and (8.4) become the Schroedinger wave equations for a system of n particles when H is the total Hamiltonian for the entire system and the wave function ψ (in the position representation) is a function of the time and of the $3n$ position coordinates of the n particles.

Problem 8.1: Give the Schroedinger wave equation for a system of n free particles each of mass m. Answer:

(8.5) $$-\frac{\hbar^2}{2m} \sum_{j=1}^{n} \left(\frac{\partial^2\psi}{\partial x_j{}^2} + \frac{\partial^2 x}{\partial y_j{}^2} + \frac{\partial^2\psi}{\partial z_j{}^2} \right) = i\hbar \frac{\partial\psi}{\partial t}$$

Problem 8.2: Give the wave equations, in the position and in the k representations, for an isotropic linear oscillator in three-space dimensions. (Hint: In (4.9), let $a = b = c$.) Answers:

(8.6)
$$\text{(a)} \quad -\frac{\hbar^2}{2m} \text{ Lap } \psi + \frac{1}{2} ar^2\psi = E\psi,$$
$$\text{(b)} \quad \frac{\hbar^2 k^2}{2m} \varphi - \frac{1}{2} a \text{ Lap}_k \varphi = E\varphi.$$

Problem 8.3: Give the Schroedinger wave equations for a hydrogen atom, taking the motion of the nucleus into account. Answer:

(8.7)
$$-\frac{\hbar^2}{2m} \text{ Lap}_1 \psi - \frac{\hbar^2}{2M} \text{ Lap}_2 \psi - \frac{e^2}{r_{12}} = E\psi,$$

where m = mass of electron, M = mass of proton, $r_{12} = |\mathbf{r}_1 - \mathbf{r}_2| =$ distance between electron and proton, and $\psi = \psi(\mathbf{r}_1, \mathbf{r}_2, t)$; $\mathbf{r}_1 = (x_1, y_1, z_1)$ and $\mathbf{r}_2 = (x_2, y_2, z_2)$ are Cartesian coordinates of the electron and the proton, respectively, referred to some fixed coordinate system.

Problem 8.4: Give the Schroedinger wave equation for the two electrons in a helium atom, neglecting the motion of the nucleus. Answer:

(8.8)
$$-\frac{\hbar^2}{2m} (\text{Lap}_1 \psi + \text{Lap}_2 \psi) + \left(\frac{e^2}{r_{12}} - \frac{2e^2}{r_1} - \frac{2e^2}{r_2}\right) \psi = E\psi,$$

where $\mathbf{r}_1 = (x_1, y_1, z_1)$ and $\mathbf{r}_2 = (x_2, y_2, z_2)$ are Cartesian coordinates of the two electrons, referred to the nucleus as origin.

Problem 8.5: Show that

(8.9)
$$\frac{\partial}{\partial t} N(\psi) = 0$$

for every proper wave function ψ satisfying the STDWE (8.3) if and only if H is Hermitean. Also show that, for any ψ satisfying (8.3), we may find a time independent constant c such that the wave function $\psi' \equiv c\psi$ has unit norm, satisfies (8.3), and gives the same expectation values as ψ does. (Refer to Problem 6.18.)

8.2. Physical Interpretation of the Wave Function. In classical continuum mechanics the equation of conservation is

(8.10)
$$\frac{\partial \rho}{\partial t} + \text{div } \mathbf{j} = 0$$

where ρ is the density and $\mathbf{j}$ is the current. When integrated over a fixed region R of space, by aid of Gauss's theorem for transforming the volume integral of a divergence into a surface integral, (8.10) gives

(8.11)
$$\frac{\partial}{\partial t} \iiint_R \rho \, dv + \iint_\sigma \mathbf{j} \cdot d\boldsymbol{\delta} = 0$$

where σ is the surface bounding the region R. There is no net flux through σ and the total amount of matter (or charge) in R remains constant when the surface integral in (8.11) vanishes.

If an equation of the form (8.10) is implied by the STDWE (8.3) we are inclined to interpret the vector whose divergence appears in the second term as a current and the quantity whose $\partial/\partial t$ appears in the first term as a density.

Starting with the STDWE in three-space dimensions,

$$(8.12) \qquad i\hbar \frac{\partial \psi}{\partial t} = -\frac{\hbar^2}{2m} \operatorname{Lap} \psi + V\psi,$$

and its complex conjugate

$$(8.13) \qquad -i\hbar \frac{\partial \psi^*}{\partial t} = -\frac{\hbar^2}{2m} \operatorname{Lap} \psi^* + V\psi^*,$$

we multiply the former by ψ^*, the latter by ψ, and subtract the resulting equations. Noting that

$$(8.14) \quad \text{(a)} \quad \psi^* \frac{\partial \psi}{\partial t} + \psi \frac{\partial \psi^*}{\partial t} = \frac{\partial}{\partial t} (\psi^*\psi),$$

$$\text{(b)} \quad \psi^* \operatorname{Lap} \psi - \psi \operatorname{Lap} \psi^* = \operatorname{div} (\psi^* \operatorname{grad} \psi - \psi \operatorname{grad} \psi^*),$$

we obtain

$$(8.15) \qquad \frac{\partial J}{\partial t} + \operatorname{div} \mathbf{S} = 0$$

where

$$(8.16) \quad \text{(a)} \quad J = \psi^*\psi,$$

$$\text{(b)} \quad \mathbf{S} = \frac{i\hbar}{2m} (\psi \operatorname{grad} \psi^* - \psi^* \operatorname{grad} \psi).$$

This is an equation of the form (8.10).

Let us picture an electron (charge e) as a *cloud of charge*[1] with density ρ varying from point to point, albeit highly concentrated in a small region, if we like. Let an infinitesimal element of the cloud be moving with velocity $\mathbf{u}$. The current $\mathbf{j} = \rho\mathbf{u}$ and the density ρ vanish at great distances from the center of the cloud. We desire to represent the cloud density and current in terms of a wave function.

Let ψ_1 satisfy the STDWE (8.3) and have finite norm. Taking $\psi = c\psi_1$, where $c = 1/\sqrt{N(\psi_1)}$ does not depend on t (see (8.9)), we obtain a wave

[1] See H. E. White, *Phys. Rev.*, **37**, 1416 (1931); **38**, 513 (1931); *Introduction to Atomic Spectra*, McGraw-Hill, 1934, p. 71; G. Herzberg, *Atomic Spectra and Atomic Structure*, Dover, 1944, p. 44.

function which satisfies the STDWE (8.3) and has unit norm. Then we may take

$$\text{(a)} \quad \rho = eJ = e\psi^*\psi,$$

(8.17)

$$\text{(b)} \quad \mathbf{j} = e\mathbf{S} = \frac{i\hbar e}{2m} (\psi \text{ grad } \psi^* - \psi^* \text{ grad } \psi)$$

as the charge density and current density in our cloud picture of the electron. ρ and $\mathbf{j}$ satisfy the continuity equation (8.10) and further

$$\text{(8.18)} \qquad \iiint \rho \, dv = e \int_\infty \psi^*\psi \, d\mathbf{r} = e,$$

since ψ has unit norm.

Problem 8.6: Show that

$$\text{(8.19)} \qquad \mathbf{S} = \frac{1}{m} Re \, (\psi^*\mathbf{p}\psi)$$

where the symbol Re denotes the real part.

Problem 8.7: Writing ψ in the form (7.45), show that

$$\text{(a)} \quad J = |\psi|^2,$$

(8.20)

$$\text{(b)} \quad \mathbf{S} = \frac{\hbar}{m} |\psi|^2 \text{ grad } \Delta.$$

Hence the magnitude of ψ determines the charge density, this and the gradient of the phase of ψ determine the charge current.

Problem 8.8: For a given ψ with unit norm define a second wave function ψ' with unit norm by

$$\text{(8.21)} \qquad \psi = \psi' e^{i\lambda t}$$

where λ is a real constant. Show that

$$\text{(a)} \quad J = \psi'^*\psi',$$

(8.22)

$$\text{(b)} \quad \mathbf{S} = \frac{i\hbar}{2m} (\psi' \text{ grad } \psi'^* - \psi'^* \text{ grad } \psi').$$

Problem 8.9: The absorption of particles from a beam may be represented by the introduction of a "negative imaginary potential" $V = V_0 - iV_1$ into the Schroedinger wave equation (8.12).[2] Show that, with J and $\mathbf{S}$ defined as in (8.16),

$$\text{(8.23)} \qquad \frac{\partial J}{\partial t} + \text{div } \mathbf{S} + \frac{2}{\hbar} V_1 J = 0.$$

[2] N. F. Mott and H. S. W. Massey, *The Theory of Atomic Collisions*, second edition, Oxford, p. 12; E. R. Rae, *Phys. Today*, **10**, 16 (1957).

When particles are absorbed at the rate α per unit volume per unit time, the continuity equation (8.10) is replaced by

$$(8.24) \qquad \frac{\partial \rho}{\partial t} + \text{div } \mathbf{j} + \alpha \rho = 0.$$

Hence

$$(8.25) \qquad \alpha = 2V_1/\hbar.$$

Problem 8.10:   Let ψ be a solution of the STDWE for a particle in a magnetic field, for which the Hamiltonian operator is (7.42). Show that

$$(8.26) \qquad \begin{array}{ll} \text{(a)} & J = \psi^*\psi, \\[2mm] \text{(b)} & \mathbf{S} = \dfrac{i\hbar}{2m} (\psi \text{ grad } \psi^* - \psi^* \text{ grad } \psi) - \dfrac{e}{mc} \psi^*\psi \mathbf{A} \end{array}$$

satisfy (8.15).

Problem 8.11:   Let ψ be a solution of the Klein-Gordon equation (5.36) for a free particle. Show that[3]

$$(8.27) \qquad \begin{array}{ll} \text{(a)} & J = \dfrac{i\hbar}{2mc^2} \left(\psi^* \dfrac{\partial \psi}{\partial t} - \psi \dfrac{\partial \psi^*}{\partial t} \right), \\[4mm] \text{(b)} & \mathbf{S} = \dfrac{i\hbar}{2m} (\psi \text{ grad } \psi^* - \psi^* \text{ grad } \psi) \end{array}$$

satisfy (8.15). Writing ψ in the form (7.46), show that

$$(8.28) \qquad J = -\frac{\hbar}{2mc^2} |\psi|^2 \frac{\partial \Delta}{\partial t}.$$

Observe that J is positive in regions in which $\dfrac{\partial \Delta}{\partial t}$ is negative but that J is negative in regions in which $\dfrac{\partial \Delta}{\partial t}$ is positive.

8.3. Stationary States.   Consider a conservative system in which the potential function V is a function of the coordinates only and not of the time. Then H_{op} does not depend explicitly on the time. We may therefore expect to be able to find solutions of (8.3) of the form

$$(8.29) \qquad \psi(\mathbf{r},t) = \psi(\mathbf{r}) \cdot T(t).$$

Since H commutes with $T(t)$ and $i\hbar \dfrac{\partial}{\partial t}$ commutes with $\psi(\mathbf{r})$, we may write

$$(8.30) \qquad T(t)H\psi(\mathbf{r}) = i\hbar\psi(\mathbf{r}) \frac{d}{dt} T(t)$$

---

[3] These expressions were proposed independently by O. Klein, *Z. Physik*, **41**, 414 (1927); E. Schroedinger, *Ann. Physik*, **82**, 267 (1927); and W. Gordon, *Z. Physik*, **33**, 879 (1927).

when we substitute from (8.29) into (8.3). In (8.30), the variables $\mathbf{r}$ and t are separable. Standard arguments lead to the separated equations

(8.31)   (a) $H\psi(\mathbf{r}) = \lambda\psi(\mathbf{r})$,   (b) $i\hbar\dfrac{d}{dt}T(t) = \lambda T(t)$,

where λ is some constant. Equation (8.31b) is readily integrated. Omitting the constant of integration since it may be absorbed by the spatially dependent factor $\psi(\mathbf{r})$, we obtain

(8.32) $T(t) = e^{-i\lambda t/\hbar}$.

From (8.32) and any solution $\psi(\mathbf{r})$ of the *eigenvalue equation* (8.31a) we obtain a solution

(8.33) $\psi(\mathbf{r},t) = \psi(\mathbf{r})e^{-i\lambda t/\hbar}$

of the Schroedinger wave equation (8.3). We observe that (8.31a) is essentially the STIWE (8.4).

From (8.17) we find that for wave functions of the form (8.33) the charge current and the charge density in the physical interpretation of the wave function of Section 8.2 are time independent. Since also (7.43) gives time independent expectation values for observables which do not depend explicitly on the time, wave functions of the form (8.33) are said to represent *stationary states*. These states, which play a central role in quantum mechanics, enter here without any *ab extra* assumption (see Bohr's assumption (b), Section 3.5).

Problem 8.12: Show that, for a wave function (8.33) with finite norm, $\lambda = \langle H \rangle$.

Problem 8.13: In the Schroedinger wave equation (8.12) let

(8.34) $\psi = Ce^{iW/\hbar}$

where $W = W(\mathbf{r},t)$. Show that, in the limit $\hbar \to 0$, W satisfies the Hamilton-Jacobi equation of classical mechanics:

(8.35) $\dfrac{1}{2m}(\operatorname{grad} W)^2 + V + \dfrac{\partial W}{\partial t} = 0$.

8.4. Time Derivatives and Constants of the Motion. For any differentiable function $u = u(q,p,t)$ the formula

(8.36) $\dfrac{du}{dt} = \sum_i \left(\dfrac{\partial u}{dq_i}\dot{q}_i + \dfrac{\partial u}{\partial p_i}\dot{p}_i \right) + \dfrac{\partial u}{\partial t}$

and Hamilton's equations of motion (4.6) give

(8.37) $\dfrac{du}{dt} = [u,H] + \dfrac{\partial u}{\partial t}$

where $[u,H]$ is the Poisson bracket defined in (7.1). From (8.37) we obtain the theorem in classical mechanics that a variable u which does not depend explicitly on the time $\left(\dfrac{\partial u}{\partial t} = 0\right)$ is a constant of the motion if and only if its Poisson bracket with the Hamiltonian function H vanishes.

Letting A be a quantum mechanical operator, combination of (7.13) and (8.37) suggests that an operator $\dfrac{dA}{dt}$ be defined by

$$(8.38) \qquad \frac{dA}{dt} = \frac{1}{i\hbar}\,(A,H) + \frac{\partial A}{\partial t}.$$

We may proceed otherwise, however, more in the spirit of the *Schroedinger picture* in which wave functions are time dependent while operators, such as x_{op} and p_{op}, are considered as time independent. Starting with the defining equation

$$(8.39) \qquad \langle A \rangle = (\psi, A\psi)/(\psi,\psi)$$

and recalling that (ψ,ψ) is independent of t (see (8.9)) when ψ satisfies the STDWE (8.3), we find by differentiating that

$$(8.40) \quad \frac{d}{dt}\langle A \rangle = \left\{\left(\frac{\partial \psi}{\partial t}, A\psi\right) + \left(\psi, A\,\frac{\partial \psi}{\partial t}\right) + \left(\psi, \frac{\partial A}{\partial t}\,\psi\right)\right\}\Big/(\psi,\psi).$$

Eliminating $\dfrac{\partial \psi}{\partial t}$ from (8.40) by means of the STDWE (8.3), we find as a consequence of the Hermiticity of H that

$$(8.41) \qquad \frac{d}{dt}\langle A \rangle = \frac{1}{i\hbar}\,\langle (A,H) \rangle + \left\langle \frac{\partial A}{\partial t} \right\rangle.$$

Comparison of (8.38) and (8.41) implies that corresponding to an operator A an operator dA/dt may be defined by

$$(8.42) \qquad \left\langle \frac{dA}{dt} \right\rangle = \frac{d}{dt}\langle A \rangle$$

for all wave functions belonging to M_A. Then the expectation value of the time derivative of A is equal to the time derivative of the expectation value of A.

An observable A will be called a *quantum mechanical constant of the motion* if and only if

$$(8.43) \qquad \frac{d}{dt}\langle A \rangle = 0$$

for all wave functions belonging to M_A. From (8.41) we obtain the important theorem: An observable A which does not depend explicitly on the time is a quantum mechanical constant of the motion if and only if the operator A commutes with the Hamiltonian operator for the system.

Problem 8.14: Show that, in the position representation, for any differentiable $f(\mathbf{r},\mathbf{p},t)$,

$$\text{(a)} \quad (f,\mathbf{p}) = i\hbar(\text{grad } f),$$

(8.44) $$\text{(b)} \quad (f,p_j{}^2) = \hbar^2 \frac{\partial^2 f}{\partial x_j{}^2} + 2\hbar^2 \frac{\partial f}{\partial x_j} \frac{\partial}{\partial x_j},$$

$$\text{(c)} \quad (f,p^2) = \hbar^2(\text{Lap } f) + 2\hbar^2(\text{grad } f) \cdot \text{grad}.$$

(Hint: See (6.23); for (b), use (a) and (6.22c). Also recall the Heisenberg commutation relations (7.15).)

Problem 8.15: Show that $\dfrac{d}{dt}\langle H\rangle = 0$ if $\dfrac{\partial H}{\partial t} = 0$.

Problem 8.16: Show that, for a particle with the Hamiltonian (8.1),

$$\text{(a)} \quad \frac{d}{dt}\langle x\rangle = \frac{1}{m}\langle p_x\rangle,$$

(8.45) $$\text{(b)} \quad \frac{d}{dt}\langle p_x\rangle = -\left\langle \frac{\partial V}{\partial x}\right\rangle,$$

$$\text{(c)} \quad \frac{d}{dt}\langle H\rangle = 0.$$

Problem 8.17: For a given operator A and for given wave functions ψ_1 and ψ_2 satisfying the STDWE (8.3) and belonging to M_A, define a *matrix element* A_{12} by

(8.46) $$A_{12} = (\psi_1, A\psi_2).$$

Show that

(8.47) $$\frac{dA_{12}}{dt} = \frac{1}{i\hbar}(A,H)_{12} + \left(\frac{\partial A}{\partial t}\right)_{12}.$$

In particular, show that

$$\text{(a)} \quad \frac{d}{dt}x_{12} = \left(\frac{\partial H}{\partial p_x}\right)_{12} = \frac{1}{m}(p_x)_{12},$$

(8.48) $$\text{(b)} \quad \frac{d}{dt}(p_x)_{12} = -\left(\frac{\partial H}{\partial x}\right)_{12} = -\left(\frac{\partial V}{\partial x}\right)_{12}$$

$$\text{(c)} \quad \frac{d}{dt}H_{12} = 0.$$

Problem 8.18: Corresponding to some particular square integrable solution ψ of the STDWE (8.3), where H does not depend explicitly on the time, define a projection operator P_ψ (see Problem 6.20) by

(8.49) $$P_\psi f = (\psi,f)\psi,$$

for all square integrable functions f. Show that

(8.50) $$\frac{d}{dt} P_\psi = 0.$$

(Assume that $\frac{\partial f}{\partial t}$ is square integrable also.)

8.5. The Heisenberg Picture. In the *Heisenberg picture*,[4] operators are time dependent and wave functions are time independent. The basic elements of the Heisenberg formalism may be developed by a transformation from the Schroedinger picture. In this development, wave functions and operators in the two pictures, the Heisenberg and the Schroedinger, will be distinguished by superscripts H and S, respectively.

First we need a formal solution of the STDWE (8.3) in the Schroedinger picture. Assuming that H does not depend explicitly on the time, (8.3) may be formally solved treating H as a constant:

(8.51) $$\psi(\mathbf{r},t) = T_-\psi(\mathbf{r},0)$$

where

(8.52) $\quad T_- = e^{-iHt/\hbar}, \; T_+ = (T_-)^\dagger = e^{-iHt/\hbar}, \; T_-T_+ = T_+T_- = 1.$

An operator e^A is defined by

(8.53) $$e^A\psi = \sum_{n=0}^{\infty} \frac{A^n\psi}{n!}$$

on the linear manifold of all functions for which A^n is defined for every positive integer n and for which the infinite series converges.

Since wave functions are time independent in the Heisenberg picture, time dependent in the Schroedinger picture, from (8.51) we obtain our clue and starting point:

(8.54) $\quad$ (a) $\quad \psi^H = \psi(\mathbf{r},0),$
$\qquad\qquad$ (b) $\quad \psi^S = \psi(\mathbf{r},t) = T_-\psi^H, \; \psi^H = T_+\psi^S.$

The relation between the two pictures A^H and A^S of an operator A is now completely and uniquely determined by the requirement that

(8.55) $$(\psi^H,A^H\psi^H) = (\psi^S,A^S\psi^S)$$

for all wave functions belonging to M_A. In fact, eliminating ψ^S from (8.55) by means of (8.54b), we find that

(8.56) $\quad (\psi^H,A^H\psi^H) = (T_-\psi^H,A^ST_-\psi^H) = (\psi^H,T_+A^ST_-\psi^H).$

[4] W. Heisenberg, *Z. Physik*, **33**, 879 (1925).

Hence, from (8.56),

(8.57)   (a) $A^H = T_+ A^S T_-$,   (b) $A^S = T_- A^H T_+$.

Problem 8.19:   Show that $A^H = A^S$ if A and H commute. In particular, $H^H = H^S$.

Problem 8.20:   Show that $(A^H, B^H) = T_+ (A^S, B^S) T_-$.

Problem 8.21:   Show that, in the Heisenberg picture, for a particle with the Hamiltonian (8.1),

$$\text{(a)}\qquad \frac{dx}{dt} = \frac{1}{m}\, p_x,$$

(8.58)   (b) $$\frac{dp_x}{dt} = -\frac{\partial V}{\partial x},$$

(c) $dH/dt = 0$.

Problem 8.22:   Matrix elements $A_{12}{}^H$ and $A_{12}{}^S$ for an operator A are defined in the Heisenberg and in the Schroedinger pictures by

(8.59) $A_{12}{}^H = (\psi_1{}^H, A^H \psi_2{}^H)$, $A_{12}{}^S = (\psi_1{}^S, A^S \psi_2{}^S)$,

(see Problem 8.17). Show that $A_{12}{}^H = A_{12}{}^S$. Hence (8.46) and (8.47) are equally valid in either picture.

Problem 8.23:   Let $\psi(x,0) = e^{ax}$. Calculate $\psi(x,t)$ from (8.51) to (8.53) using $H = p^2/2m = \dfrac{-\hbar^2}{2m}\dfrac{d^2}{dx^2}$. Show that $\psi(x,t)$ satisfies (8.3). Answer: $\psi(x,t) = e^{ax + i\hbar a^2 t/2m}$.

Problem 8.24:   Work Problem 8.5, using (8.55) and the time independence of ψ^H.

8.6. References for Supplementary Reading.

Section 8.1:   Bohm, 191–2; Born, 132–9; Finkelnburg, 206–12; Frenkel, 47–8; Kemble, 14–19, 21–4; Kramers, 27–40; Landé, 48–50; Mandl, 22–31; McConnell, 97–9; Mott and Sneddon, 102–3; Pauling and Wilson, 50–58, 84–8; Peaslee and Mueller, 224–7; Persico, 152–60; Schaefer, 250–59; Schiff, 18–21.

Section 8.2:   Bohm, 83–8, 355–7; Born, 144–7; French, 188–91; Frenkel, 49–51; Kemble, 29–32; Kramers, 41–51; March, 45–9; McConnell, 36–8; Mott and Massey, 1–5, 10–12; Mott and Sneddon, 27–30; Pauling and Wilson, 63–7, 88–90; Persico, 160–62; Schiff, 21–7.

Section 8.3:   Bohm, 225–8; Kramers, 51–61, 116–20; Mandl, 31–4; Mott and Sneddon, 41–4, 46–8.

Section 8.4:   Bohm, 192–8; Born, 380–87; Frenkel, 62–8; Houston, 67–70; Mott and Sneddon, 362–3; Persico, 346–51; Schiff, 138–9.

Section 8.5:   McConnell, 68–71.

CHAPTER 9

SECTIONALLY CONSTANT POTENTIALS

9.1. Some Specific Quantum Effects Exhibited by Sectionally Constant Potentials. In order to illustrate certain specifically quantum effects, that is, (1) the reflection of electrons at a sharp change of potential (Sections 9.3 and 9.4), (2) the penetration of barriers (Section 9.5), (3) transmission resonance (Section 9.6), and (4) the existence of discrete energy states of particles held in a narrow region by an attractive force (Sections 9.7 and 9.8), we solve in this chapter several special problems involving *sectionally constant* potentials. With the idealization to sectionally constant potentials the Schroedinger equation can be solved by elementary methods.

As an introduction to the methods of solution and of interpretation, we consider first the wave equation for free particles in three-space dimensions. Following this, in Sections 9.3 to 9.8, various sectionally constant potentials in one-space dimension are selected to illustrate the quantum effects noted above. Finally, in Section 9.9, general conclusions concerning free states, reflecting states, penetrating states, and bound states are inferred from solutions for sectionally constant potentials. No attempt is made to extend these general conclusions to particles in three-space dimensions.

9.2. Streams of Free Particles. The spatial part of the wave function for free particles in three-space dimensions satisfies the STIWE

$$(9.1) \qquad -\frac{\hbar^2}{2m}\left(\frac{\partial^2}{\partial x^2} + \frac{\partial^2}{\partial y^2} + \frac{\partial^2}{\partial z^2}\right)\psi = E\psi.$$

The time factor, $e^{-i\omega t}$, where $\omega = E/\hbar$, will be supplied when its presence encourages interpretation. By standard methods it is found that (9.1) possesses separated solutions $X(x)\,Y(y)\,Z(z)$ with $X(x)$, $Y(y)$, and $Z(z)$ satisfying the ordinary differential equations

$$(9.2) \quad X'' + k_1{}^2X = 0, \qquad Y'' + k_2{}^2Y = 0, \qquad Z'' + k_3{}^2Z = 0,$$

provided

$$(9.3) \qquad k_1{}^2 + k_2{}^2 + k_3{}^2 = k^2 = 2mE/\hbar^2.$$

Taking the exponential solutions of (9.2) and inserting the time factor, we obtain a particular solution of (9.1):

$$(9.4) \qquad\qquad \psi = A e^{i(\mathbf{k} \cdot \mathbf{r} - \omega t)}.$$

The wave function (9.4) does not possess finite norm. Nevertheless, it may be given a physical interpretation (see Section 8.2) as the unique wave function representing a stream of noninteracting particles with given number density ρ and given number current $\mathbf{j}$ which determine $|A|$ and $\mathbf{k}$ by the equations

$$(9.5) \qquad \begin{aligned} &\text{(a)} \quad \rho = |\psi|^2 = |A|^2, \\ &\text{(b)} \quad \mathbf{j} = \frac{\hbar}{m} |\psi|^2 \operatorname{grad} \Delta = \frac{\hbar}{m} |A|^2 \mathbf{k} = \frac{\hbar}{m} \rho \mathbf{k}. \end{aligned}$$

The wave function (9.4) implies no information about the location of a particle, in agreement with the Heisenberg uncertainty principle which states that precise knowledge of the particle momentum implies absence of information about the particle position: $\Delta p_x = 0$, implies that $\Delta x = \infty$, etc.

9.3. Reflection at a Potential Jump.   Consider a beam of particles directed toward $+x$ against a potential which jumps from $V = 0$ for

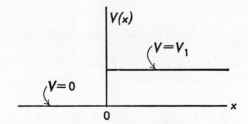

Fig. 9.1. A potential jump.

$x < 0$ to $V = V_1 > 0$ for $x > 0$. Classically, the particles would be reflected without loss of speed if $E < V_1$, they would be transmitted, passing over the potential jump with reduced speed $u = \sqrt{2(E - V_1)/m}$ if $E > V_1$.

Quantum mechanically, all information about the beam can be obtained from a wave function which satisfies the STIWE

$$(9.6) \quad \text{(a)} \quad \frac{d^2\psi}{dx^2} + k_0{}^2\psi = 0, \, x < 0, \qquad \text{(b)} \quad \frac{d^2\psi}{dx^2} + k_1{}^2\psi = 0, \, x > 0,$$

where

$$(9.7) \qquad \text{(a)} \quad \hbar^2 k_0{}^2 = 2mE, \qquad \text{(b)} \quad \hbar^2 k_1{}^2 = 2m(E - V_1).$$

The trigonometric form of the solution of (9.6), including the time factor $e^{-i\omega t}$,

(9.8)   (a) $\psi = \psi_0 = (a \cos k_0 x + b \sin k_0 x)e^{-i\omega t},\ x < 0,$
           (b) $\psi = \psi_1 = (c \cos k_1 x + d \sin k_1 x)e^{-i\omega t},\ x > 0,$

represents the wave function in terms of standing waves. Helpful for detailed interpretation is an exponential form of solution

(9.9)   (a) $\psi = \psi_0 = (Ae^{ik_0 x} + Be^{-ik_0 x})e^{-i\omega t},\ x < 0,$
           (b) $\psi = \psi_1 = (Ce^{ik_1 x} + De^{-ik_1 x})e^{-i\omega t},\ x > 0,$

since the exponential terms with pure imaginary exponents can be interpreted as incident, as transmitted, or as reflected beams.

Consider first the case $E > V_1$, making both k_0 and k_1 real and, for convenience of exposition, positive. Then (9.9a) represents ψ_0 as a superposition of an "A" beam incident from $-x$ and a "B" beam traveling toward $-x$. Similarly (9.9b) represents ψ_1 as a superposition of a "D"

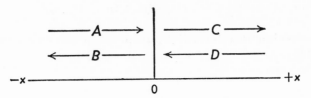

Fig. 9.2. The wave function (9.9) as a superposition of traveling waves.

beam incident from $+x$ and a "C" beam traveling toward $+x$. (See Fig. 9.2.) Before proceeding with this interpretation, we impose the conditions that ψ and $d\psi/dx$ be continuous at $x = 0$, obtaining from (9.9),

(9.10)   (a) $A + B = C + D,$ (b) $k_0(A - B) = k_1(C - D).$

Uniqueness of solution can be obtained only by imposing a third condition. Arbitrarily assuming that there is no beam incident from $+x$, we set $D = 0$ and find from (9.10) that

(9.11)   (a) $A = \dfrac{1}{2}\left(1 + \dfrac{k_1}{k_0}\right)C,$ (b) $B = \dfrac{1}{2}\left(1 - \dfrac{k_1}{k_0}\right)C.$

From (9.5), (9.9) and (9.11) we find

(9.12)   (a) $\rho_A = \dfrac{1}{4}\left|1 + \dfrac{k_1}{k_0}\right|^2 |C|^2,$ $j_A = \rho_A\left(\dfrac{\hbar k_0}{m}\right),$

                (b) $\rho_B = \dfrac{1}{4}\left|1 - \dfrac{k_1}{k_0}\right|^2 |C|^2,$ $j_B = -\rho_B\left(\dfrac{\hbar k_0}{m}\right),$

                (c) $\rho_C = |C|^2,$ $j_C = \rho_C\left(\dfrac{\hbar k_1}{m}\right),$

for the number densities and currents in (a) the incident "A" beam, (b) the reflected "B" beam, and (c) the transmitted "C" beam. The coefficients of reflection and transmission, R and T, are, respectively,

(9.13)

$$\text{(a)} \quad R = \left| \frac{j_B}{j_A} \right| = \left(\frac{k_0 - k_1}{k_0 + k_1} \right)^2,$$

$$\text{(b)} \quad T = \left| \frac{j_C}{j_A} \right| = 4 \left(\frac{k_1}{k_0 + k_1} \right)^2.$$

Since $R + T = 1$, R and T may be jointly graphed (Fig. 9.3) as functions of $\alpha = \dfrac{k_1}{k_0} = \sqrt{(E - V_1)/E}$.

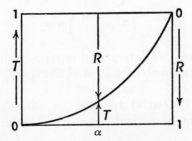

Fig. 9.3. The transmission and reflection coefficients for a beam directed toward a potential jump, as functions of $\alpha = \sqrt{(E - V_1)/E}$.

When $0 < E < V_1$, k_1 as defined in (9.7b) is pure imaginary. Letting $k_1 = i\mu$, (9.9) becomes

(9.14)

$$\text{(a)} \quad \psi = \psi_0 = (Ae^{ik_0 x} + Be^{-ik_0 x})e^{-i\omega t}, \quad x < 0,$$

$$\text{(b)} \quad \psi = \psi_1 = (Ce^{-\mu x} + De^{\mu x})e^{-i\omega t}, \quad x > 0.$$

Continuity of ψ and of $d\psi/dx$ at $x = 0$ gives (9.10) with k_1 replaced by $i\mu$. Taking $\mu > 0$ without loss of generality, and requiring that the wave function be bounded for all x, we see from (9.14b) that $D = 0$.

For this case, $0 < E < V_1$, (9.14a) still represents ψ_0 as a superposition of two beams, an "A" beam incident from $-x$ and a reflected "B" beam traveling toward $-x$. But with $k_1 = i\mu$, μ real, (9.12a) and (9.12b) become

(9.15)

$$\text{(a)} \quad \rho_A = \frac{1}{4}\left(1 + \frac{\mu^2}{k_0{}^2}\right)|C|^2, \qquad j_A = \rho_A\left(\frac{\hbar k_0}{m}\right),$$

$$\text{(b)} \quad \rho_B = \frac{1}{4}\left(1 + \frac{\mu^2}{k_0{}^2}\right)|C|^2, \qquad j_B = -\rho_B\left(\frac{\hbar k_0}{m}\right).$$

From (9.15) we see that

(9.16)

$$\text{(a)} \quad \rho_A = \rho_B, \qquad \text{(b)} \quad j_A = -j_B.$$

There is total reflection at the potential jump. But with $k_1 = i\mu$, μ real, instead of (9.12c) we obtain, from (9.5) and (9.14b) with $D = 0$,

(9.17)   (a) $\rho_C = |C|^2 e^{-2\mu x}$,   (b) $j_C = 0$.

Althouth total reflection is predicted by classical mechanics for the case $E < V_1$, not predicted is the possibility that, in interaction with the potential jump, sufficient energy may be imparted to particles to enable their detection in the region $x > 0$.

Problem 9.1:   Show, in the case $E > V_1$, that

$$\text{(a)}\quad \rho_0 \equiv |\psi_0|^2 = \left(1 - \frac{V_1}{E} \sin^2 \frac{x}{\hbar}\sqrt{2mE}\right)|C|^2,$$

(9.18)

$$\text{(b)}\quad \rho_A + \rho_B = \left(\frac{2E - V_1}{E}\right)|C|^2.$$

That $\rho_0 \neq \rho_A + \rho_B$ may be interpreted in terms of interference: ρ_0 is an observable; to attempt to observe ρ_A or ρ_B abrogates the statement of the problem. (Hint: Use (9.7), (9.9a) and (9.11).)

9.4. An Infinite Potential Jump.   An infinite potential jump (Fig. 9.4) is an idealization of a rigid boundary. The infinite jump may be

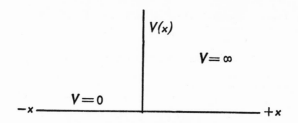

Fig. 9.4. An infinite potential jump.

treated as the limit as $V_1 \to \infty$ of a finite potential jump (Fig. 9.1) primarily for the purpose of examining the modification of the continuity conditions on the wave function by the presence of rigid boundaries.

Keeping E fixed, we see from (9.7) that k_0 remains fixed and $k_1 = i\mu \to i\infty$ as $V_1 \to \infty$. Then (9.11) implies that A and B cease to be finite unless $C \to 0$. Letting $C = k_0 c/k_1 i$, keeping c fixed, we have $A \to c/2i$, $B \to -c/2i$, $C \to 0$ as $V_1 \to \infty$. Then from (9.14), with $D = 0$, we obtain in the limit $V_1 = \infty$,

(9.19)   (a) $\psi = \psi_0 = c(\sin k_0 x)e^{-i\omega t}$, $x < 0$
                  (b) $\psi = \psi_1 = 0$, $x > 0$.

From (9.19) we see that the wave function remains continuous everywhere, but its derivative $d\psi/dx$ is discontinuous at the potential wall.

The condition that $d\psi/dx$ be continuous is replaced by the condition that $\psi = 0$ in regions where $V = \infty$.

Problem 9.2: Solve the STIWE (9.6a), (9.7a) for the region $x < 0$ for $E > 0$, subject to the condition $\psi = 0$ at $x = 0$. Supply the time factor and interpret the solution as a superposition of two waves. Answer: (9.19a).

9.5. Barrier Penetration. According to classical mechanics, a beam of particles with energy $E < V_0$ directed toward a potential barrier (Fig. 9.5) will be entirely reflected. Quantum mechanically, a calculable part is transmitted. This property of barrier penetration, the "tunnel effect," is not restricted to sectionally constant potentials, but exists for all kinds of potentials. The tunnel effect is especially important in the theory of radioactive decay and in the theory of cold emission of electrons from metals.

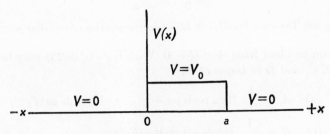

Fig. 9.5. A potential barrier.

The STIWE for the barrier of Fig. 9.5, for the case $0 < E < V_0$, is

$$\text{(a)} \quad \frac{d^2\psi}{dx^2} + k^2\psi = 0, \qquad x < 0 \text{ and } x > a,$$

(9.20)

$$\text{(b)} \quad \frac{d^2\psi}{dx^2} - \mu^2\psi = 0, \qquad 0 < x < a,$$

where

(9.21)   (a) $\hbar^2 k^2 = 2mE$,   (b) $\hbar^2 \mu^2 = 2m(V_0 - E)$.

The general solution, including the time factor, is

(9.22)
(a) $\psi = \psi_0 = (Ae^{ikx} + Be^{-ikx})e^{-i\omega t}, x < 0,$
(b) $\psi = \psi_1 = (Ce^{\mu x} + De^{-\mu x})e^{-i\omega t}, 0 < x < a,$
(c) $\psi = \psi_2 = (Fe^{ikx} + Ge^{-ikx})e^{-i\omega t}, x > a.$

In (9.22), the wave function is represented as a superposition of waves traveling as indicated in Fig. 9.6; there are no waves in the barrier region $0 < x < a$.

Continuity of the wave function (9.22) and of its derivative at $x = 0$ and at $x = a$ give

(9.23)
$$
\begin{align}
\text{(a)} \quad & A + B = C + D \\
\text{(b)} \quad & ik(A - B) = \mu(C - D), \\
\text{(c)} \quad & Ce^{\mu a} + De^{-\mu a} = Fe^{ika} + Ge^{-ika}, \\
\text{(d)} \quad & \mu(Ce^{\mu a} - De^{-\mu a}) = ik(Fe^{ika} - Ge^{-ika}).
\end{align}
$$

Uniqueness in the solution may be obtained by imposing a further condition. This we arbitrarily obtain by considering the case in which there

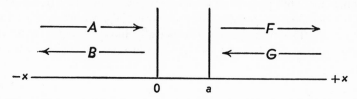

Fig. 9.6. The wave function (9.22) as a superposition of traveling waves.

is no beam incident from $+x$: $G = 0$. With $G = 0$, (9.23) may be solved for A, B, C, and D in terms of F:

(9.24)
$$
\begin{align}
\text{(a)} \quad & A = \frac{1}{2k\mu} \{2k\mu \cosh \mu a + i(\mu^2 - k^2) \sinh \mu a\} Fe^{ika}, \\
\text{(b)} \quad & B = \frac{1}{2ik\mu} (k^2 + \mu^2) \sinh \mu a Fe^{ika}, \\
\text{(c)} \quad & C = \frac{1}{2\mu} (\mu + ik) Fe^{ika-\mu a}, \\
\text{(d)} \quad & D = \frac{1}{2\mu} (\mu - ik) Fe^{ika+\mu a}.
\end{align}
$$

From (9.5), (9.22) and (9.24) we readily find for the currents in the incident "A" beam, the reflected "B" beam, and the transmitted "F" beam,

(9.25)
$$
\begin{align}
\text{(a)} \quad & j_A = \frac{\hbar}{m} |A|^2 k = \frac{\hbar}{4mk\mu^2} \{4k^2\mu^2 + (k^2 + \mu^2)^2 \sinh^2 \mu a\} |F|^2, \\
\text{(b)} \quad & j_B = -\frac{\hbar}{m} |B|^2 k = \frac{-\hbar}{4mk\mu^2} (k^2 + \mu^2)^2 \sinh^2 \mu a |F|^2, \\
\text{(c)} \quad & j_F = \frac{\hbar}{m} |F|^2 k,
\end{align}
$$

respectively. The coefficients of reflection and transmission,

(9.26)
$$
\begin{align}
\text{(a)} \quad & R = \left| \frac{j_B}{j_A} \right| = \frac{(k^2 + \mu^2)^2 \sinh^2 \mu a}{4k^2\mu^2 + (k^2 + \mu^2)^2 \sinh^2 \mu a}, \\
\text{(b)} \quad & T = \left| \frac{j_F}{j_A} \right| = \frac{4k^2\mu^2}{4k^2\mu^2 + (k^2 + \mu^2)^2 \sinh^2 \mu a},
\end{align}
$$

are functions of

(9.27) (a) $\dfrac{k}{\mu} = \sqrt{E/(V_0 - E)}$,   (b) $\mu a = \dfrac{a}{\hbar}\sqrt{2m(V_0 - E)}$.

To aid in obtaining a graph of R and T as functions of μa for fixed k/μ, or

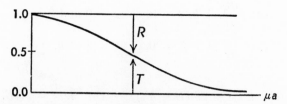

Fig. 9.7. Coefficients of reflection and transmission by a potential barrier as functions of its width, for fixed E and V_0.

as functions of a for fixed k and μ (Fig. 9.7), we observe from (9.26) that $R + T = 1$ and that

(9.28)

(a) $R \cong \dfrac{1}{4}\left(\dfrac{\mu}{k} + \dfrac{k}{\mu}\right)^2 (\mu a)^2, \ \mu a \ll 1$,

(b) $T \cong 16\left(\dfrac{\mu}{k} + \dfrac{k}{\mu}\right)^{-2} e^{-2\mu a}, \ \mu a \gg 1$.

9.6. Transmission Resonance. According to classical mechanics, a beam of particles with energy $E > V_0$ directed toward the potential well (Fig. 9.8) would be transmitted without any reflection. According to wave theory, we expect some particles to be reflected at the sharp edges. We

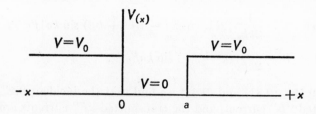

Fig. 9.8. A potential well.

shall find, however, that there is appreciable transmission only in the neighborhoods of certain values of E. An interesting example of this phenomenon, *transmission resonance*, occurs in the scattering of electrons from atoms of noble gases, such as argon and neon. As a first approximation, the potential energy of an electron inside such an atom may be represented by a well of radius about 2 Ängstroms. The effective depth and radius of the well are such that there is a transmission resonance for very slow electrons: $E - V_0 = 0.1$ electron volts. This effect was first observed by Ramsauer and is called the *Ramsauer effect*,[1] or the *Ramsauer-Townsend* effect.[2]

The STIWE for the potential well of Fig. 9.8, for the case $E > V_0$, may be written in the form

(9.29)

$$\text{(a)} \quad \frac{d^2\psi}{dx^2} + k_0{}^2\psi = 0, \qquad x < 0 \text{ and } x > a,$$

$$\text{(b)} \quad \frac{d^2\psi}{dx^2} + k^2\psi = 0, \qquad 0 < x < a,$$

where

(9.30)   (a) $\hbar^2 k_0{}^2 = 2m(E - V_0),$ (b) $\hbar^2 k^2 = 2mE.$

The general solution including the time factor is

(9.31)
$$\text{(a)} \quad \psi = \psi_0 = (Ae^{ik_0x} + Be^{-ik_0x})e^{-i\omega t}, \; x < 0,$$
$$\text{(b)} \quad \psi = \psi_1 = (Ce^{ikx} + De^{-ikx})e^{-i\omega t}, \; 0 < x < a,$$
$$\text{(c)} \quad \psi = \psi_2 = (Fe^{ik_0x} + Ge^{-ik_0x})e^{-i\omega t}, \; x > a.$$

Let a beam be directed toward the well from $-x$, none from $+x$. Then $G = 0$. Continuity of ψ and of $d\psi/dx$ at $x = 0$ and at $x = a$ gives

(9.32)
$$\text{(a)} \quad A + B = C + D,$$
$$\text{(b)} \quad ik_0(A - B) = ik(C - D),$$
$$\text{(c)} \quad Ce^{ika} + De^{-ika} = Fe^{ik_0a},$$
$$\text{(d)} \quad k(Ce^{ika} - De^{-ika}) = k_0Fe^{ik_0a}.$$

Solution of (9.32) for A and B in terms of F gives

(9.33)
$$\text{(a)} \quad A = \frac{1}{2kk_0} \{2kk_0 \cos ka - i(k^2 + k_0{}^2) \sin ka\} Fe^{ik_0a},$$
$$\text{(b)} \quad B = \frac{i}{2kk_0} (k^2 - k_0{}^2) \sin ka Fe^{ik_0a}.$$

From (9.5b), (9.31) and (9.33) we find that the incident "A" current, the reflected "B" current, and the transmitted "F" currents are

$$\text{(a)} \quad j_A = \frac{\hbar}{m} |A|^2 k_0 = \frac{\hbar}{4mk^2k_0} \{4k^2k_0{}^2 + (k^2 - k_0{}^2)^2 \sin^2 ka\}|F|^2,$$

(9.34)
$$\text{(b)} \quad j_B = -\frac{\hbar}{m} |B|^2 k_0 = \frac{-\hbar}{4mk^2k_0} (k^2 - k_0{}^2)^2 \sin^2 ka|F|^2,$$

$$\text{(c)} \quad j_F = \frac{\hbar}{m} |F|^2 k_0.$$

[1] C. Ramsauer, *Ann. Physik*, **64**, 513 (1921); **66**, 545 (1921).
[2] J. S. Townsend and V. A. Bailey, *Phil. Mag.*, **43**, 593 (1922); **44**, 1033 (1922).

From (9.34) we readily calculate the coefficients of reflection and transmission:

(9.35)

(a) $R = \left| \dfrac{j_B}{j_A} \right| = \dfrac{(k^2 - k_0{}^2)^2 \sin^2 ka}{4k^2k_0{}^2 + (k^2 - k_0{}^2)^2 \sin^2 ka}$,

(b) $T = \left| \dfrac{j_F}{j_A} \right| = \dfrac{4k^2k_0{}^2}{4k^2k_0{}^2 + (k^2 - k_0{}^2)^2 \sin^2 ka}$.

From (9.35) we see that R and T are functions of k/k_0 and ka, periodic in ka with period π, and that $R + T = 1$. To aid in obtaining graphs of R and T as functions of ka for fixed k/k_0, we observe that $T = T_{\max} = 1$ when $\sin ka = 0$, $ka = n\pi$, and that $T = T_{\min} = 4k^2k_0{}^2/(k^2 + k_0{}^2)^2$ when $\sin ka = \pm 1$, $ka = (2n + 1)\pi/2$. With this we readily obtain Fig. 9.10.

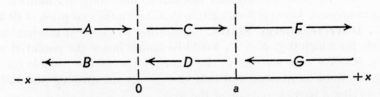

Fig. 9.9. The wave function (9.31) as a superposition of traveling waves.

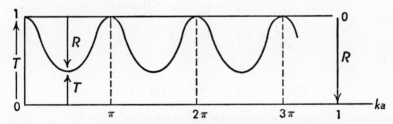

Fig. 9.10. Transmission and reflection coefficients for the potential well of Fig. 9.8, as functions of ka for fixed k/k_0.

There is complete transmission when $ka = n\pi$, n an integer. Since k is given in terms of the de Broglie wavelength in the well by $k = 2\pi/\lambda$, complete transmission occurs when $n(\lambda/2) = a$, that is, when there are an integral number of half wavelengths within the well.

The resonance is sharp if T rises sharply from, say, 50 per cent transmission to 100 per cent transmission. From (9.35b) and (9.30) we find that $T = \frac{1}{2}$ when

(9.36) $\sin^2 ka = \dfrac{4k^2k_0{}^2}{(k^2 - k_0{}^2)^2} = \dfrac{4E(E - V_0)}{V_0{}^2}$.

Since resonance occurs when $\sin ka = 0$, the 50 per cent transmission point is near the resonance if $4(E - V_0)/V_0 \ll 1$. Hence resonance is sharp for particles of low energy passing over deep wells.

Problem 9.3:   Express (9.35) in terms of E and V_0 and show that, near a resonance,

$$(9.37) \qquad T \cong 1 - \frac{mV_0{}^2}{2\hbar^2(E - V_0)} \left(a - \frac{n\pi\hbar}{\sqrt{2mE}} \right)^2.$$

Problem 9.4:   How deep does a well of 2×10^{-8} cm wide have to be to provide a transmission resonance for electrons of 0.1 ev kinetic energy? ($E - V_0 = 0.1$ ev). Answer: $V_0 \geq 9.4$ ev.

Problem 9.5:   Solve the STIWE for the barrier of Fig. 9.5 for the case $E > V_0$, letting $\hbar^2 k_0{}^2 = 2mE$, $\hbar^2 k^2 = 2m(E - V_0)$. Obtain and sketch the coefficients of reflection and transmission as functions of $k_0 a$ for fixed k/k_0. Discuss transmission resonance, obtaining a condition for sharp resonance. Answer: See (9.29) to (9.35) with the exception of (9.30).

9.7. Discrete Energy States.   According to classical mechanics, a particle for which $0 \leq E < V_0$ would be bound inside the potential well of Fig. 9.8. We shall see that in the quantum theory the possible energy levels are finite in number and that there is a nonvanishing probability of observing a particle outside of the well.

The STIWE is

$$(9.38) \qquad \begin{aligned} &\text{(a)} \quad \frac{d^2\psi}{dx^2} - \mu^2\psi = 0, \qquad x < 0 \text{ and } x > a, \\ &\text{(b)} \quad \frac{d^2\psi}{dx^2} + k^2\psi = 0, \qquad 0 < x < a, \end{aligned}$$

where

$$(9.39) \qquad \text{(a)} \quad \hbar^2\mu^2 = 2m(V_0 - E) \qquad \text{(b)} \quad \hbar^2 k^2 = 2mE.$$

The general solution, omitting the time factor, is

$$(9.40) \qquad \begin{aligned} &\text{(a)} \quad \psi = \psi_0 = Ae^{\mu x} + Be^{-\mu x}, \, x < 0, \\ &\text{(b)} \quad \psi = \psi_1 = Ce^{ikx} + De^{-ikx}, \, 0 < x < a, \\ &\text{(c)} \quad \psi = \psi_2 = Fe^{\mu x} + Ge^{-\mu x}, \, x > a. \end{aligned}$$

Taking $\mu > 0$, we see from (9.40) that $\psi_0 \to \infty$ as $x \to -\infty$ unless $B = 0$ and that $\psi_2 \to \infty$ as $x \to \infty$ unless $F = 0$. Hence, to obtain a bounded solution, we take $B = 0$ and $F = 0$.

With $B = F = 0$, continuity of ψ and of $d\psi/dx$ at $x = 0$ and at $x = a$ gives

$$(9.41) \qquad \begin{aligned} &\text{(a)} \quad A = C + D, \\ &\text{(b)} \quad \mu A = ik(C - D), \\ &\text{(c)} \quad Ce^{ika} + De^{-ika} = Ge^{-\mu a}, \\ &\text{(d)} \quad ik(Ce^{ika} - De^{-ika}) = -\mu Ge^{-\mu a}. \end{aligned}$$

These four equations for A, C, D, and G are consistent if

$$(9.42) \qquad \begin{vmatrix} 1 & -1 & -1 & 0 \\ \mu & -ik & ik & 0 \\ 0 & e^{ika} & e^{-ika} & -e^{-\mu a} \\ 0 & ike^{ika} & -ike^{-ika} & \mu e^{-\mu a} \end{vmatrix} = 0.$$

Expansion of the determinant (9.42) gives

$$(9.43) \qquad e^{-\mu a}\{(\mu + ik)^2 e^{ika} - (\mu - ik)^2 e^{-ika}\} = 0.$$

For consistency we must have either of the two cases:

$$(9.44) \qquad \begin{aligned} &\text{(a)} \quad (\mu + ik)e^{ika/2} = (\mu - ik)e^{-ika/2}, \\ &\text{(b)} \quad (\mu + ik)e^{ika/2} = -(\mu - ik)e^{-ika/2}. \end{aligned}$$

These may be expressed in the forms

$$(9.45) \qquad \text{(a)} \quad \tan (ka/2) = -k/\mu, \qquad \text{(b)} \quad \tan (ka/2) = \mu/k,$$

respectively.

V_0 is considered as given and E is determined by k: $E = \hbar^2 k^2/2m$. Let $w = ka/2$ and $2\hbar^2 b^2 = mV_0 a^2$. Then, by (9.39), (9.45) becomes

$$(9.46) \qquad \text{(a)} \quad \tan w = \frac{-w}{\sqrt{b^2 - w^2}}, \qquad \text{(b)} \quad \tan w = \frac{\sqrt{b^2 - w^2}}{w}.$$

To solve (9.46) for w, we plot the curves

$$(9.47)$$

$$\text{(a)} \quad y_0 = \tan w, \qquad \text{(b)} \quad y_1 = \frac{-w}{\sqrt{b^2 - w^2}} \qquad \text{(c)} \quad y_2 = \frac{\sqrt{b^2 - w^2}}{w},$$

for positive values of w, Fig. 9.11. The branches of the graph of $y_0 = \tan w$ are asymptotic to the lines $w = (2n + 1)\pi/2$, $n = $ any integer. The curve

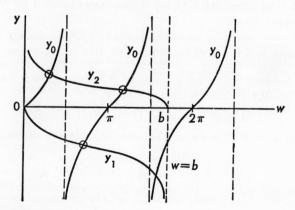

Fig. 9.11. Graphical solution of (9.47) for $3\pi/2 \leq b < 2\pi$, giving four energy levels.

for y_1 proceeds downward in the fourth quadrant from the origin, approaching the line $w = b$ asymptotically. The curve for y_2 lies in the first quadrant, being asymptotic to the y axis and meeting the w axis at $w = b$.

From Fig. 9.11 we see that for a given value of b there are a finite, determined number of points of intersection of the y_0 curve with the y_1 and the y_2 curves. In fact there are, not including the intersection at the origin, n points of intersection when $(n - 1)\pi/2 < b \leq n\pi/2$. Hence for given b there are n discrete energy levels, where $2b/\pi \leq n < \dfrac{2b}{\pi} + 1$.

A value of w at a point of intersection gives a value of $k = 2w/a$ for which the equations (9.41) may be solved for A, C, and D in terms of G, giving bounded wave functions (9.40) which satisfy the continuity conditions. For each wave function there is a calculable, nonvanishing probability of observing a particle outside the region $0 < x < a$. The discussion at the end of Section 9.3 applies.

Problem 9.6: Show how the energy levels can be obtained by plotting on a ξ, w plane the circle $\xi^2 + w^2 = b^2$ and the curves $\xi = -w \cot w$, $\xi = w \tan w$, where $\xi = \mu a/2$.[3]

9.8. The Particle in a Box.

Let V_0 in the potential well of Fig. 9.8 approach ∞, keeping $E < V_0$ and the width a fixed. Since, according to (9.39a), $\mu \to \infty$ as $V_0 \to \infty$, the equations (9.45) determining k become

$$(9.48) \qquad \text{(a)} \quad \tan (ka/2) = 0, \qquad \text{(b)} \quad \cot (ka/2) = 0.$$

One or the other of these equations is satisfied by taking $k = n\pi/a$, n an integer. Thus are obtained the discrete energy levels for a particle in a one-dimensional box of width a:

$$(9.49) \qquad E_n = \frac{\hbar^2 k_n{}^2}{2m} = \frac{\hbar^2}{2m}\left(\frac{n\pi}{a}\right)^2 = \frac{\hbar^2 n^2}{8ma^2}.$$

The result is identical with (4.49) which was obtained by Wilson-Sommerfeld quantization.

When $\mu \to \infty$ and $k \to n\pi/a$ the equations (9.41) do not remain consistent unless $A \to 0$ and $G \to \infty$ properly. However, letting

$$(9.50) \qquad A = ck/\mu, \qquad G = -(ck/\mu)e^{(\mu - ik)a},$$

we find from (9.41) that we have

$$(9.51) \qquad A = 0, \ C = c/2i, \ D = -c/2i, \ G = 0$$

in the limit $\mu = \infty$, $k = n\pi/a$. The wave function (9.40) becomes

$$(9.52) \qquad \begin{aligned} &\text{(a)} \quad \psi = 0, \ x < 0 \text{ and } x > a, \\ &\text{(b)} \quad \psi = c \sin (n\pi x/a), \ 0 < x < a. \end{aligned}$$

The conclusions at the end of Section 9.4 apply.

[3] See L. I. Schiff, *Quantum Mechanics*, second edition, McGraw-Hill, 1955, p. 37.

Problem 9.7:   Determine c in (9.52) so that $N(\psi) = 1$. Also show that wave functions (9.52) corresponding to different values of n are orthogonal. Answer: $c = \sqrt{2/a}$.

Problem 9.8:   Solve the STIWE for a free particle in the region $-a < x < a$, imposing the conditions that the wave function vanish at $x = -a$ and at $x = a$. Obtain the energy values and the normalized wave functions. Show that wave functions corresponding to different energy values are orthogonal. Answer: See (9.49), (9.52) and Problem 9.7.

Problem 9.9:   Obtain separated solutions of (9.1) for the three-dimensional box $0 \leq x \leq a$, $0 \leq y \leq b$, $0 \leq z \leq c$, which vanish on the faces of the box. What are the possible energy values? Normalize the solutions, and show that distinct solutions are orthogonal.

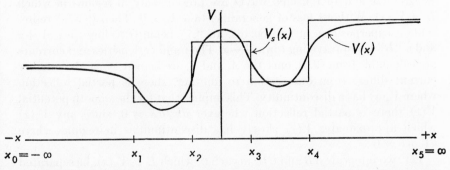

Fig. 9.12. Approximation to a smooth potential $V(x)$ by a sectionally constant potential $V_s(x)$.

9.9. Generalization of Principal Results.   From results obtained by studying the STIWE for sectionally constant potentials, conclusions of general validity for reasonably smooth potentials $V(x)$ may be drawn. Any such $V(x)$ may be approximated to any desired degree of accuracy by a sectionally constant potential $V_s(x)$ (see Fig. 9.12, where a crude approximation is depicted).

For simplicity of discussion let us consider a potential $V(x)$ which is bounded as well as reasonably smooth. Let $V(x)$ be approximated by $V_s(x)$ which is constant over n sections $-\infty = x_0 < x_1 < x_2 < \cdots < x_n = +\infty$:

(9.53) $V_s(x) = V_\lambda,$ $x_{\lambda-1} < x < x_\lambda,$ $\lambda = 1, 2, \ldots, n,$

where

(9.54) $V_1 = \lim_{x \to -\infty} V(x),$ $V_n = \lim_{x \to +\infty} V(x).$

In a region $x_{i-1} < x < x_i$ where $E > V_i$ we write the STIWE in the form

(9.55) $\dfrac{d^2\psi}{dx^2} = k_i{}^2\psi = 0, \qquad \hbar^2 k_i{}^2 = 2m(E - V_i).$

In a region $x_{j-1} < x < x_j$ where $E < V_j$ we write it in the form

(9.56) $\dfrac{d^2\psi}{dx^2} - \mu_j{}^2\psi = 0, \qquad \hbar\mu_j{}^2 = 2m(V_j - E).$

General solutions of (9.55) and (9.56) are

(9.57)   (a) $\psi = \psi_i = A_i e^{ik_i x} + B_i e^{-ik_i x}, \; x_{i-1} < x < x_i,$
              (b) $\varphi = \psi_j = C_j e^{\mu_j x} + D_j e^{-\mu_j x}, \; x_{j-1} < x < x_j.$

Progressive and/or reflected waves are present only in regions in which $E > V_s(x)$. Without loss of generality, take $k_i > 0$. Then (9.57a) represents a superposition of two beams, an "A" beam traveling toward $+x$ and a "B" beam traveling toward $-x$. The number densities and currents are calculable from (9.5), once the A_i and B_i are known. Since the number current differs from one section to another, there is partial reflection where $V_s(x)$ has a discontinuity. This implies that for the smooth potential $V(x)$ there is partial reflection wherever $dV/dX \neq 0$, since any $V_s(x)$ which approximates $V(x)$ closely has discontinuities in regions where $dV/dx \neq 0$.

Let two intervals AB and CD, in each of which $E > V_s(x)$, be separated by an interval BC in which $E < V_s(x)$. Waves appear in AB and CD, but not in BC. Thus the interval BC acts as a barrier through which waves penetrate. The conclusion remains equally valid for a smooth potential $V(x)$ when intervals AB and CD in each of which $E > V(x)$ are separated by an interval BC in which $E < V(x)$. The phenomenon of barrier penetration is not restricted to sectionally constant potentials.

Transmission resonance is also explainable in terms of smooth, non-repulsive potentials, but the mathematical treatment is beyond the scope of this book. A theoretical explanation of the Ramsauer-Townsend effect was suggested by M. Bohr and shown to be quantitatively reasonable by H. Faxen and J. Holtsmark.[4] A brief mathematical discussion is given by Schiff.[5] The experimental results, an observed low minimum in the scattering cross section of electrons by rare gas atoms at about 0.7 ev bombarding energy, are summarized by R. Kollath.[6]

Consideration of the continuity and boundary conditions on the wave functions lead to important distinctions between "bound" states and "free"

[4] H. Faxen and J. Holtsmark, Z. Physik, 45, 307 (1927).
[5] L. I. Schiff, op. cit., p. 108f.
[6] R. Kollath, Physik Z., 31, 985 (1931).

states. Continuity of ψ and of $d\psi/dx$ at $x_1, x_2, \ldots, x_{n-1}$ imposes $2n - 2$ linear homogeneous conditions on the $2n$ coefficients in the general solution (9.57) of the Schroedinger equation for $V_s(x)$. For other conditions we distinguish special cases, assuming for definiteness of description that there exist one or more regions in which $V_s(x) < V_1$.

Case 1. $E < V_1$. The wave function is of the form (9.57b) in the regions $x < x_1$ and $x > x_{n-1}$. Hence there are no waves outside of the region $x_1 > x < x_{n-1}$; particles are "bound" within the region.

Boundedness of ψ at $x = \pm \infty$ leads to the conditions $D_1 = 0, C_n = 0$. The continuity conditions reduce to $2n - 2$ linear homogeneous equations for $2n - 2$ unknowns. These equations are consistent if and only if the determinant of their coefficients, considered as a function of E, vanishes (see (9.42)). This condition leads to discrete energy solutions, the finite number of such increasing, in general, with various potentials, as V_1 increases until, as in the case of a particle in a box (Section 9.8) or of the harmonic oscillator (Chapter 11), there are an infinite number of discrete energy states.

The wave function (9.57) is certainly square integrable over the finite region $x_1 < x < x_{n-1}$. Since it is of the form $C_1 e^{\mu x}$ for $x < x_1$ and of the form $D_n e^{-\mu_n x}$ for $x > x_{n-1}$, it is also square integrable outside of this region. Hence it is square integrable on $(-\infty, \infty)$.

The conclusion that "bound" states exist only for discrete energy levels, the wave functions representing such states being square integrable, is readily extended to any reasonably smooth potential $V(x)$.

Case 2. $V_1 < E < V_n$. The wave function is of the form (9.57a) in the region $x < x_1$, of the form (9.57b) in the region $x > x_{n-1}$. Hence there are no waves in the region $x > x_{n-1}$: particles are entirely reflected at $x = x_{n-1}$. There exists, however, a wave incident from $-x$ and a wave reflected toward $-x$.

Boundedness of ψ at $x = +\infty$ leads to the condition $C_n = 0$. There are no further conditions, other than this and the $2n - 2$ continuity conditions. With $C_n = 0$ the continuity conditions reduce to $2n - 2$ linear homogeneous conditions in $2n - 1$ unknowns. Since this system is always solvable, E may have any value, $V_1 < E < V_n$.

The wave function (9.57) is square integrable over the region $x > x_1$ but not over the region $x < x_1$, where it is of the form (9.57a). Hence the wave function is not square integrable over $(-\infty, \infty)$.

The conclusion that "reflecting" states exist for a continuum of energy levels, the wave functions representing such states being not square integrable, is readily extended to any reasonably smooth potential $V(x)$.

Case 3. $E > V_n$. In the regions $x < x_1$ and $x > x_{n-1}$ the wave function is of the form (9.57a). Hence there are waves in both extreme regions.

Uniqueness of solution for the wave function can be obtained only by

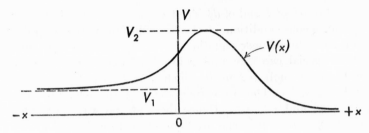

Fig. 9.13. The potential for problem 9.10.

imposing a condition in addition to the $2n - 2$ continuity conditions. Arbitrarily limiting considerations to a case in which there is no beam incident from $+x$, we set $B_n = 0$. With $B_n = 0$, the $2n - 2$ continuity conditions reduce to $2n - 2$ linear homogeneous equations in $2n - 1$ unknowns. These equations are always solvable nontrivially, E having any value in the continuum $E > V_n$. The wave function is square integrable except over the regions $x < x_1$ and $x < x_{n-1}$, where it is of the form (9.57a).

We conclude that "free" states exist for a continuum of levels for any bounded, reasonably smooth potential. The wave functions representing "free" states are not square integrable.

The general theory of wave functions belonging to energy values in a continuum has been extensively developed by H. Weyl[7] and others. Although the treatment is beyond the scope of this book, we remark that such wave functions may be superposed by integration to yield square integrable wave functions and "eigendifferentials." An important example is that of the free particle wave functions (9.4), which may be superposed in the Fourier integral (5.51), yielding a square integrable wave function.

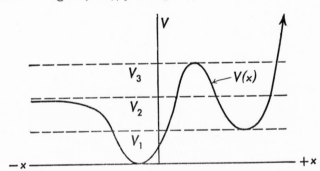

Fig. 9.14. The potential for problem 9.11.

[7] H. Weyl, *Math. Ann.*, **68**, 220 (1910); J. R. Oppenheimer, *Z. Physik*, **41**, 268 (1927); H. A. Kramers, *Quantum Mechanics*, Interscience, 1957, pp. 76, 130; also see E. C. Kemble, *The Fundamental Principles of Quantum Mechanics*, Dover, Ch. VI.

Problem 9.10: Describe the solutions of the Schroedinger wave equation, the energy levels (discrete or continuous), and the states (bound, reflecting, penetrating, free) for the potential pictured in Fig. 9.13. Consider the three cases (1) $0 < E < V_1$, (2) $V_1 < E < V_2$, and (3) $E > V_2$, separately.

Problem 9.11: Describe the solutions of the Schroedinger wave equation, the energy levels, and the states for the potential pictured in Fig. 9.14. Consider the four cases (1) $0 < E < V_1$, (2) $V_1 < E < V_2$, (3) $V_2 < E < V_3$, and (4) $E > V_3$, separately.

9.10. References for Supplementary Reading.

Section 9.1: Bohm, 229–32.

Section 9.2: Pauling and Wilson, 90–95; Persico, 198–202.

Section 9.3: Bohm, 232–8; French, 201–4; Frenkel, 1–7; Mandl, 36–8; Mott and Massey, 7–9; Mott and Sneddon, 13–15; Persico, 174–8; Sproull, 143–6.

Section 9.4: Schiff, 29–36.

Section 9.5: Bohm, 238–42; Finkelnburg, 234–6; Landé, 75–77; Mott and Sneddon, 15–19; Persico, 186–91; Schiff, 92–5.

Section 9.6: Bohm, 242–7; Mott and Massey, 200–204; Schiff, 108–10.

Section 9.7: Bohm, 247–51; French, 341–2; Houston, 83–90; Persico, 178–80; Schiff, 36–40; Shankland, 337–8; Sherwin, 41–8; Sproull, 139–42.

Section 9.8: Bohm, 251–7; French, 198–201; Landé, 50–51; Mandl, 38–43; Mott and Sneddon, 48–9; Pauling and Wilson, 95–100; Peaslee and Mueller, 227–30; Persico, 202–3; Sherwin, 48–50, 66–71.

Section 9.9: Pauling and Wilson, 58–63; Persico, 165–74, 193–5; a very helpful discussion of the "staircase method" is given by J. Frenkel in *Wave Mechanics, Elementary Theory* (Dover, 1950), 99–124.

CHAPTER 10

EIGENFUNCTIONS AND EIGENVALUES

10.1. The Eigenvalue Problem. Let A be a linear operator defined over a linear manifold M. If for any particular f in M there exists a number a such that

(10.1) $$Af = af,$$

then f is called an *eigenfunction* of A and a is called an *eigenvalue* of A. Briefly we say that *f is an eigenfunction of A for $A = a$*. If M is an *inner product space*, that is, if an inner product (f,g) having the properties (6.6) is defined for all f, g, . . . in M, then (10.1) and (6.6c) imply that

(10.2) $$(f,Af) = a(f,f)$$

when f is an eigenfunction of A for $A = a$. Hermiticity of A over M implies that it has only real eigenvalues (see Problem 6.16) and that eigenfunctions belonging to different eigenvalues are orthogonal (see Problem 6.17). Recall that Hermiticity, as well as anti-Hermiticity and the adjoint of an operator, is defined only over inner product spaces (see (6.14)-(6.19)).

When f is an eigenfunction of a Hermitean operator A, then $\Delta A = 0$ (see Problem 6.16). A converse theorem is readily proved: Let A be Hermitean and let $\Delta A = 0$ for some f. Then f is an eigenfunction of A. To prove this, we note that since A is Hermitean, $a = \langle A \rangle$ is real and $B = A - a$ is Hermitean. Then, by (6.12), $(\Delta A)^2 = \langle B^2 \rangle$. Problem 6.15 now implies that if $\Delta A = 0$, then $Bf = Af - af = 0$. Hence f is an eigenfunction of A for $A = a$.

A central problem in quantum mechanics is that of finding the eigenvalues and eigenfunctions of linear operators associated with real observables. Of particular importance are the energy and the angular momentum eigenvalues and eigenfunctions. The linear manifolds in which eigenfunctions are sought are frequently, but not necessarily, inner product spaces.

Problem 10.1: Let M be the linear manifold of functions $f(x)$ which are bounded and differentiable for all x, $-\infty < x < \infty$. Find the eigenfunctions and eigenvalues of $p = -i\hbar\dfrac{d}{dx}$. Answer: Set of all $f = ce^{ipx/\hbar}$, p real.

Problem 10.2: Let f be an eigenfunction of a linear operator A for $A = a$. Show that for any c, $f' = cf$ is also an eigenfunction of A for $A = a$. For an inner product space, c may be chosen so that $N(f') = 1$. (See Problem 6.4.)

Problem 10.3: Let f be an eigenfunction of A for $A = a$, in an inner product space. Show that, for any polynomial $f(x)$, $\langle f(A) \rangle = f(a)$. In particular, $\langle A^n \rangle = a^n$.

Problem 10.4: Let f be an eigenfunction of A for $A = a$. Show that f is an eigenfunction of $B = A - c$ for $B = a - c$, where c is any constant.

Problem 10.5: A Hermitean operator A such that $(f,Af) > 0$ for all f is said to be *positive definite*. If $(f,Af) \geq 0$ for all f, A is said to be positive semi-definite. Show that all eigenvalues of a positive definite Hermitean operator are positive. Show also that if A is Hermitean, then A^2 is positive semi-definite. In particular, x^2 and p^2 are positive definite.

Problem 10.6: Let f be an eigenfunction of A for $A = a$. Prove that if A and B commute, then either $Bf = 0$ or Bf is an eigenfunction of A for $A = a$.

Problem 10.7: Let f and f' be eigenfunctions of a Hermitean operator A for $A = a$ and $A = a'$, respectively, $a \neq a'$. Show that, if a Hermitean operator B commutes with A, then $(f,Bf') = 0$.

10.2. Degeneracy of Eigenvalues; Linear Dependence and Independence. Very frequently there occur cases in which at least two linearly independent eigenfunctions belong to the same eigenvalue, that is, there exist at least two functions f and g such that, for some a, $Af = af$ and $Ag = ag$, but no c exists such that $f = cg$. This is known as *degeneracy*: An eigenvalue to which there belong $k > 1$ linearly independent eigenfunctions is said to be *k-fold degenerate*. A nondegenerate eigenvalue is called a *simple eigenvalue*.

Let us recall the definitions of linear dependence and independence: A set of k functions f_i is said to be a *linearly dependent* set if there exist k constants c_i, not all zero, such that

$$(10.3) \qquad \sum_{i=1}^{n} c_i f_i = 0.$$

A set of k functions f_i is said to be a *linearly independent* set if there exist no constants c_i, except $c_i = 0$, such that (10.3) holds. Differently stated, k functions f_i are linearly independent if a relation of the form (10.3) implies all $c_i = 0$; they are linearly dependent if a relation of the form (10.3) does not necessarily imply all $c_i = 0$.

In the case of linear dependence, at least one of the f_i's may be expressed in terms of other f_i's. For example, if in (10.3) $c_1 \neq 0$, we may write

$$(10.4) \qquad f_1 = \frac{-1}{c_1} \sum_{i=2}^{n} c_i f_i.$$

Problem 10.8: Taking M and p as in Problem 10.1, show that the non-zero eigenvalues of p^2 are doubly degenerate and that zero is a simple eigenvalue. Answer: The functions $f_+ = c_+ e^{ipx/h}$ and $f_- = c_- e^{ipx/h}$ belong to the same eigenvalue, $p^2 > 0$, p real.

Problem 10.9: Prove that any linear combination of eigenfunctions of an operator A for $A = a$ is also an eigenfunction of A for $A = a$.

Problem 10.10: Show that any k mutually orthogonal functions are linearly independent.

Problem 10.11: Show that, if k functions in an inner product space are linearly dependent, they are not mutually orthogonal.

Problem 10.12: Let k functions f_i be mutually orthogonal. Show that, if $\sum_{i=1}^{k} c_i f_i = \sum_{i=1}^{k} d_i f_i$, then $c_i = d_i$.

Problem 10.13: Obtain the conclusion of Problem 10.12 for k linearly independent functions, not necessarily in an inner product space.

Problem 10.14: Taking k orthonormal functions f_i in an inner product space M and k real constants a_i, define an operator A over M by

$$(10.5) \qquad Af = \sum_{i=1}^{k} a_i f_i (f_i, f)$$

whenever f belongs to M. Show that A is Hermitean and that f_i is an eigenfunction of A for $A = a_i$.

Problem 10.15: Taking n orthogonal functions f_i in an inner product space M, and a function f in M, determine n constants c_i so that

$$(10.6) \qquad f' = f + \sum_{i=1}^{n} c_i f_i$$

is orthogonal to each f_i. Answer:

$$(10.7) \qquad c_i = - (f_i, f)/(f_i, f_i).$$

10.3. Gram-Schmidt Orthogonalization. The proof (Problem 6.17) that eigenfunctions belonging to distinct eigenvalues of a Hermitean operator are orthogonal gives no information concerning orthogonality of eigenfunctions belonging to a degenerate eigenvalue. Indeed, of k linearly independent functions which are obtained as eigenfunctions of a Hermitean operator for a k-fold degenerate eigenvalue, some pairs may be orthogonal, some not. However, for theoretical purposes it is important to know that there exist k mutually orthogonal eigenfunctions belonging to a k-fold degenerate eigenvalue. A process which was discovered by J. P. Gram[1] in 1883 and rediscovered by E. Schmidt[2] in 1907 gives a straightforward, though perhaps tedious in application, method for obtaining k mutually orthogonal linear combinations of any k linearly independent functions in an inner product space.

The method is implied by Problem 10.15, (10.6), and (10.7). Take $f_1' = f_1$. Then, writing

$$(10.8) \qquad f_2' = f_2 + c_1 f_1',$$

we determine c_1 so that

$$(10.9) \qquad (f_1', f_2') = (f_1', f_2) + c_1(f_1', f_1') = 0.$$

This is possible since $(f_1', f_1') \neq 0$.

Next, writing

$$(10.10) \qquad f_3' = f_3 + c_1 f_1' + c_2 f_2',$$

we determine c_1 and c_2 so that

$$(10.11) \qquad \begin{array}{ll} \text{(a)} & (f_1', f_3') = (f_1', f_3) + c_1(f_1', f_1') + c_2(f_1', f_2') = 0, \\ \text{(b)} & (f_2', f_3') = (f_1', f_3) + c_1(f_2', f_1') + c_2(f_2', f_2') = 0. \end{array}$$

Due to (10.9), this requires simply

$$(10.12) \qquad \begin{array}{ll} \text{(a)} & (f_1', f_3') = (f_1', f_3) + c_1(f_1', f_1') = 0, \\ \text{(b)} & (f_2', f_3') = (f_2', f_3) + c_2(f_2', f_2') = 0. \end{array}$$

Solution of (10.12) for c_1 and c_2 is possible since $(f_1', f_1') \neq 0$ and $(f_2', f_2') \neq 0$. Confusion of c_1 in (10.8) and (10.9) with c_1 in (10.10)—(10.12) is not legitimate.

Continuing, we write

$$(10.13) \qquad f_4' = f_4 + c_1 f_1' + c_2 f_2' + c_3 f_3',$$

and, using the orthogonality of f_1', f_2', and f_3', determine the new c_1, c_2, and c_3 by

$$(10.14) \qquad \begin{array}{ll} \text{(a)} & (f_1', f_4') = (f_1', f_4) + c_1(f_1', f_1') = 0, \\ \text{(b)} & (f_2', f_4') = (f_2', f_4) + c_2(f_2', f_2') = 0, \\ \text{(c)} & (f_3', f_4') = (f_3', f_4) + c_3(f_3', f_3') = 0. \end{array}$$

The process is continued until a set of mutally orthogonal functions f_1', f_2', $\ldots$ f_k' is obtained. These may then be normalized without

[1] J. P. Gram, *J. für Math.*, **94**, 41 (1883).
[2] E. Schmidt, *Dissertation*, Göttingen, 1905; *Math. Ann.*, **63**, 433 (1907).

destroying the orthogonality. Problem 10.10 implies that the orthonormal functions thus obtained are linearly independent.

Problem 10.16: What happens in the Gram-Schmidt process when the f_i are linearly dependent? (Hint: Start by assuming f_1 and f_2 linearly dependent.)

Problem 10.17: Let $f_1 = 1$, $f_2 = x$, $f_3 = x^2$. Define the inner product (f,g) by $(f,g) = \int_0^1 f^*g\, dx$. Apply the Gram-Schmidt process, obtaining orthonormal functions f_1', f_2', and f_3'.

10.4. The Expansion Problem. The orthogonality of the eigenfunctions of the Hamiltonian operator for a system, together with a property known as *completeness*, provides a means for determining the wave function $\psi(\mathbf{r},t)$ at any time t, given the wave function $\psi(\mathbf{r})$ at $t = 0$. Suppose for simplicity that the eigenvalue spectrum of H is entirely discrete and that there exists a lowest energy eigenvalue E_0 but no greatest energy eigenvalue. This happens, for example, with the particle in a box (Section 9.8), with the harmonic oscillator (Chapter 11) and with many other systems of interest. Further, the methods here described are frequently applicable with other types of eigenvalue spectra.

Since the energy eigenvalue spectrum is assumed to be entirely discrete, with a lowest energy level E_0, and with degenerate eigenvalues having finite degrees of degeneracy, we may order the energy eigenvalues,

$$(10.15) \qquad E_0 \leq E_1 \leq E_2 \leq E_3 \leq \cdots ,$$

and the corresponding eigenfunctions of the Hamiltonian H,

$$(10.16) \qquad \psi_0, \psi_1, \psi_2, \psi_3, \ldots ,$$

where

$$(10.17) \qquad H\psi_j = E_j\psi_j, \qquad j = 0, 1, 2, 3, \ldots .$$

By allowing groups of two or more of the energy values to be equal we include the possibility of degenerate energy levels. Hermiticity of H implies orthogonality of eigenfunctions for distinct energy values. The Gram-Schmidt process permits us to choose orthogonal eigenfunctions belonging to degenerate energy levels. Thus, choosing in (10.16) orthonormal eigenfunctions, we have, for all j, $k \geq 0$,

$$(10.18) \qquad (\psi_k,\psi_j) = \delta_{kj}.$$

By means of (10.17), we may readily verify that the function

$$(10.19) \qquad \psi_j(\mathbf{r},t) = \psi_j(\mathbf{r})e^{-iE_jt/\hbar}$$

satisfies the STDWE (8.3). Then we may readily verify that the function

$$(10.20) \qquad \psi(\mathbf{r},t) = \sum_{j=0}^{\infty} c_j \psi_j(\mathbf{r},t) = \sum_{j=0}^{\infty} c_j \psi_j(\mathbf{r}) e^{-iE_j t/\hbar}$$

also satisfies the STDWE (8.3), provided any questions about convergence can be answered satisfactorily. Leaving such questions aside for the present, we readily see from (10.20) that

$$(10.21) \qquad \psi(\mathbf{r},0) = \sum_{j=0}^{\infty} c_j \psi_j(\mathbf{r}).$$

We wish to determine the c_j in (10.20) and (10.21) so that $\psi(\mathbf{r},0) = \psi(\mathbf{r})$, where $\psi(\mathbf{r})$ is given. For arbitrary $\psi(\mathbf{r})$, it is quite evidently necessary that there be an infinite number of eigenfunctions $\psi_j(\mathbf{r})$. In general it is also necessary that $\psi(\mathbf{r})$ have a finite norm. Purely formally, however, we readily see that (10.21) implies that, for $k = 0, 1, 2, 3, \ldots$,

$$(10.22) \qquad (\psi_k, \psi) - \left(\psi_k, \sum_{j=0}^{\infty} c_j \psi_j\right).$$

Here and henceforth we write ψ and ψ_j in place of $\psi(\mathbf{r})$ and $\psi_j(\mathbf{r})$. By the distributive property (6.6c) of the inner product, (10.22) gives

$$(10.23) \qquad (\psi_k, \psi) = \sum_{j=0}^{\infty} c_j (\psi_k, \psi_j).$$

Finally, by the orthonormality of the eigenfunctions, expressed by (10.18), this gives, for $k = 0, 1, 2, 3, \ldots$,

$$(10.24) \qquad c_k = (\psi_k, \psi).$$

By means of (10.20) and (10.24) we have formally solved the problem of finding the wave function $\psi(\mathbf{r},t)$ at any time t, given the wave function $\psi = \psi(\mathbf{r})$ at time $t = 0$. In the remaining sections of this chapter we examine more closely the validity of this solution.

Problem 10.18: Orthonormal energy eigenfunctions for a particle in a one-dimensional box $0 \leq x \leq a$ were found in (9.52b) and Problem 9.7 to be, for $n = 1, 2, 3, \ldots$

$$(10.25) \qquad \psi_n = \sqrt{\frac{2}{a}} \sin (n\pi x/a).$$

Find $\psi(x,t)$, given the wave function $\psi(x) = 1$, $0 \leq x \leq a$, at $t = 0$. Answer:

$$(10.26) \qquad \psi(x,t) = \frac{4}{\pi} \sum_{n \text{ odd}} \frac{1}{n} \sin \left(\frac{n\pi x}{a}\right) e^{-in^2\pi\hbar t/4ma^2}$$

Problem 10.19:   Obtain a series solution of

$$(10.27) \qquad H\psi(\mathbf{r}) - \lambda\psi(\mathbf{r}) = \Psi(\mathbf{r})$$

for given $\Psi(\mathbf{r})$, assuming that $\lambda \neq E_j$ for any j, and waiving questions of convergence. Hint: First write, according to (10.21) and (10.24),

$$(10.28) \qquad \Psi = \sum_{j=0}^{\infty} d_j\psi_j, \qquad d_j = (\psi_j, \Psi)$$

Answer:

$$(10.29) \qquad \psi = \sum_{j=0}^{\infty} C_j\psi_j, \qquad C_j = d_j/(E_j - \lambda).$$

10.5. Bessel's Inequality. Conditions sufficient for the validity of the expansions in the preceding section can be examined by the use of Bessel's inequality, which we now proceed to derive. Let us define, for a finite number n of orthonormal functions f_i in an inner product space M and arbitrary coefficients c_i, a function R_n by

$$(10.30) \qquad R_n = f - \sum_{i=1}^{n} c_i f_i,$$

where f is a given function in M. From (6.6b) we have $(R_n, R_n) > 0$ unless $R_n = 0$, which may occur when f is linearly dependent on the n functions f_i (see Section 10.6). In any case, the minimum value of (R_n, R_n), obtained by allowing the c_i's in (10.30) to vary, is nonnegative. We proceed to find this minimum value.

Using the distributive property (6.6c) of the inner product, we find from (10.30) that

$$(10.31) \quad (R_n, R_n) = \left(f - \sum_{i=1}^{n} c_i f_i, f - \sum_{j=1}^{n} c_j f_j\right)$$

$$= (f, f) - \sum_{j=1}^{n} c_j(f, f_j) - \sum_{i=1}^{n} c_i^*(f_i, f) + \sum_{i,j=1}^{n} c_i^* c_j(f_i, f_j).$$

But for orthonormal f_i (see (10.18)) we have

$$(10.32) \qquad \sum_{i,j=1}^{n} c_i^* c_j(f_i, f_j) = \sum_{i,j=1}^{n} c_i^* c_j \delta_{ij} = \sum_{i=1}^{n} c_i^* c_i.$$

Hence, from (10.31) and (10.32),

$$(10.33) \quad (R_n, R_n) = (f, f) - \sum_{i=1}^{n} c_i^*(f_i, f) - \sum_{i=1}^{n} c_i(f, f_i) + \sum_{i=1}^{n} c_i^* c_i.$$

For the minimum value of (R_n, R_n) we must have, according to (10.33),

(10.34)

(a) $\quad \dfrac{\partial}{\partial c_i} (R_n, R_n) = -(f, f_i) + c_i^* = 0,$

(b) $\quad \dfrac{\partial}{\partial c_i^*} (R_n, R_n) = -(f_i, f) + c_i = 0,$

for each i. Since $(f_i, f)^* = (f, f_i)$, the requirements (10.34a) and (10.34b) are not distinct. We conclude that the minimum value of (R_n, R_n) is given by taking

(10.35) $\qquad\qquad c_i = (f_i, f), \qquad c_i^* = (f, f_i).$

Using (10.35) to eliminate the inner products (f_i, f) and (f, f_i) from (10.33). we find that

(10.36) $\qquad\qquad (R_n, R_n)_{\min} = (f, f) - \sum_{i=1}^{n} c_i c_i^*$

where the c_i and c_i^* are given by (10.35). From (10.36) and the relation $(R_n, R_n) \geq 0$ we obtain *Bessel's inequality:*

(10.37) $\qquad\qquad (f, f) \geq \sum_{i=1}^{n} c_i c_i^*$

where the c_i and c_i^* are given by (10.35), the f_i being orthonormal.

Problem 10.20: Let $R_n = f - \sum_{i=1}^{n} c_i f_i$ where the f_i are orthonormal and where, for each i, $c_i = (f_i, f)$. Further let $A f_i = a_i f_i$. Show that, for any positive integer m,

(10.38) $\qquad\qquad (R_n, A^m R_n) = (f, A^m f) - \sum_{i=1}^{n} a_i^m c_i c_i^*.$

Problem 10.21: Define R_n as in Problem 10.20, and define S_n by $S_n = g - \sum_{i=1}^{n} d_i f_i$, where $d_i = (f_i, g)$. Show that

(10.39) $\qquad\qquad (R_n, S_n) = (f, g) - \sum_{i=1}^{n} c_i^* d_i.$

10.6. The Completeness Relation. Let f_1, f_2, f_3, ... be an infinite sequence of orthonormal functions in an inner product space M, and let f be a function in M. Defining R_n for some finite n by (10.30) and taking the c_i as given by (10.35), we have the inequality in (10.37) unless

(10.40) $\qquad\qquad f = \sum_{i=1}^{n} c_i f_i, \qquad c_i = (f_i, f),$

that is, unless f is linearly dependent on the first n of the f_i.

There may exist functions f in M such that (10.40) holds for no finite n. For such functions, $(R_n,R_n)_{min} > 0$ for all n. Very important is the case when, for any f in M,

$$(10.41) \qquad\qquad \lim_{n \to \infty} (R_n,R_n)_{min} = 0.$$

In its more customary form, this *completeness relation* is that, for any f in M,

$$(10.42) \qquad \lim_{n \to \infty} \sum_{i=1}^{n} c_i{}^*c_i = (f,f), \qquad c_i = (f_i,f).$$

A sequence $f_1, f_2, f_3, \ldots$ of orthonormal functions in an inner product space M is said to be *complete in M* if (10.42) holds for every f in M. The completeness relation (10.42) does not necessarily imply (10.40) for some finite n dependent on f. However, when (10.40) is not valid for some finite n, we write, contingent on the completeness relation,

$$(10.43) \qquad \lim_{n \to \infty} \sum_{i=1}^{n} c_i f_i = f, \qquad c_i = (f_i,f),$$

where "lim" is read "limit in the mean." It is in this sense that equalities appear in (10.20), (10.21), (10.28), and (10.29).

Problem 10.22:   Let (10.40) hold for some finite n. Show that it holds for all $m \geq n$.

Problem 10.23:   Let a sequence $f_1, f_2, j_3, \ldots$ of orthonormal functions be complete in an inner product space M. Show that the sequence obtained by deleting one of the members of this sequence, say f_j, is not complete in M.

Problem 10.24:   A set or sequence $\{f_i\}$ is said to be *closed* relative to a linear manifold M if the statement that $(f_i,f) = 0$ for any f in M and for every f_i in the set implies that $f = 0$. Prove that a complete set is closed. (Hint: Assume that $f \neq 0$ but that $(f_i,f) = 0$ for every f_i in the set. Then show that the completeness relation is not satisfied, contradicting the hypothesis of completeness.)

Problem 10.25:   Let $c_i = (f_i,f)$, $d_i = (f_i,g)$. Assuming that the completeness relation is satisfied, obtain *Parseval's relation*

$$(10.44) \qquad \lim_{n \to \infty} \sum_{i=1}^{n} c_i{}^*d_i = (f,g).$$

(Hint: Apply the Schwartz inequality (6.9) to (R_n,S_n), where R_n and S_n are defined as in Problems 10.20 and 10.21. Then apply (10.41) to (R_n,R_n) and to (S_n,S_n). Finally, use (10.39).)

10.7. Extremal and Minimal Properties of Eigenvalues. In this section six theorems relating the eigenvalues of a Hermitean operator A to extremal values of $\langle A \rangle$ and of $(\psi, A\psi)$ are stated and proved. A problem at the end of the section provides a simple illustration of the application of the theorems to the estimation of eigenvalues. Theorem VI will be used in Section 10.8 in a proof that certain conditions are sufficient to ensure completeness of the set of eigenfunctions of a Hermitean operator.

THEOREM I: Let A be a Hermitean operator. Any extremal value of $\langle A \rangle$ is an eigenvalue of A.

Proof: A variation $\delta\psi$ in ψ produces a variation $\delta\langle A \rangle$ in $\langle A \rangle$ which, by (6.11) and the rules of the variational calculus is

$$(10.45) \qquad \delta\langle A \rangle = \frac{(\psi, \delta A\psi) + (\delta\psi, A\psi)}{(\psi, \psi)} - \lambda \left\{ \frac{(\psi, \delta\psi) + (\delta\psi, \psi)}{(\psi, \psi)} \right\}$$

where $\lambda = \langle A \rangle$. Since A is Hermitean, λ is real for all ψ. Also $\delta(A\psi) = A(\delta\psi)$. Hence

$$(10.46) \quad \begin{aligned} \delta\langle A \rangle &= \{ (A\psi, \delta\psi) + (\delta\psi, A\psi) - (\lambda\psi, \delta\psi) - (\delta\psi, \lambda\psi) \} \div (\psi, \psi) \\ &= \{ (A\psi - \lambda\psi, \delta\psi) + (\delta\psi, A\psi - \lambda\psi) \} \div (\psi, \psi). \end{aligned}$$

Extremals of $\langle A \rangle$ are determined by the condition $\delta\langle A \rangle = 0$ for all $\delta\psi$. Let us take

$$(10.47) \qquad\qquad \delta\psi = \epsilon(A\psi - \lambda\psi),$$

where ϵ is real. Then, from (10.46)

$$(10.48) \qquad\qquad \delta\langle A \rangle = 2\epsilon(A\psi - \lambda\psi, A\psi - \lambda\psi) \div (\psi, \psi).$$

From (6.6b) and (10.48) we see that $\delta\langle A \rangle = 0$ for all $\delta\psi$ given by (10.47) if and only if $A\psi - \lambda\psi = 0$. Hence necessary for an extremal is that ψ be an eigenfunction of A and $\langle A \rangle$ an eigenvalue of A.

Characteristic of practically all quantum mechanical systems of interest is a state of minimum energy. The Hamiltonian for any such system possesses a smallest eigenvalue. Theorem I is readily adapted to any Hermitean operator possessing a smallest eigenvalue:

THEOREM II: Let a Hermitean operator A possess a smallest eigenvalue λ_0, with corresponding eigenfunction ψ_0 belonging to M_A. Then $\lambda_0 = $ the minimum value of $\langle A \rangle$ for all wave functions ψ belonging to M_A.

Frequently a modified version of Theorem I is useful:

THEOREM III: Let A be a Hermitean operator. Any extremal value of $(\psi, A\psi)$ for all ψ such that $(\psi, \psi) = 1$ is an eigenvalue of A.

Proof: By the rules of the variational calculus and the condition on (ψ,ψ) we have

$$(10.49) \quad \begin{array}{ll} \text{(a)} & \delta(\psi,A\psi) = (\psi,\delta A\psi) + (\delta\psi,A\psi) = (A\psi,\delta\psi) + (\delta\psi,A\psi), \\ \text{(b)} & \delta(\psi,\psi) = (\psi,\delta\psi) + (\delta\psi,\psi). \end{array}$$

Now using *Lagrange's method of undetermined multipliers*, we multiply (10.49b) by real λ and subtract from (10.49a), obtaining as the condition for an extremal

$$(10.50) \quad (A\psi - \lambda\psi,\delta\psi) + (\delta\psi,A\psi - \lambda\psi) = 0.$$

For $\delta\psi$ given by (10.47) this becomes

$$(10.51) \quad 2\epsilon(A\psi - \lambda\psi,A\psi - \lambda\psi) = 0.$$

Hence, as before, $A\psi - \lambda\psi = 0$ for an extremal.

Evident from Theorem III is a restatement of Theorem II:

THEOREM IV: Let a Hermitean operator A possess a smallest eigenvalue λ_0 with corresponding eigenfunction ψ_0 belonging to M_A. Then $\lambda_0 =$ the minimum value of $(\psi,A\psi)$ for all normalized wave functions in M_A.

A generalization of Theorem IV is of practical as well as of theoretical importance:

THEOREM V: Let a Hermitean operator A possess a discrete eigenvalue spectrum with a minimum eigenvalue λ_0. Let the eigenvalues and eigenfunctions be ordered as in (10.15) and (10.16), degenerate eigenvalues having finite degrees of degeneracy and the eigenfunctions being mutually orthogonal. Then $\lambda_k =$ the minimum value of $(\psi,A\psi)$ for all wave functions ψ belonging to M_A subject to the normalization condition $(\psi,\psi) = 1$ and to the k orthogonality conditions $(\psi,\psi_j) = 0$ for $j = 0, 1, 2, \ldots, k - 1$.

Proof: In proving Theorem III we found that ψ gives an extremal of $(\psi,A\psi)$ for all ψ such that $(\psi,\psi) = 1$ only if $A\psi = \lambda\psi$ and $(\psi,\psi) = 1$. Then $(\psi,A\psi) = \lambda(\psi,\psi) = \lambda =$ an eigenvalue of A. We have only to pick out the smallest eigenvalue not less than λ_{k-1}. By the ordering, we may take $\lambda = \lambda_k$, $\psi = \psi_k$.

Theorem V may be restated in the form:

THEOREM VI: Let a Hermitean operator A possess a discrete eigenvalue spectrum with a minimum eigenvalue λ_0. Let the eigenvalues be ordered as in (10.15), the corresponding eigenfunctions, (10.16), being mutually orthogonal and degenerate eigenvalues having finite degrees of degeneracy. Then $\lambda_k =$ the minimum value of $\langle A \rangle$ for all wave functions ψ belonging to M_A subject to the k supplemental orthogonality conditions $(\psi,\psi_j) = 0$, $j = 0, 1, 2, \ldots, k - 1$.

Theorems II and IV are directly applicable in obtaining upper bounds to the smallest eigenvalue λ_0 of a given Hermitean operator A. Taking a function ψ which depends on certain parameters α, β, . . . , for which (ψ,ψ) and $(\psi,A\psi)$ can be computed as functions of the parameters, we obtain the minimum value μ of $(\psi,A\psi)/(\psi,\psi)$, or of $(\psi,A\psi)$ subject to the condition $(\psi,\psi) = 1$. Then $\lambda_0 \leq \mu$. For fortunate choice of ψ, sometimes obtained by using a large number of parameters, requiring high speed computing machines, the value of μ thus obtained may be very close to the smallest eigenvalue λ_0, coinciding with λ_0 when ψ happens to be the eigenfunction for the ground state.

Problem 10.26: Find the value of σ in the Gaussian wave packet (5.56) for which $\langle H \rangle$ is minimized, where H is the Hamiltonian for a harmonic oscillator in one-space dimension (see (11.8) or (11.6)). Also compute $\langle H \rangle_{min}$. Then, using the method of Lagrangian multipliers, find the value of σ for which $(\psi,H\psi)$ is minimized, subject to the condition $(\psi,\psi) = 1$. (Aid: See (5.72) and (5.73b).) Answers:

$$(10.52) \quad \text{(a)} \quad \sigma = \frac{1}{2\pi} (h/2m\nu)^{1/2}, \quad \text{(b)} \quad \langle H \rangle_{min} = E_0 = \tfrac{1}{2}h\nu,$$

where ν is the classical frequency.

10.8. A Sufficient Condition for Completeness. THEOREM VII: Let the eigenvalue spectrum of a Hermitean operator be entirely discrete, with a finite minimum eigenvalue λ_0 but no maximum eigenvalue, degenerate eigenvalues being of finite degree. Then the eigenfunctions of A form a complete set over the linear manifold of all functions belonging to M_A.

Proof: Let the eigenvalues and the eigenfunctions be ordered as in (10.15) and in (10.16). A succession of $k - 1$ equality signs in the ordering of the eigenvalues indicates k-fold degeneracy of the eigenvalue. Without loss of generality, take orthonormal eigenfunctions. Let

$$(10.53) \qquad R_n = \psi - \sum_{i=0}^{n-1} c_i\psi_i, \; c_i = (\psi_i,\psi).$$

It is readily verified from the definition of R_n and the orthonormality of the eigenfunctions that $(\psi_j,R_n) = c_j - c_j = 0$ for $0 \leq j \leq n - 1$. This orthogonality and Theorem VI, Section 10.7 now imply that

$$(10.54) \qquad \lambda_n \leq (R_n,AR_n)/(R_n,R_n).$$

By hypothesis, there is no maximum eigenvalue, that is, $\lambda_n \to \infty$ as $n \to \infty$. Hence, according to (10.54), either $(R_n,R_n) \to 0$ or $(R_n,AR_n) \to \infty$ as $n \to \infty$. By showing that (R_n,AR_n) does not approach infinity as

n approaches infinity we show that $(R_n,R_n) \to 0$ as $n \to \infty$. This is the completeness relation (10.41).

By (10.38) we may write

$$(10.55) \qquad (R_n,AR_n) = (\psi,A\psi) - \sum_{i=0}^{n-1} \lambda_i |c_i|^2.$$

Since $\lambda_n \to \infty$, there exists some positive integer k such that $\lambda_i > 0$ for all $i \geq k$. Therefore for $n > k$ we write (10.55) in the form

$$(10.56) \qquad (R_n,AR_n) = (\psi,A\psi) - \sum_{i=0}^{k-1} \lambda_i |C_i|^2 - \sum_{i=k}^{n-1} \lambda_i |c_i|^2.$$

Since the first summation in (10.56) contains a fixed number of terms and since every term in the second summation in (10.56) is positive, we see that (R_n,AR_n) does not approach $+\infty$ as n approaches infinity. Hence we conclude that $(R_n,R_n) \to 0$ as $n \to \infty$.

The conditions of Theorem VII are sufficient but not necessary for the existence of a complete set of eigenfunctions. Problem 10.27 presents an interesting and important linear operator whose eigenvalue spectrum contains only the two points $+1$ and -1. The degree of degeneracy of each eigenvalue is infinite. Yet the eigenfunctions form a complete set.

Problem 10.27:   The reflection operator R is defined for all $f(x)$ on $(-\infty,\infty)$ by $Rf(x) = f(-x)$. Show that, for any $f(x)$, $R^2f(x) = f(x)$, that is, $R^2 = 1$. Show further that $Rf(x) = \lambda f(x)$ only for $\lambda^2 = 1, \lambda = +1$ or $\lambda = -1$. Each eigenvalue is degenerate of infinite degree. *Even* functions of x are those for which $R = 1$, *odd* functions of x are those for which $R = -1$. Define inner products (f,g) by $(f,g) = \int_{-\infty}^{\infty} f^*g \, dx$. Show that R is Hermitean over the linear manifold of all square integrable functions. Show that eigenfunctions belonging to different eigenvalues are orthogonal. For given $f(x)$, find orthonormal eigenfunctions $f_e(x)$ and $f_0(x)$, belonging to the eigenvalues $R = 1$ and $R = -1$, respectively, and constants c_e and c_0 such that $f(x) = c_e f_e(x) + c_0 f_0(x)$. Show finally that $R^n f(x) = c_e f_e(x) + (-1)^n c_0 f_0(x)$. Answer: $c_e f_e(x) = \{f(x) + f(-x)\}/2 = \mathcal{E}f(x)$ where $\mathcal{E} = (1 + R)/2$; $|c_e|^2 = (\mathcal{E}f,\mathcal{E}f) = (f,\mathcal{E}f)$; $c_0 f_0(x) = \{f(x) - f(-x)\}/2 = \mathcal{O}f(x)$ where $\mathcal{O} = (1 - R)/2$; $|c_0|^2 = (\mathcal{O}f,\mathcal{O}f) = (f,\mathcal{O}f)$.

Problem 10.28:   Show that the operators $\mathcal{E}$ and $\mathcal{O}$ defined in the solution of Problem 10.27 are Hermitean. Show further that $\mathcal{E}^2 = \mathcal{E}$, that $\mathcal{O}^2 = \mathcal{O}$, and that $\mathcal{E}\mathcal{O} = \mathcal{O}\mathcal{E} = 0$. Find the eigenvalues and the eigenfunctions of $\mathcal{E}$ and of $\mathcal{O}$. Answer: Any even function of x for $\mathcal{E} = 1$ and for $\mathcal{O} = 0$; any odd function of x for $\mathcal{E} = 0$ and for $\mathcal{O} = 1$.

Problem 10.29:   Let a_0 and b_0 be the minimum eigenvalues of two Hermitean operators A and B, respectively. Show that the minimum eigenvalue of $A + B$ is not less than $a_0 + b_0$.

10.9. References for Supplementary Reading.

Section 10.1:   Bohm, 209–20; French, 195–8; Frenkel, 54–6; Landé, 77–80; Persico, 85–98, 155–7.

Section 10.4: Bohm, 220–23; Houston, 93–4; Kemble, 113–14; Kramers, 61–8; Mott and Sneddon, 64–6; Persico, 98–105, 157–9; Schaefer, 255–66·

Section 10.6:   Kemble, 119–21.

Section 10.7:   Frenkel, 68–75; Kramers, 202–7; Landé, 98–102; Pauling and Wilson, 180–91; Schiff, 171–80; Sproull, 473–9.

Section 10.8: Kemble, 132–9.

CHAPTER 11

THE HARMONIC OSCILLATOR

11.1. Classical Description. The problem of the harmonic oscillator is of great importance both in classical and in quantum mechanics. Many systems can be represented approximately by harmonic oscillators. The radiation field acts like a collection of harmonic oscillators. Further, the solution for the harmonic oscillator serves to introduce methods used in solving many other problems.

Frequently, the potential energy of two atoms as a function of their distance of separation gives a curve of the type shown in Fig. 11.1, with

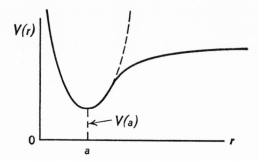

Fig. 11.1. Potential energy of two atoms, with parabolic approximation.

a minimum at some distance $r = a$. In the neighborhood of this point, the curve is approximated by a parabola,

(11.1) $V(r) = V(a) + V'(a)(r - a) + \frac{1}{2}V''(a)(r - a)^2$.

But $V'(a) = 0$. Choosing the arbitrary zero of potential so that $V(a) = 0$, and letting $V''(a) = k$, $r - a = x$, we have, approximately, $V = kx^2/2$.

The classical solution

(11.2) $x = A \sin(\omega t + \varphi),\ \omega = \sqrt{k/m}$,

for the harmonic oscillator, for which $V(x) = kx^2/2$, is readily obtained by solving Newton's equation of motion,

(11.3) $m\ddot{x} = -\dfrac{\partial V}{\partial x} = -kx$.

126

From (11.2) it is readily verified that the total energy is a constant of the motion:

(11.4) $\quad E = T + V = \frac{1}{2}m\dot{x}^2 + \frac{1}{2}kx^2 = \frac{1}{2}m\omega^2 A^2 = \frac{1}{2}kA^2.$

The total energy may have any nonnegative value.

11.2. Power Series Method of Obtaining Energy Eigenfunctions and Eigenvalues. Since the Hamiltonian for a harmonic oscillator in one-space dimension is

(11.5) $\qquad\qquad H = p_x^2/2m + m\omega^2 x^2/2, \; m\omega^2 = k,$

the STIWE to be solved is

(11.6) $\qquad\qquad -\dfrac{\hbar^2}{2m}\dfrac{d^2\psi}{dx^2} + \dfrac{1}{2}m\omega^2 x^2\psi = E\psi.$

Solutions square integrable on $(-\infty, \infty)$ are desired. Only for these may expectation values of H, x, p_x and, more generally, of x^n and p_x^n be defined.

We start by introducing into (11.6) a new independent variable ξ by the change of scale $x = \alpha\xi$, where α will be chosen so as to obtain a differential equation with simpler coefficients. In terms of ξ as independent variable (11.6) becomes

(11.7) $\qquad\qquad -\dfrac{\hbar^2}{2m\alpha^2}\dfrac{d^2\psi}{d\xi^2} + \dfrac{1}{2}m\omega^2\alpha^2\xi^2\psi = E\psi.$

The coefficients of the two terms on the left-hand side of (11.7) are equal except for the minus sign if we choose

(11.8) $\qquad\qquad \alpha = (\hbar/m\omega)^{\frac{1}{2}} = (\hbar^2/mk)^{\frac{1}{4}}.$

Setting

(11.9) $\qquad\qquad\qquad E = \hbar\omega\epsilon,$

we simplify (11.7) to

(11.10) $\qquad\qquad \dfrac{d^2\psi}{d\xi^2} - \xi^2\psi + 2\epsilon\psi = 0.$

The series

(11.11) $\qquad\qquad\qquad \psi = \sum_{s=0}^{\infty} c_s \xi^s$

satisfies (11.10) at least formally if the c_s are chosen so that

(11.12) $\quad \sum_{s=0}^{\infty} s(s-1)c_s\xi^{s-2} - \sum_{s=0}^{\infty} c_s\xi^{s+2} + 2\epsilon\sum_{s=0}^{\infty} c_s\xi^s = 0$

for all values of y. Picking out the coefficients of ξ^{s+2}, we would require that

(11.13) $$(s + 4)(s + 3)c_{s+4} - c_s + 2\epsilon c_{s+2} = 0$$

for all nonnegative s. This is a *three-term recurrence relation*. Further consideration of it and of the *ansatz* (11.11) would lead to tedious computations.

The difficulty of three-term recurrence relations can be avoided frefrequently by first separating a factor known as the *asymptotic* solution. Consider the function

(11.14) $$\psi_{\pm} = c_{\pm}e^{\pm\xi^2/2}.$$

By differentiation we readily verify that

(11.15) $$\frac{d^2\psi_{\pm}}{d\xi^2} - \xi^2\psi_{\pm} \mp \psi_{\pm} = 0.$$

By comparing (11.10) and (11.15), we see that the function $\psi_{\pm}$ satisfies (11.10) if $\epsilon = \mp\frac{1}{2}$. Also, if $\epsilon = \mp\frac{1}{2}$, $\psi_{\pm}$ is an approximate solution for large values of ξ. However, to obtain a square integrable solution, we must reject ψ_+ as the solution for $\epsilon = -\frac{1}{2}$ and as the approximate solution for other values of ϵ.

We proceed to an accurate solution of (11.10) by setting

(11.16) $$\psi = v(\xi)e^{-\xi^2/2}$$

and then determining a power series representation for $v(\xi)$. Differentiating (11.16) twice, we obtain

(11.17)
(a) $$\frac{d\psi}{d\xi} = \left(\frac{dv}{d\xi} - \xi v\right)e^{-\xi^2/2},$$
(b) $$\frac{d^2\psi}{ds^2} = \left(\frac{d^2v}{ds^2} - 2\xi\frac{dv}{ds} + \xi^2v - v\right)e^{-\frac{1}{2}\xi^2}.$$

Substituting from (11.17) into (11.10), we find that (11.16) gives a solution of (11.10) if $v(\xi)$ satisfies the equation

(11.18) $$\frac{d^2v}{d\xi^2} - 2\xi\frac{dv}{d\xi} + (2\epsilon - 1)v = 0.$$

Setting

(11.19) $$v(\xi) = \sum_{s=0}^{\infty} c_s\xi^s,$$

and substituting into (11.18), we obtain

$$(11.20) \quad \sum_{s=0}^{\infty} s(s-1)c_s \xi^{s-2} - 2 \sum_{s=0}^{\infty} sc_s \xi^s + (2\epsilon - 1) \sum_{s=0}^{\infty} c_s \xi^s = 0.$$

This equation is satisfied for all values of ξ if, for all nonnegative s,

$$(11.21) \quad (s+2)(s+1)c_{s+2} - 2sc_s + (2\epsilon - 1)c_s = 0.$$

From this *two-term recurrence relation* we may calculate successively c_2, c_4, c_6, c_8, etc., in terms of c_0, and c_3, c_5, c_7, c_9, etc., in terms of c_1. Hence we may write

$$(11.22) \quad v(\xi) = c_0 P_0(\xi) + c_1 P_1(\xi)$$

where $P_0(\xi)$ contains only even powers of ξ and $P_1(\xi)$ contains only odd powers of ξ. The coefficients in each depend on ϵ. Evidently $c_{n+2} = 0$ if $\epsilon = n + \frac{1}{2}$. Then $c_{n+m+2} = 0$ for all positive even integers m. Hence if $\epsilon = n + \frac{1}{2}$, where n is an even integer, $P_0(\xi)$ is a polynomial of degree n and $P_1(\xi)$ is an infinite series. If $\epsilon = n + \frac{1}{2}$, where n is an odd integer, $P_1(\xi)$ is a polynomial of degree n and $P_0(\xi)$ is an infinite series. If $\epsilon \neq n + \frac{1}{2}$ for some integer n, both $P_0(\xi)$ and $P_1(\xi)$ are infinite series.

In order to determine whether (11.16) and (11.19) give a square integrable wave function, we note from (11.21) that $c_{s+2} \cong 2c_s/(s+2)$ when $s \gg \epsilon$. Since the same behavior is exhibited by the coefficients in the series expansions of e^{ξ^2} and of ξe^{ξ^2} we conclude that, for large values of ξ, $P_0(\xi)$ behaves like e^{ξ^2} unless ϵ is such that $P_0(\xi)$ is a polynomial, and $P_1(\xi)$ behaves like ξe^{ξ^2} unless ϵ is such that $P_1(\xi)$ is a polynomial. Evidently, ψ in (11.16) is not square integrable if either or both of $P_0(\xi)$ and $P_1(\xi)$ are present in (11.22) as infinite series. We can avoid the presence of an infinite series in (11.22) by taking $c_1 = 0$ and choosing ϵ to make $P_0(\xi)$ a polynomial, or by taking $c_0 = 0$ and choosing ϵ to make $P_1(\xi)$ a polynomial. This requires taking $\epsilon = n + \frac{1}{2}$ and taking $c_1 = 0$ for n even, $c_0 = 0$ for n odd. Then $v(\xi)$ is a polynomial of degree n, parity that of n. The polynomials thus obtained are proportional to the famous *Hermite polynomials* which have many interesting properties and which occur very frequently in physical mathematics. Some of these properties will be deduced by more elegant methods in the remaining sections of this chapter.

Returning to (11.9), we see that the values of E for which the STIWE (11.6) has square integrable solutions are the energy eigenvalues

$$(11.23) \quad E_n = (n + \frac{1}{2})\hbar\omega = (n + \frac{1}{2})h\nu, \qquad \nu = \frac{\omega}{2\pi} = \frac{1}{2\pi}\sqrt{\frac{k}{m}}.$$

The energy eigenfunctions are

$$(11.24) \qquad \psi_n(x) = v_n\left(\frac{x}{\alpha}\right) e^{-x^2/2\alpha^2}, \qquad \alpha = \sqrt{\hbar/m\omega},$$

where

$$(11.25) \qquad v_n(\xi) = \sum_{s=0}^{n} c_s \xi^s, \qquad c_{s+2} = \frac{2(s-n)c_s}{(s+1)(s+2)}.$$

Here $\qquad c_0 = 0$, n odd; $\qquad c_1 = 0$, n even.

Problem 11.1: Obtain $v_0(\xi)$, $v_1(\xi)$, $v_2(\xi)$, and $v_3(\xi)$. Answers:

$$(11.26) \qquad \begin{array}{ll} \text{(a)} \quad v_0 = c_0, & \text{(c)} \quad v_2 = c_0(1 - 2\xi^2), \\ \text{(b)} \quad v_1 = c_1\xi, & \text{(d)} \quad v_3 = c_1(\xi - \tfrac{2}{3}\xi^3), \end{array}$$

where none of the c_0's or of the c_1's need be equal.

Problem 11.2: Using the method of separation of variables, obtain the energy eigenfunctions and eigenvalues for an isotropic harmonic oscillator in two-space dimensions, for which the Hamiltonian is

$$(11.27) \qquad H = \frac{1}{2m}(p_x^2 + p_y^2) + \frac{1}{2}m\omega^2(x^2 + y^2)$$

Answer:

$$(11.28) \qquad \begin{array}{ll} \text{(a)} & \psi_{pq}(x,y) = \psi_p(x)\psi_q(y), \\ \text{(b)} & E_{pq} = \hbar(p + q + 1)\omega, \end{array}$$

where p and q are nonnegative integers.

Problem 11.3: From (11.28b) it is evident that the degree of degeneracy of the n'th energy level for an isotropic harmonic oscillator in two-space dimensions is equal to the number of partitions of n into nonnegative integers p and q, that is, the number of ways in which the equation $p + q = n$ may be satisfied by nonnegative integers p and q. Evidently, this is equal to $n + 1$. Show that this is also equal to the coefficient of x^n in the expansion, by long multiplication, of $f(x) = (1 + x + x^2 + \cdots)^2$. Then observe that $f(x) = (1 - x)^{-2}$.

Problem 11.4: Using the method of separation of variables, obtain the energy eigenfunctions and eigenvalues for an isotropic harmonic oscillator in three-space dimensions, for which the Hamiltonian is

$$(11.29) \qquad H = \frac{1}{2m}(p_x^2 + p_y^2 + p_z^2) + \frac{1}{2}m\omega^2(x^2 + y^2 + z^2).$$

Answer:

$$(11.30) \qquad \begin{array}{ll} \text{(a)} & \psi_{p,q,r}(x,y,z) = \psi_p(x)\psi_q(y)\psi_r(z), \\ \text{(b)} & E_{pqr} = \hbar(p + q + r + \tfrac{3}{2})\omega \end{array}$$

where p, q, and r are nonnegative integers.

Problem 11.5: From (11.30b) it is evident that the degree of degeneracy of the n'th energy level for an isotropic harmonic oscillator in three-space dimensions is equal to the number of partitions of n into triplets of nonnegative integers p, q, and r. This is the number of ways in which the equation $p + q + r = n$ may be satisfied by nonnegative integers. Show that this is equal to the coefficient of x^n in the expansion, by long multiplication, of $f(x) = (1 + x + x^2 + \cdots)^3$. Then, observing that $f(x) = (1 - x)^{-3}$, obtain the degree of degeneracy of the n'th energy level. Answer: $(n + 1)(n + 2)/2$.

Problem 11.6: Show that the Hamiltonians (11.5), (11.27), and (11.29) have only positive eigenvalues. (Hint: See Problem 10.5.)

11.3. Operator Relations for the Harmonic Oscillator. Factorization of the classical Hamiltonian function (11.5), permitted by the commutativity of ordinary multiplication, into either of the two forms

$$(11.31) \quad H = \frac{1}{2m} (p + im\omega x)(p - im\omega x) = \frac{1}{2m} (p - im\omega x)(p + im\omega x),$$

suggests introduction of the operators

$$(11.32) \qquad L_+ = p + im\omega x, \qquad L = p - im\omega x.$$

Since x and p are Hermitean, L_+ and L_- are adjoint operators (see Problem 6.33). In forming operator products L_+L_- and L_-L_+ we must take account of the noncommutativity of the operators x and p. Using the Heisenberg commutation relation $xp - px = i\hbar$, we readily find from (11.5) and (11.32) that

$$(11.33) \quad \text{(a)} \quad L_+L_- = p^2 + m^2\omega^2x^2 + im\omega(xp - px) = 2mH - m\omega\hbar,$$
$$\qquad \text{(b)} \quad L_-L_+ = p^2 + m^2\omega^2x^2 - im\omega(xp - px) = 2mH + m\omega\hbar.$$

Hence

$$(11.34) \quad \text{(a)} \quad H = \frac{1}{2m} L_+L_- + \tfrac{1}{2}\omega\hbar,$$
$$\qquad \text{(b)} \quad H = \frac{1}{2m} L_-L_+ - \tfrac{1}{2}\omega\hbar.$$

Commutation rules connecting H with L_+ and with L_- are readily deduced from (11.33) and the associative property of operator multiplication. Starting with $(L_+L_-)L_+ = L_+(L_-L_+)$, (11.33) gives

$$(11.35) \qquad (2mH - m\omega\hbar)L_+ = L_+(2mH + m\omega\hbar).$$

Similarly, starting with $(L_-L_+)L_- = L_-(L_+L_-)$, (11.33) gives

$$(11.36) \qquad (2mH + m\omega\hbar)L_- = L_-(2mH - m\omega\hbar).$$

From (11.35) and (11.36) we readily obtain the desired relations:

(11.37)
$$\text{(a)} \quad HL_+ = L_+H + \omega\hbar L_+,$$
$$\text{(b)} \quad HL_- = L_-H - \omega\hbar L_-.$$

11.4. The Ground State. For a state described by a proper wave function, we find from (11.34a) that

(11.38)
$$\langle H \rangle = \frac{1}{2m} \langle L_+L_- \rangle + \frac{1}{2} \omega\hbar.$$

It is to be stressed that (11.38) is valid only for a state described by a proper wave function, as defined in Section 7.5. Since L_+ and L_- are adjoint operators, $\langle L_+L_- \rangle$ is nonnegative. Hence the ground state, corresponding to the lowest energy level $E_0 = \frac{1}{2}\omega\hbar$, is determined by the vanishing of $\langle L_+L_- \rangle$, that is, according to Problem 6.34, by the equation

(11.39)
$$L_-\psi = 0,$$

provided this equation has a proper wave function as a solution.

In the position representation, $p = -i\hbar \dfrac{d}{dx}$ and

(11.40)
$$L_\pm = -i\hbar \frac{d}{dx} \pm im\omega x = -\frac{i\hbar}{\alpha}\left(\frac{d}{d\xi} \pm \xi\right),\ \alpha = \sqrt{\frac{\hbar}{m\omega}},\ x = \alpha\xi.$$

The ground state, ψ_0, is therefore determined, except for normalization, by the first-order ordinary differential equation

(11.41)
$$L_-\psi_0 = -\frac{i\hbar}{\alpha}\left(\frac{d}{d\xi} + \xi\right)\psi_0 = 0.$$

From (11.41) we readily obtain

(11.42)
$$\psi_0 = c_0 e^{-\xi^2/2} = c_0 e^{-\frac{x^2}{2\alpha^2}},$$

where c_0 may be determined by normalization. The corresponding ground state energy level is

(11.43)
$$E_0 = \frac{1}{2}\hbar\omega.$$

Problem 11.7: Normalize ψ_0. Answer: In (11.42),

(11.44)
$$c_0 = \{\alpha \sqrt{\pi}\}^{-\frac{1}{2}}.$$

Problem 11.8: Solve (11.39) in the k representation. Answer:

(11.45)
$$\varphi_0 = c_0' e^{-\alpha^2 k^2/2}.$$

Problem 11.9: Show that, for a state described by a proper wave function,

(11.46) $$\langle H \rangle = \frac{1}{2m} \langle L_- L_+ \rangle - \frac{1}{2} \omega \hbar.$$

Hence, according to Problem 6.34, by solving the equation $L_+ \psi = 0$ we might expect to obtain a state of negative energy. Solve this equation in the position representation and state why the solution is not acceptable.

11.5. Excited States. From (11.37a) we have, for any wave function ψ,

(11.47) $$H(L_+ \psi) = L_+(H\psi) + \omega \hbar (L_+ \psi).$$

If ψ is an eigenfunction of H for $H = E$, then $H\psi = E\psi$ and, from (11.47),

(11.48) $$H(L_+ \psi) = (E + \omega \hbar)(L_+ \psi).$$

This states that $L_+ \psi$ is an eigenfunction of H for $H = E + \omega \hbar$.

Replacing the eigenfunction ψ in (11.47) by $L_+ \psi$, which is also an eigenfunction of H but for $H = E + \omega \hbar$, we find that $L_+(L_+ \psi) = (L_+)^2 \psi$ is an eigenfunction of H, for $H = E + 2\omega \hbar$. Continuing, we find that $(L_+)^n \psi$ is an eigenfunction of H for $H = E + n\omega \hbar$ if ψ is an eigenfunction of H for $H = E$.

The process may be started with the normalized ground state eigenfunction ψ_0, (11.42) and (11.44). Then the eigenfunction for the n'th excited state is

(11.49) $$\psi_n = C_n (L_+)^n \psi_0,$$

where C_n may be determined by normalization. The function ψ_n is an eigenfunction of H for $H = E_0 + n\omega \hbar = E_n$ where, in view of (11.43),

(11.50) $$E_n = (n + \tfrac{1}{2})\omega \hbar.$$

In normalizing the energy eigenfunction ψ_n, it is convenient to write (11.49) in the form

(11.51) $$c_n \psi_n = L_+ \psi_{n-1}, \qquad n = 1, 2, 3, \cdots.$$

From (11.49) and (11.51) it follows that $C_n = C_{n-1}/c_n$, but we shall not need the C_n. To determine c_n, we start with equality of inner products which follows directly from (11.51):

(11.52) $$(c_n \psi_n, c_n \psi_n) = (L_+ \psi_{n-1}, L_+ \psi_{n-1}).$$

Hence

(11.53) $$|c_n|^2 (\psi_n, \psi_n) = (\psi_{n-1}, L_- L_+ \psi_{n-1})$$

since L_- is the adjoint of L_+. Using (11.33b), we find that $L_-L_+ = 2mn\omega\hbar$ for $H = E_{n-1} = (n - \frac{1}{2})\omega\hbar$. Hence, from (11.53),

$$(11.54) \qquad |c_n|^2(\psi_n,\psi_n) = 2mn\omega\hbar(\psi_{n-1},\psi_{n-1}).$$

From (11.54) we readily see that ψ_n is normalized if ψ_{n-1} is normalized and if

$$(11.55) \qquad |c_n|^2 = 2mn\omega\hbar = 2n\hbar^2/\alpha^2, \quad \alpha^2 = \hbar/m\omega.$$

The phase of c_n is not determined by (11.55). Inserting L_+ from (11.40) into (11.51), we see that ψ_n is real valued if ψ_{n-1} is real valued and if c_n is pure imaginary. Hence we take

$$(11.56) \qquad c_n = i|c_n| = i\frac{\hbar}{\alpha}\sqrt{2n}, \quad \alpha = \sqrt{\hbar/m\omega}.$$

In resumé, from (11.40), (11.42), (11.44), (11.51), and (11.56) we have the orthonormal energy eigenfunctions for the harmonic oscillator:

$$(11.57) \qquad \begin{array}{ll} \text{(a)} & \psi_0 = \dfrac{1}{\sqrt{\alpha}\sqrt{\pi}}\, e^{-\xi^2/2}, \qquad \xi = \dfrac{x}{\alpha}, \\[2mm] \text{(b)} & \psi_n = \dfrac{1}{\sqrt{2n}}\left(\xi - \dfrac{d}{d\xi}\right)\psi_{n-1}, \qquad n = 1, 2, 3, \cdots, \end{array}$$

belonging to the energy eigenvalues (11.50).

Problem 11.10: From (11.57), obtain ψ_1, ψ_2, and ψ_3. Answer: See (11.26).

Problem 11.11: Show by induction that ψ_n has the parity of n, and hence that $\psi_n(0) = 0$ when n is odd.

Problem 11.12: Show that

$$(11.58) \qquad L_-\psi_n = -c_n\psi_{n-1}, \qquad n = 1, 2, 3, \cdots.$$

(Hint: Operate on both members of (11.51) with L_-, then use (11.33b) and (11.56).)

Problem 11.13: A precise measurement of the position of a harmonic oscillator indicates that, at $t = 0$, it is in its equilibrium position at $x = 0$. Find $\psi(x,t)$, taking $\psi(x,0) = \delta(x)$ where $\delta(x)$ is the highly singular *Dirac delta function*[1] having the property that, for any function $f(x)$ continuous at $x = 0$,

$$(11.59) \qquad \int_{-\infty}^{\infty} f(x)\,\delta(x)\,dx = f(0).$$

Answer:

$$(11.60) \qquad \psi(x,t) = \sum_{n=0}^{\infty} \psi_{2n}(0)\psi_{2n}(x)e^{-i(2n+\frac{1}{2})\omega t}.$$

[1] See P. A. M. Dirac, *Principles of Quantum Mechanics*, fourth edition, Oxford, 1958, p. 58f. or L. I. Schiff, *Quantum Mechanics*, second edition, McGraw-Hill, 1955, p. 50f.

11.6. Dirac's Bra and Ket Symbols; Matrix Elements. A very convenient and frequently used notation developed by Dirac[2] replaces the generic symbol ψ for a wave function by a *ket* symbol $|>$. In this notation, the Schroedinger equation $H\psi = E\psi$ is written $H|> = E|>$. The symbol ψ_n for the n'th of an ordered set of wave functions is replaced by the ket symbol $|n>$. Thus, the equation $H\psi_n = E_n\psi_n$ becomes $H|n> = E_n|n>$. Generally, the symbol $A\psi$ becomes $A|>$.

Since the complex conjugate ψ^* of a solution ψ of the STDWE (8.3) is not a solution of this equation, but of the complex conjugate equation,

$$(11.61) \qquad H\psi^* = -i\hbar \frac{\partial \psi^*}{\partial t},$$

the functions ψ and ψ^* are considered to be in distinct linear manifolds, or preferably, *dual linear manifolds*. Dirac replaced the generic symbol ψ^* for functions in the dual linear manifold by a *bra* symbol $<|$. The symbol ψ_n^* for the complex conjugate of ψ_n is replaced by $<n|$.

Quite evidently, the *bra-ket* notation for an inner product $(\psi_m, A\psi_n)$ is $\langle m|A|n \rangle$. Since $(\psi_m, A\psi_n) = (A\dagger\psi_m, \psi_n)$ where A and $A\dagger$ are adjoint operators, the symbol $(A\dagger\psi)^*$ becomes the bra symbol $<|A$. Hence the inner product $\langle m|A|n \rangle$ may be formed symbolically by uniting the bra symbol $\langle m|$ and the ket symbol $A|n\rangle$, or by uniting the bra symbol $\langle m|A$ and the ket symbol $|n\rangle$. This inner product is defined to be the *matrix element*, A_{mn}, of the operator A between the states m and n (see Problem 8.17):

$$(11.62) \qquad A_{mn} = (\psi_m, A\psi_n) = \langle m|A|n \rangle.$$

The elements A_{nn} are called the *diagonal* matrix elements of A. A is said to be in *diagonal form* if $A_{mn} = 0$ for $m \neq n$.

Matrix elements play a central role in Heisenberg's formulation of quantum mechanics and in numerous calculational procedures in Schroedinger's formulation. Further, according to the semi-classical, semi-quantum mechanical theory of radiation, a *first-order* transition between energy states $|m>$ and $|n>$ is forbidden if the matrix element x_{mn} vanishes (see Section 15.10). Other matrix elements, e.g. x_{mn}^2, p_{mn}, p_{mn}^2, and H_{mn} are important in various calculations.

Problem 11.14: Show that for a Hermitean operator A, $A_{mn} = (A_{nm})^*$, and that for an anti-Hermitean operator B, $B_{mn} = -(B_{nm})^*$.

11.7. Matrix Elements for the Harmonic Oscillator. As the first step in calculating $x_{mn} = \langle m|x|n \rangle$ for the linear harmonic oscillator,

[2] P. A. M. Dirac, loc. cit. p. 18f.

where $|m>$ and $|n>$ are the m'th and n'th energy eigenstates (11.57), we solve (11.32) for x, obtaining

$$(11.63) \qquad x = \frac{1}{2im_0\omega}(L_+ - L_-),$$

where the symbol m_0 represents the mass of the oscillator. Hence, from (11.63),

$$(11.64) \qquad \langle m|x|n \rangle = \frac{1}{2im_0\omega}\{\langle m|L_+|n\rangle - \langle m|L_-|n\rangle\}.$$

From (11.51) and (11.58) we have

$$(11.65) \quad \text{(a)} \quad L_+|n> = c_{n+1}|n+1>, \qquad \text{(b)} \quad L_-|n> = -c_n|n-1>.$$

Hence, from (11.64) and (11.65),

$$(11.66) \qquad \langle m|x|n \rangle = \frac{1}{2im_0\omega}\{c_{n+1}\langle m|n+1\rangle + c_n\langle m|n-1\rangle.$$

Using (11.56) and the orthonormality of the energy eigenfunctions, we readily reduce (11.66) to

$$\text{(a)} \quad \langle m|x|n \rangle = 0, \, m \neq n \pm 1,$$

$$(11.67) \quad \text{(b)} \quad \langle m|x|n \rangle = \frac{1}{2im_0\omega}c_{n+1} = \frac{\alpha}{2}\sqrt{2m}, \qquad m = n+1,$$

$$\text{(c)} \quad \langle m|x|n \rangle = \frac{1}{2im_0\omega}c_n = \frac{\alpha}{2}\sqrt{2n}, \qquad m = n-1.$$

This gives the selection rule for the harmonic oscillator: *Transitions occur only between adjacent states.*

Problem 11.15:   Calculate the matrix elements of p. Answer:

$$\text{(a)} \quad \langle m|p|n \rangle = 0, \, m \neq n \pm 1,$$

$$(11.68) \quad \text{(b)} \quad \langle m|p|n \rangle = \frac{1}{2}c_m = \frac{i\hbar}{2\alpha}\sqrt{2m}, \qquad m = n+1,$$

$$\text{(c)} \quad \langle m|x|n \rangle = -\frac{1}{2}c_n = \frac{-i\hbar}{2\alpha}\sqrt{2n}, \qquad m = n-1.$$

Problem 11.16:   Calculate the matrix elements of H.   Answer:

$$(11.69) \qquad \langle m|H|n \rangle = E_n\delta_{mn} = (n+\tfrac{1}{2})\hbar\omega\,\delta_{mn}.$$

Problem 11.17:   Calculate the diagonal matrix elements of x^2. (Hint: Obtain x^2 from (11.63).) Answer:

$$(11.70) \qquad \langle n|x^2|n \rangle = \frac{-1}{4m_0^2\omega^2}(c_n^2 + C_{n+1}^2) = \frac{\alpha^2}{2}(2n+1).$$

Problem 11.18: Calculate the diagonal matrix elements of p^2. Answer:

$$(11.71) \qquad \langle n|p^2|n \rangle = -\frac{1}{4}\left(c_n{}^2 + c_{n+1}{}^2\right) = \frac{\hbar^2}{2\alpha^2}(2n+1).$$

Problem 11.19: Calculate Δx and Δp for a harmonic oscillator in the energy eigenstate ψ_n. Observe that $(\Delta x)(\Delta p) = (2n+1)\hbar/2 \geq \hbar/2$.

11.8. References for Supplementary Reading.

Section 11.1: Finkelnburg, 365–8; Sproull, 146–8.

Section 11.2: Bohm, 351–5; Born, 350–52; Finkelnburg, 219–21; Kemble, 87–90; Landé, 54–7; Mandl, 43–6; March, 57–62; Mott and Sneddon, 50–53, 376–9; Pauling and Wilson, 67–83, 100-11; Persico, 180–86; Schaefer, 279–82; Schiff, 60–69; Sherwin, 335–40.

Section 11.5: Bohm, 296–306; Houston, 55–66, 71–3, 277–8; Sherwin, 50–54; Sproull, 148–52.

Section 11.6: Dirac, 14–34, 136–40; Mandl, 101–2.

Section 11.7: Bohm, 429–33; Kemble, 469–70; Landé, 72–3; March, 70–80; Pauling and Wilson, 81–2; Persico, 269–70; Sproull, 153–7.

CHAPTER 12

STATISTICAL INTERPRETATION OF THE WAVE FUNCTION

12.1. Probability Densities and Expectation Values in Classical Mechanics. Consider a particle moving along the x axis, subject to a force $F(x)$. According to classical mechanics, $x(t)$ and $p(t) = mv(t)$ are uniquely determined by Newton's second law and given initial values $x(0)$ and $p(0) = mv(0)$. In the absence of contrary information, it may be assumed that observations of the position and momentum of the particle are distributed at random in time. Let $P(t)|dt| =$ the probability that an observation is made within the time interval dt. Then

$$(12.1) \qquad\qquad P(t)\, dt = C\, dt.$$

When the motion is periodic, the proportionality factor C may be determined by normalizing $P(t)$ over a period T:

$$(12.2) \qquad \int_0^T P(t)\, dt = \int_0^T C\, dt = CT = 1,\ C = 1/T.$$

Since $x(t)$ and $p(t) = mv(t)$ are determined functions of t, the probabilities $P(x)|dx|$, $P(v)|dv|$ and $P(p)|dp|$ that x is in the interval dx, that v is in the interval dv, and that p is in the interval dp at the moment of observation must each be equal to $P(t)|dt|$:

$$(12.3) \qquad P(t)|dt| = P(x)|dx| = P(v)|dv| = P(p)|dp|.$$

Then the normalization (12.2) of $P(t)$ implies normalization of $P(x)$, $P(v)$, and $P(p)$:

$$(12.4) \quad \int_0^T P(t)\, dt = \oint P(x)|dx| = \oint P(v)|dv| = \oint P(p)|dp| = 1.$$

The normalized probability functions $P(w)$, where $w = t$, x, v, or p, are called *probability densities*. Probabilistic concepts are useful even when the functions $P(w)$ are not normalizable, as in the case of free motion, $P(w)$ then being called a *relative probability density*.

138

The experimental basis for the definition of a normalized probability density $P(w)$ is that

$$(12.5) \qquad \lim_{N \to \infty} (dN_w/N) = P(w)|dw|,$$

where dN_w/N is the relative number of members of an assemblage of N identical, independent systems for which the value of w is observed to be in the interval dw.

Complete additivity of probabilities for mutually exclusive events implies that the probability $P(w' \leq w \leq w'')$ that an observation of w results in a value in the interval $w' \leq w \leq w''$ is

$$(12.6) \qquad P(w' \leq w \leq w'') = \int_{w'}^{w''} P(w)|dw|,$$

it being understood that normalization has been effected if possible. The *average, mean value,* or *expectation value* $f(w)$ of a function $f(w)$ is defined by

$$(12.7) \qquad \overline{f(w)} = \oint f(w)P(w)|dw| \Big/ \oint P(w)|dw|$$

provided the numerator and the denominator exist. The mean value of a function $f(w)$ when w is restricted to the range $w' \leq w \leq w''$ is defined by

$$(12.8) \qquad \overline{(f(w))}_{w' \leq w \leq w''} = \int_{w'}^{w''} f(w)P(w)|dw| \Big/ \int_{w'}^{w''} P(w)|dw|,$$

provided the numerator and the denominator exist. The definition of *mean value* is readily extended to functions of two or more of the variables t, x, v, and p since, classically, any one of these variables is determined as a function of any other.

Problem 12.1:   For the linear harmonic oscillator, $x = A \sin(\omega t + \theta)$ where $\omega = 2\pi/T = \sqrt{k/m}$. (a) Find the normed probability densities $P(t)$, $P(x)$, $P(v)$, and $P(p)$; (b) Calculate $\bar{x}$, $\bar{v}$, $\overline{kx^2/2}$, $\overline{mv^2/2}$, and $\overline{xp}$; (c) Calculate $P(-A/2 \leq x \leq A/2)$ and $P(-\omega A/2 \leq v \leq \omega A/2)$; (d) Calculate $\overline{(v)}_{v>0}$. Answers: (a) $1/T$, $1/2\pi \sqrt{A^2 - x^2}$, $1/2\pi \sqrt{\omega^2 A^2 - v^2}$, $1/2\pi \sqrt{m^2\omega^2 A^2 - p^2}$; (b) 0, 0, $kA^2/4$, $kA^2/4$, 0; (c) $\frac{1}{6}$, $\frac{1}{6}$; (d) $4A/T = 2v_{max}/\pi$.

12.2. Quantum Mechanical Probability Densities and Expectation Values.

The wave mechanical expectation values of functions $f(x)$ and $g(p)$, defined for wave functions for which the integrals exist by

$$(12.9) \quad \begin{aligned} &\text{(a)} \quad \langle f(x) \rangle = \frac{(\psi, f\psi)}{(\psi, \psi)} = \int_{-\infty}^{\infty} \psi^* f\psi \, dx \Big/ \int_{-\infty}^{\infty} \psi^* \psi \, dx, \\[2mm] &\text{(b)} \quad \langle g(p) \rangle = \frac{(\Phi, g\Phi)}{(\Phi, \Phi)} = \int_{-\infty}^{\infty} \Phi^* g\Phi \, dp \Big/ \int_{-\infty}^{\infty} \Phi^* \Phi \, dp, \end{aligned}$$

are readily correlated with classical expectation values (12.7) by the identifications

(12.10)

$$\text{(a)} \quad P(x) = \frac{\psi^*\psi}{\int_{-\infty}^{\infty} \psi^*\psi \, dx} = \frac{\psi^*\psi}{(\psi,\psi)},$$

$$\text{(b)} \quad P(p) = \frac{\Phi^*\Phi}{\int_{-\infty}^{\infty} \Phi^*\Phi \, dp} = \frac{\Phi^*\Phi}{(\Phi,\Phi)}.$$

When the wave function has been normed, we have the simpler relations

$$(12.11) \qquad \text{(a)} \quad P(x) = \psi^*\psi, \qquad \text{(b)} \quad P(p) = \Phi^*\Phi,$$

for wave mechanical probability densities. A normed wave function is frequently called a *probability amplitude*, the square of its absolute value a *probability density*. For wave functions which cannot be normed *relative probability densities* are defined by (12.11).

The quantum mechanical probability densities $P(x)$ and $P(p)$ are not related as in (12.3), there being no quantum mechanical relations $x = x(t)$, $p = p(t)$. Absence of such relations introduces the problem of defining probability densities $P(f)$ for functions $f(x,p)$. For the calculation of the quantum mechanical expectation value of a function $f(x,p)$, either the x, the k, or the p representation, or a matrix representation, may be used. Progress in this latter direction is made, in the sections which follow, by the introduction of discrete probability distributions for quantized observables.

12.3. Discrete Probability Distributions. The discussion in Sections 12.1 and 12.2 is based on the concept of observables whose values belong to continua. If an observable A assumes only discrete values a_k, we define $P(A = a)$, the probability that an observation of A gives the value $A = a$, to be zero when a is not a member of the set of discrete values a_k. Note that the symbol "A" represents an observable, the symbols "a" and "a_k" represent observed or observable values of A. For brevity, we frequently write $P(a)$ rather than $P(A = a)$ and we need not always repeat that $P(a) = 0$ when a is nonexistent as a value of A.

The experimental basis for the definition of a normalized discrete probability distribution $P(a)$ is that

$$(12.12) \qquad \lim_{N \to \infty} (N_k/N) = P(a_k),$$

where N_k/N is the relative number of members of an assemblage of N identical systems for which the value of A is observed to be a_k. This definition leads naturally to a normal probability distribution. A distribution which is not normed may be normed, in many cases, by choosing an arbitrary factor in $P(a_k)$ to make

$$(12.13) \qquad\qquad \sum_k P(a_k) = 1.$$

Here the summation extends over all a_k for which $P(a_k) \neq 0$.

The expectation value of a function $f(A)$ is defined by

$$(12.14) \qquad\qquad \overline{f(A)} = \sum_k f(a_k)P(a_k) \Big/ \sum_k P(a_k),$$

the denominator being 1 when $P(a)$ has been normalized. Frequently we are interested in the expectation value of a function $f(A)$ over a subset of the set a_k, say over those values of A such that $a' \leq a \leq a''$. Let $P(a' \leq a \leq a'')$ be the probability that an observation of A gives a value a such that $a' \leq a \leq a''$. Complete additivity of probabilities for mutually exclusive events gives

$$(12.15) \qquad P(a' \leq a \leq a'') = \sum_{a' \leq a_k \leq a''} P(a_k) \Big/ \sum_k P(a_k)$$

and, in the absence of further information concerning the probability distribution outside of the range $a' \leq a \leq a''$, the restricted expectation value is

$$(12.16) \qquad \overline{f(A)}_{a' \leq a \leq a''} = \sum_{a' \leq a_k \leq a''} f(a_k)P(a_k) \Big/ \sum_{a' \leq a_k \leq a''} P(a_k).$$

This may also be formulated in terms of a conditional probability distribution. Let $P(a|a' \leq a \leq a'')$ be the probability that $A = a$, subject to the condition that $a' \leq a \leq a''$. Then

$$(12.17) \quad P(a|a' \leq a \leq a'') = 0, a \neq a_k \text{ where } a' \leq a_k \leq a'',$$
$$= p(a_k) \Big/ \sum_{a' \leq a_k \leq a''} P(a_k), a = a_k, a' \leq a_k \leq a''.$$

Applying (12.17) to (12.16) we see that

$$(12.18) \qquad \overline{f(A)}_{a' \leq a \leq a''} = \sum_{a' \leq a_k \leq a''} f(a_k)P(a_k|a' \leq a_k \leq a'').$$

It is important to recognize that a relation of the form (12.14) or (12.18) for arbitrary $f(x)$ serves to determine the corresponding probability distribution. This is a consequence of the theorem that the probability distribution for an observable A is uniquely determined by the expectation values of a sufficient number of independent functions of A.

Problem 12.2: Let A = the number of heads observed when four coins are tossed. The possible values of A are 0, 1, 2, 3, 4. For unbiased coins, $P(0) = P(4) = \frac{1}{16}$, $P(1) = P(3) = \frac{1}{4}$, $P(2) = \frac{3}{8}$. (a) What are the expectation values of A and of A^2? (b) What are the expectation values of A and of A^2 if only cases in which $A = 2$ and $A = 3$ are considered? (c) What is $P(2 \leq a \leq 3)$?

Problem 12.3: A man loses \$1 each time a certain coin shows tails and he wins \$2 each time it shows heads. (a) What is the man's expectation if the coin is unbiased? (b) What is the probability of heads if the man's expectation is zero?

12.4. The Postulates of Quantum Mechanics. In this section, attempt is made to justify two postulates which provide the foundation for *Born's statistical interpretation* of the wave function.[1] In order to ensure proper perspective, statement of the two statistical postulates, Postulates IV and V, is preceded by the statement of three postulates of which extensive use has already been made.

POSTULATE I: A state of a mechanical system is completely specified by a wave function ψ. All possible information about the system can be derived from its wave function.

POSTULATE II: To every observable there corresponds a Hermitean operator with a complete set of eigenfunctions.

POSTULATE III: For every system there exists a Hermitean operator H, the Hamiltonian operator, which determines the time variation of the wave function during any time interval in which the system is not disturbed, through the time dependent Schroedinger wave equation (8.3).

These three postulates, which leave open the interpretation of the wave function, need not be further discussed at this point, except for the remark that *superposition of states*, required by experimental evidence, implies that quantum mechanical operators be linear. The study of a linear operator culminates in its *spectral resolution*, which consists essentially in the determination of its eigenvalues and eigenfunctions. Postulate IV tells how knowledge of these and of the wave function are used in predicting the results of a measurement. Postulate V tells how the wave function is affected by measurements.

POSTULATE IV: Let the wave function ψ describing the state of a system, or of any member of an assemblage of noninteracting systems, be expansible in terms of the orthonormal eigenfunctions of a Hermitean operator A associated with an observable A:

$$(12.19) \quad \psi = \sum_k c_k \psi_k, \qquad A\psi_k = a_k \psi, \qquad (\psi_j, \psi_k) = \delta_{jk}, \qquad c_k = (\psi_k, \psi).$$

[1] M. Born, *Z. Physik*, **37**, 863 (1926); *Nature*, **119**, 354 (1927).

Then the probability of finding for A a value lying in the interval $a' \leq a \leq a''$, in any measurement of A, either on the system or on members of the assemblage of systems, is

$$(12.20) \qquad P(a' \leq a \leq a'') = \sum_S c_k{}^* c_k / c^2,$$

where S is the set of all k such that $a' \leq a_k \leq a''$ and where

$$(12.21) \qquad c^2 = \sum_{\text{all } k} c_k{}^* c_k.$$

This postulate is frequently presented in a simplified version:

POSTULATE IV′:   The only possible values which a precise measurement of an observable can yield are the eigenvalues of the operator associated with the observable.

This simplified version follows as a special case of Postulate IV which implies that, in case a_j is a nondegenerate eigenvalue of A,

$$(12.22) \qquad P(a = a_j) = c_j{}^* c_j / c^2.$$

When a_j is a k-fold degenerate eigenvalue of A, there are k terms $c_{ji}\psi_{ji}$, $i = 1, 2, \ldots, k$, in (12.19), for which $A = a_j$. Then, from (12.20),

$$(12.23) \qquad P(a = a_j) = \sum_{i=1}^{k} c_{ji}{}^* c_{ji} / c^2.$$

To justify Postulate IV, we note that, for any polynomial $f(x)$,

$$(12.24) \qquad f(A)\psi_k = f(a_k)\psi_k$$

where ψ_k is an eigenfunction of A for $A = a_k$. Waiving questions of convergence, we calculate $\langle f(A) \rangle$ in terms of the components c_k in (12.19):

$$(12.25) \qquad \langle f(A) \rangle = \frac{(\psi, f(A)\psi)}{(\psi, \psi)} = \frac{(\Sigma_j c_j \psi_j, f(A) \Sigma_k c_k \psi_k)}{(\Sigma_j c_j \psi_j, \Sigma_k c_k \psi_k)}$$
$$= \sum_k f(a_k) c_k{}^* c_k / c^2.$$

In the simplification of (12.25), use has been made of (12.24), of the distributive properties of the inner product, and of the orthonormality of the eigenfunctions ψ_k.

Comparison of (12.25) with (12.14) readily gives (12.22) and (12.23). Complete additivity of probabilities for mutually exclusive events then gives (12.20).

In appreciation of Postulate V which follows it should be realized that many measuring processes (e.g. energy measurements with velocity selectors) are based on the separation of an assemblage of noninteracting systems into sub-assemblages for each of which an observable A has a value within certain limits, the separation process not altering the value of A for any system of the assemblage. Except when the observable measured is a constant of the motion (see Section 8.4), of which the energy of a conservative system is an example, Postulate V gives the wave function only immediately after the separation process. This limitation is to be expected inasmuch as the wave function describing an undisturbed system varies in time as determined by the STDWE (8.3).

We assume that the wave function ψ is known immediately before a measurement, of the type described above, of an observable A. In the measurement of A, there is an interaction between the systems in the assemblage and the measuring apparatus. This interaction is not included in the Hamiltonian for the systems of the assemblage, whence the STDWE (8.3) does not account for the change in the wave function produced by the interaction. We treat this change as being discontinuous, calculating the wave function ψ' for a sub-assemblage of systems for each of which it is known only that the observable A has a value within the limits a', a'', from our knowledge of the wave function ψ before the separation of the sub-assemblage.

Let the wave function ψ be expanded in terms of the eigenfunctions of A, with coefficients c_k, as in (12.19). A similar expansion exists for ψ':

$$(12.26) \qquad \psi' = \sum_k c_k' \psi_k, \qquad c_k' = (\psi_k, \psi').$$

ψ' will be known when the c_k' are determined.

Let $P'(a)$ be the probability that, for a system of the sub-assemblage, the observable A has the value a. Since it is known that $a' \leq a \leq a''$ for systems in the sub-assemblage, we have $P'(a) = P(a | a' \leq a \leq a'')$ or, according to (12.17),

$$(12.27) \qquad \begin{aligned} P'(a) &= 0, \, a < a' \text{ and } a > a'', \\ &= P(a_j) \Big/ \sum_S P(a_j), \qquad a = a_j, \qquad a' \leq a_j \leq a'', \end{aligned}$$

where S is the set of all a_j such that $a' \leq a_j \leq a''$. But, according to (12.23),

$$(12.28) \qquad P'(a_j) = \sum_{i=1}^{k} c_{ji}'^* c_{ji}' / c'^2, \qquad P(a_j) = \sum_{i=1}^{k} c_{ji}^* c_{ji} / c^2$$

where k is the degree of degeneracy of a_j. Hence, substituting from (12.28) into (12.27), we obtain

$$(12.29) \qquad \sum_{i=1}^{k} c_{ji}'^* c_{ji}' = 0, \qquad a_j < a' \text{ and } a_j > a'',$$

$$= \sum_{i=1}^{k} c_{ji}^* c_{ji} \Big/ \sum_{S} c_j^* c_j.$$

For nondegenerate a_j (12.29) gives

$$(12.30) \qquad \begin{aligned} c_j' &= 0, \qquad a_j < a' \text{ and } a_j > a'', \\ c_j' &= c_j, \qquad a' \le a_j \le a''. \end{aligned}$$

The extension of (12.30) to degenerate a_j does not follow from (12.28). However, in the absence of further observational information, we make the extension, as implied by:

POSTULATE V: Let ψ' be the wave function describing the state of any member of an assemblage of noninteracting systems, for which it is known that $a' \le a \le a''$, immediately after their separation from an assemblage for which (12.19) describes the state of any member. Then

$$(12.31) \qquad \psi' = \sum_{S} c_k \psi_k$$

where S is the set of all a_k such that $a' \le a_k \le a''$.

Problem 12.4: Study and check: Orthonormal energy eigenfunctions for noninteracting particles in a box $0 \le x \le a$ are given in (10.25). Having no information about the position of a particle at $t = 0$, other than $0 \le x \le a$, we take $P(x) = C$, $0 \le x \le a$ and determine C to normalize $P(x)$: $\int_0^a C \, dx = 1$, $C = 1/a$. From $P(x) = \psi^* \psi$ and $P(x) = 1/a$, we have

$$(12.32) \qquad \psi(x) = e^{i\delta}/\sqrt{a}, \qquad 0 \le x \le a.$$

Using (10.25) and (10.26), we write the normalized wave function $\psi(x,t)$ in the form

$$(12.33) \qquad \psi(x,t) = \sum_{k \text{ odd}} c_k(t) \psi_k(x)$$

where

$$(12.34) \qquad c_k(t) = \frac{2\sqrt{2}}{k\pi} e^{i\delta - iE_k t/\hbar}.$$

Then

$$(12.35) \qquad c^2 = \sum_k |c_k|^2 = \frac{8}{\pi^2} \sum_{k \text{ odd}} \frac{1}{k^2}.$$

We observe that $c^2 = (\psi, \psi)$ is independent of t. But $(\psi, \psi) = 1$, from (12.32). Hence $c^2 = 1$. Then, according to (12.22) and (12.34),

(12.36) $P(E_k) = 0$, k even; $P(E_k) = c_k{}^*c_k = 8/k^2\pi^2$, k odd.

The lowest energy state is most heavily occupied. In fact, $P(E_1) = 8/\pi^2 \cong 0.8$. However, as readily verified from (12.35), high energy states are so heavily occupied that $\langle E \rangle$ is not defined.

If by some process of separation we remove from the box all particles of energy $E > E_n$, without changing the energy distribution of the remaining particles, then the wave function

$$(12.37) \qquad \psi' = \sum_{k=1, k \text{ odd}}^{N} c_k(t)\psi_k(x),$$

where $c_k(t)$ is given by (12.34), describes the state of any particle remaining in the box. Taking, for example, $N = 5$ (or 6), we find

$$
(12.38) \quad
\begin{aligned}
(c')^2 &= |c_1|^2 + |c_3|^2 + |c_5|^2 = 2072/225\pi^2, \\
P'(E_1) &= |c_1|^2/(c')^2 = 225/259, \\
P'(E_3) &= |c_3|^2/(c')^2 = 25/259, \\
P'(E_5) &= |c_5|^2/(c')^2 = 9/259, \\
\langle E' \rangle &= E_1 P'(E_1) + E_3 P'(E_3) + E_5 P'(E_5) \\
&= 675 h^2/2072 m a^2.
\end{aligned}
$$

For $k \neq 1$, 3, or 5, $P'(E_k) = 0$.

Problem 12.5: A separation is effected on an assemblage of noninteracting harmonic oscillators each of which is in the state described by the wave function (11.60), removing all particles with energy $E > E_3$. Let there be N particles for which $E \leq E_3$. (a) Calculate the numbers of oscillators with energies E_0, E_1, E_2, and E_3. (b) Find the expectation value of E for the N particles. (c) What is the wave function describing the state of any member of the assemblage, immediately after the separation? Answers: (a) $2N/3$, 0, $N/3$, 0; (b) $7\hbar\omega/6$.

Problem 12.6: Consider an assemblage of N similar, noninteracting systems for each of which the Hamiltonian H possesses nondegenerate eigenvalues E_k with a complete set of orthonormal eigenfunctions $\psi_k(\mathbf{r})$. Let N_k systems be in the state described by the eigenfunction $\psi_k(\mathbf{r})$ at $t = 0$, $\sum_k N_k = N$. What is $\psi(\mathbf{r}, t)$? Answer:

$$(12.39) \qquad \psi(\mathbf{r}, t) = \sum_k \sqrt{N_k/N}\, \psi_k(\mathbf{r}) e^{-iE_k t/\hbar}.$$

Problem 12.7: Show that, if a precise measurement of A certainly gives a value a, then $a = a_k$, an eigenvalue of A, and the wave function describing the state of the system is ψ_k, an eigenfunction of A for $A = a_k$. Show conversely that, if the wave function is an eigenfunction of A for $A = a_k$, then a precise measurement of A will certainly give a value $a = a_k$.

12.5. Transition Probabilities. Suppose that a system is initially in a stationary state (i.e. an energy eigenstate) ψ_n, the energy being an energy eigenvalue E_n. We desire to calculate the probability $P_{nk}(t)$ that the system will be in the energy eigenstate ψ_k, with energy E_k, at time $t > 0$, if the system is subjected to a possibly time dependent perturbing field U during the time interval $(0,t)$. The stationary states, viz.

$$(12.40) \qquad \psi_j(\mathbf{r},t) = \psi_j(\mathbf{r})e^{-iE_j t/\hbar},$$

satisfy the unperturbed STDWE

$$(12.41) \qquad i\hbar\,\frac{\partial\psi_j}{\partial t} = H\psi_j,$$

but during the presence of the perturbing field the wave function ψ satisfies

$$(12.42) \qquad i\hbar\,\frac{\partial\psi}{\partial t} = (H + U)\psi.$$

In the absence of the perturbing field the wave function $\psi(\mathbf{r},t)$ can be expanded in the form

$$(12.43) \qquad \psi(\mathbf{r},t) = \sum_j c_j\psi_j(\mathbf{r},t)$$

where the c_j are constants, independent of t. Let us assume that during the perturbation the wave function $\psi(\mathbf{r},t)$, which must satisfy (12.42), may still be expanded in the form (12.43), but with the c_j time dependent, $c_j = c_j(t)$. Then, when (12.43) is substituted into (12.42), we obtain

$$(12.44) \qquad i\hbar \sum_j \left(c_j\,\frac{\partial\psi_j}{\partial t} + \psi_j\,\frac{dc_j}{dt} \right) = \sum_j c_j(H\psi_j + U\psi_j).$$

By means of (12.41) this simplifies to

$$(12.45) \qquad i\hbar \sum_j \psi_j\,\frac{dc_j}{dt} = \sum_j c_j U\psi_j.$$

The term by term inner product of (12.45) with ψ_k gives, when use is made of the orthonormality of the unperturbed energy eigenfunctions ψ_j,

$$(12.46) \qquad i\hbar\,\frac{dc_k(t)}{dt} = \sum_j U_{kj}(t)c_j(t),$$

where U_{kj} is the matrix element of U between the k'th and j'th unperturbed energy eigenstates (12.40), *including their time factors.*

In (12.46) we have an infinite system of simultaneous differential equations for the $c_j(t)$, for which an approximate solution can easily be obtained in case the perturbation is small. With this restriction, we replace the $c_j(t)$ in the right-hand member of (12.46) by their initial values, namely, $c_j(0) = 0$, $j \neq n$, $c_n(0) = 1$. From the resulting system of equations,

$$(12.47) \qquad i\hbar \frac{d}{dt} c_k(t) = U_{kn}(t), \ k \neq n,$$

we readily obtain the approximate solution

$$(12.48) \qquad c_k(t) = \frac{1}{i\hbar} \int_0^t U_{kn}(t) \, dt, \ k \neq n$$

of (12.46). From (12.22) we see that (12.48) gives the probability $P_{nk}(t)$ of a transition from the n'th stationary state to the j'th stationary state, by means of the formula

$$(12.49) \qquad P_{nk}(t) = |c_k(t)|^2.$$

In order that the approximation (12.48) be valid, it is necessary that the total probability for transitions from the n'th state be small compared to unity. It may happen that there exist one or more states labeled j for which P_{nj} and P_{jk} are nonvanishing. Then calculations for virtual transitions, from the state n to the state j and from the state j to the state k, would be in order.

Bohm[2] discusses time dependent perturbation theory in great detail for cases in which (a) $U(\mathbf{r},t)$ is independent of t after it is initiated at $t = t_0$, (b) $U(\mathbf{r},t)$ oscillates trigonometrically with time, and (c) $U(\mathbf{r},t)$ increases slowly to a time dependent value. The general theory was first developed by Dirac.[3]

Problem 12.8: Obtain $P_{nk}(t)$ in case the perturbing potential U is time independent. Answer:

$$(12.50) \quad P_{nk}(t) = 4|U_{nk}(0)|^2 \sin^2 (\pi\nu_{nk}t)/(h\nu_{nk})^2, \ h\nu_{nk} = E_n - E_k.$$

Problem 12.9: Suppose that a constant force $F_x = \lambda = -\partial U/\partial x$, $U = -\lambda x$, is applied beginning at $t = 0$, to each of a system of harmonic oscillators initially in the n'th stationary state. Find the relative number which will be in the k'th stationary state at time $t > 0$. What is a suffi-

---

[2] D. Bohm, *Quantum Theory*, Prentice-Hall, 1951, Ch. 18.
[3] P. A. M. Dirac, *Proc. Roy. Soc. (London)*, **112A**, 661 (1926); **114A**, 243 (1927).

cient condition for validity of the approximations? (Hint: Use (11.67) and (12.50).) Answers:

(12.51)
$$P_{n,n-1} = 2n\lambda^2 \sin^2 (\omega t/2)/m\hbar\omega^3,$$
$$P_{n,n+1} = 2(n + 1)\lambda^2 \sin^2 (\omega t/2)/m\hbar\omega^3,$$
$$P_{n,k} = 0, \; k \neq n \pm 1.$$

The approximations are valid if $P_{n,n\pm1} \ll 1$.

Problem 12.10: Show that if the perturbing potential $U(\mathbf{r},t)$ has even parity, that is, if $U(-\mathbf{r},t) = U(\mathbf{r},t)$, transitions do not occur between energy eigenstates of opposite parity. Show also that if $U(\mathbf{r},t)$ has odd parity, that is, if $U(-\mathbf{r},t) = -U(\mathbf{r},t)$, transitions do not occur between states of the same parity.

12.6. References for Supplementary Reading.

Section 12.1: Bohm, 81–2, 117–8.

Section 12.2: Bohm, 82–3, 95–8, 178–82; Peaslee and Mueller, 240–42; Persico, 145–8.

Section 12.4: Houston, 31–54; Mandl, 60–70; Oldenberg, 28; Peaslee and Mueller, 50–52; Schaefer, 371–80; Shankland, 8, 52; Sherwin, 12–25, 62–5.

Section 12.5: Bohm, 407–29; Born, 389–92; Dirac, 167–8, 172–81; Houston, 95–8; Mott and Massey, 350–60; Pauling and Wilson, 294–9; Persico, 385–90; Schaefer, 425–31; Schiff, 195–205; Sherwin, 239–78.

CHAPTER 13

QUANTUM THEORY OF MEASUREMENTS

13.1. Simultaneous and Repeatable Measurements. In analyzing the results of repeated measurements, we must consider (1) the effect of each measurement on the state of the system, and (2) changes in the state of the system between measurements. Any measurement on a system is effected by an interaction between the system and the apparatus of measurement, including the observer. Extreme cases occur when (a) the interaction radically alters the value of the observable being measured, and when (b) the alteration is negligible. An example of the former extreme is the determination of the energy of a charged particle by observing the length of its track in a Wilson cloud chamber. An example of the second extreme is the determination of energy by measuring the radius of curvature in a magnetic field. In this text we deal exclusively with the latter extreme, the observations serving to separate an assemblage into sub-assemblages, reducing the wave function as indicated by Postulate V, Section 12.4.

A measurement of an observable A is repeatable only if (1) the measurement does not affect the value of A, and if (2) the expectation value of A does not change during the time interval between measurements. If A is not a constant of the motion, the expectation value of A changes during a time interval in which the system is not disturbed, at a rate given by (8.41). By a *disturbance* is meant any interaction of the system with its environment, not included in the Hamiltonian for the system. Disturbances produce changes in the wave function not accounted for by the STDWE for the system.

Even in the absence of disturbances, $d\langle A \rangle / dt = 0$ only if A is a constant of the motion. Hence we can not generally expect the equality of results obtained by measuring an observable A at two different times even if the system is not disturbed in the time interval between the measurements. We may, however, suppose that the two measurements are made within such a short time interval that the change in $\langle A \rangle$ during this time interval is so small that it may be neglected. We shall speak of such measurements as being *made in rapid succession* or as being *simultaneous measurements*.

13.2. Compatible Observables, Commuting Operators, and Complete Sets of Simultaneous Eigenfunctions. Suppose that a measurement of an observable A giving a value a in a range $a' \le a \le a''$

is followed immediately by a measurement of an observable B. The measurement of B disturbs the system and, if it is followed by a remeasurement of A, there may or may not be obtained a value a in the range $a' \leq a \leq a''$, even if the measurements are made in rapid succession. This suggests the **definition**: The measurement of B is *compatible with* the measurement of A if the immediate remeasurement of A *necessarily* gives a value a in the range $a' \leq a \leq a''$ containing the result of the first measurement of A, for *arbitrary intervals* (a',a''). Compatibility means that successive measurements in quick succession give repetitious results.

The major theorem of this chapter will show the close relation between (1) compatibility of measurements, (2) commutativity of the associated operators, and (3) the existence of a complete set of simultaneous eigenfunctions. It should be recalled that two operators A and B commute over a linear manifold M if and only if $A(B\psi) = B(A\psi)$ for every ψ in M. A wave function ψ is a *simultaneous eigenfunction* of A and B if it is an eigenfunction of A and also an eigenfunction of B, that is, if there exists an a and a b such that $A\psi = a\psi$ and $B\psi = b\psi$. There is no requirement that $a = b$. The fact that one, or even a set of the eigenfunctions of an operator A happen also to be eigenfunctions of an operator B does not imply much. Very significant it is, however, if there exists a *complete set of simultaneous eigenfunctions* of A and B. In fact, the existence of a complete set of simultaneous eigenfunctions implies compatibility. Fortunately, the following major theorem states much more than this inasmuch as it provides a practicable test for compatibility: commutativity.

MAJOR THEOREM: Assuming that A and B possess complete sets of eigenfunctions, then, of the three statements:

(1) A and B are compatible,

(2) A and B possess a complete set of simultaneous eigenfunctions,

(3) A and B commute,

any one implies the other two.

In Section 13.3 we prove the equivalence of (1) and (2) by proving in Theorem I that (2) implies (1) and in Theorem II that (1) implies (2). The proof of the major theorem is finally completed in Section 13.4 where, in Theorem III, it is proven that (2) implies (3) and in Theorem IV that (3) implies (2).

Problem 13.1: Show that if two noncommuting operators A and B possess a simultaneous eigenfunction, then the operator $C = i(A,B)$ possesses zero as an eigenvalue. Hence show in particular that x_i and p_i do not possess a simultaneous eigenfunction.

13.3. Compatible Observables and Complete Sets of Simultaneous Eigenfunctions. THEOREM I: Let A and B possess a complete set of simultaneous eigenfunctions. Then A and B are compatible.

Proof: Let ψ be the wave function immediately prior to the measurement of A. Expand ψ in terms of simultaneous, orthonormal eigenfunctions ψ_k of A and B:

$$(13.1) \qquad \psi = \sum_k c_k \psi_k, \qquad c_k = (\psi_k, \psi), \qquad (\psi_j, \psi_k) = \delta_{jk},$$

where $A\psi_k = a_k \psi_k$ and $B\psi_k = b_k \psi_k$. According to Postulate V, Section 12.4, the measurement of A reduces the wave function. If the result of the measurement of A is in the interval (a', a''), the wave function immediately after this measurement is

$$(13.2) \qquad \psi' = \sum_{a' \leq a_k \leq a''} c_k \psi_k.$$

Let a measurement of B, immediately after the measurement of A, give a value b in the interval (b', b''). This again reduces the wave function. To obtain the new wave function, we separate the simultaneous eigenfunctions ψ_k in (13.2) into three disjoint sets, those for which $b_k < b'$, those for which $b' \leq b_k \leq b''$, and those for which $b'' < b_k$, thus obtaining

$$(13.3) \quad \psi' = \sum_{a' \leq a_k \leq a'',\, b_k < b'} c_k \psi_k + \sum_{a' \leq a_k \leq a'',\, b' \leq b_k \leq b''} c_k \psi_k + \sum_{a' \leq a_k \leq a'',\, b'' < b_k} c_k \psi_k.$$

Applying Postulate V again, we see from this that the wave function, immediately after the measurement of B, is

$$(13.4) \qquad \psi'' = \sum_{a' \leq a_k \leq a'',\, b' \leq b_k \leq b''} c_k \psi_k.$$

From (13.4) we readily obtain, according to Postulate IV, Section 12.4, the probability distribution $P''(a)$ immediately after the measurement of B:

$$(13.5) \quad P''(a < a') = 0, \; P''(a' \leq a \leq a'') = 1, \; P''(a > a'') = 0.$$

This states that an immediate remeasurement of A will certainly yield a value a in the interval (a', a''). The result is valid no matter how small the interval (a', a''). Hence B is compatible with A if A and B possess a complete set of simultaneous eigenfunctions. By interchanging the roles of A and B in the proof, we show that A is compatible with B under the same hypothesis. Hence the phrase "A and B are compatible" is legitimated.

THEOREM II: Let A and B be compatible and let A and B possess complete sets of eigenfunctions. Then A and B possess a complete set of simultaneous eigenfunctions.

Proof: We are to prove that if A and B are compatible, and if, A and B possess complete sets of eigenfunctions, then any wave function ψ can be expanded in a set of functions each of which is a simultaneous eigenfunction of A and B. First, expand the wave function in terms of the eigenfunctions of A, as in (13.1), where $A\psi_k = a_k\psi_k$ but not necessarily $B\psi_k = b_k\psi_k$. Suppose then that each eigenfunction ψ_k of A can be expanded in terms of simultaneous eigenfunctions of A and B:

$$(13.6) \qquad \psi_k = \sum_j d_{jk}\psi_j',$$

where $A\psi_j' = a_j\psi_j'$ and $B\psi_j' = b_j\psi_j'$. Then the arbitrary wave function ψ can also be expanded as a series in the simultaneous eigenfunctions ψ_j', for, upon substituting from (13.6) into (13.1), we have

$$(13.7) \qquad \psi = \sum_k c_k \left(\sum_j d_{jk}\psi_j' \right) = \sum_j \left(\sum_k c_k d_{jk} \right) \psi_j'.$$

We therefore need only to prove that if A and B are compatible, then any eigenfunction of ψ_k of A can be expanded in terms of simultaneous eigenfunctions of A and B. This we proceed to do.

In the definition of compatibility, the interval (a',a'') is arbitrarily small. Let it be so small that it contains only the one eigenvalue a_k of A. Then, subsequent to the measurement of A, the wave function is ψ_k, where $A\psi_k = a_k\psi_k$. Let ψ_k be expanded in terms of eigenfunctions ψ_j' of B as in (13.6), where $B\psi_j' = b_j\psi_j'$ and where we wish to prove that compatibility of A and B implies that each ψ_j' is also an eigenfunction of A.

Immediately after a sharp measurement of A gives the value $a = a_k$, let a sharp measurement of B give a value $b = b_{j_0}$. Following the method used in writing (13.3), we write, before the measurement of B,

$$(13.8) \quad \psi = \psi_k = \sum_j d_{jk}\psi_j' = \sum_{b_j < b_{j_0}} d_{jk}\psi_j' + d_{j_0k}\psi_{j_0}' + \sum_{b_{j_0} < b_j} d_{jk}\psi_j'.$$

The sharp measurement of B disturbs the wave function, reducing it to

$$(13.9) \qquad \psi' = d_{j_0k}\psi_{j_0}'.$$

By the hypothesis of compatibility, a measurement now of A certainly has to give the value a_k. This means that ψ_{j_0}' is an eigenfunction of A for $A = a_k$ (see Problem 12.7). Since b_{j_0} is any eigenvalue of B for which $d_{j_0k} \neq 0$, each eigenfunction of B appearing in (13.6) is an eigenfunction of A for $A = a_k$. Thus any eigenfunction of A can be expanded in terms of simultaneous eigenfunctions of A and B. From this it follows that, if A and B are compatible, any wave function can be expanded in terms of simultaneous eigenfunctions of A and B. But this is equivalent to the statement that A and B possess a complete set of simultaneous eigenfunctions.

Problem 13.2:   The function $f = c_1 \sin \alpha x + c_2 \cos \alpha x + c_3 \sinh \alpha x + c_4 \cosh \alpha x$ is an eigenfunction of $A = \dfrac{d^4}{dx^4}$ for $A = \alpha^4$. Express f in terms of simultaneous eigenfunctions of A and of $B = \dfrac{d}{dx}$.

13.4. Complete Sets of Simultaneous Eigenfunctions and Commutativity.   THEOREM III: Let A and B possess a complete set of simultaneous eigenfunctions. Then A and B commute.

Proof: Expanding an arbitrary wave function ψ in terms of simultaneous eigenfunctions of A and B as in (13.1) we readily obtain

$$(13.10) \qquad A(B\psi) = A(\Sigma_k c_k b_k \psi_k) = \Sigma_k c_k b_k a_k \psi_k,$$

and also

$$(13.11) \qquad B(A\psi) = B(\Sigma_k c_k a_k \psi_k) = \Sigma_k c_k a_k b_k \psi_k.$$

Hence $A(B\psi) = B(A\psi)$ for any ψ. A and B commute.

A proof of the converse of Theorem III is preceded by the proofs of two lemmas.

Lemma I: Let A and B commute and let ψ be an eigenfunction of A belonging to a nondegenerate eigenvalue. Then ψ is also an eigenfunction of B.

Proof: By hypothesis, $A\psi = a\psi$ for some a.   Hence $B(A\psi) = B(a\psi)$. But a is a c- number and by hypothesis, B commutes with A. Hence $A(B\psi) = a(B\psi)$, that is, $B\psi$ is an eigenfunction of A for $A = a$. Since a is a nondegenerate eigenvalue of A, by hypothesis, there must exist some b such that $B\psi = b\psi$. Hence ψ is an eigenfunction of B as well as of A.

Lemma II: Let A and B commute and let a be a k-fold degenerate eigenvalue of A. Then there exist k linearly independent, simultaneous eigenfunctions of A and B for $A = a$.

Proof: By hypothesis, there exist k linearly independent eigenfunctions ψ_j of A for $A = a$. Then for any constants c_{ji} the function

$$(13.12) \qquad \psi_i' = \sum_{j=1}^{k} c_{ji} \psi_j$$

is an eigenfunction of A for $A = a$ (see Problem 10.9). We want to show that, if A and B commute, there exist k sets of constants c_{ji} (i fixed for any one set) such that (13.12) gives k linearly independent, simultaneous eigenfunctions of A and B.

We start the proof by writing

$$(13.13) \qquad B\psi_i' = \sum_{j=1}^{k} c_{ji}(B\psi_j).$$

Since A and B commute, either $B\psi_j = 0$ or $B\psi_j$ is an eigenfunction of A for $A = a$ (see Problem 10.6). If $B\psi_j = 0$, ψ_j is a simultaneous eigenfunction of A and B, for $A = a$ and for $B = 0$. We need consider further only the case $B\psi_j \neq 0$.

By hypothesis, there are just k linearly independent eigenfunctions of A for $A = a$. Hence for each j, $j = 1, 2, \ldots, k$, there exist k constants $d_{lj}, l = 1, 2, \ldots, k$ such that

$$(13.14) \qquad B\psi_j = \sum_{l=1}^{k} d_{lj}\psi_l.$$

If we start with orthonormal ψ_j, we have $d_{lj} = (\psi_l, B\psi_j)$. In any case, we consider the d_{lj} as being known. Substituting from (13.14) into (13.13), we obtain

$$(13.15) \qquad B\psi_i' = \sum_{j=1}^{k} c_{ji}\left(\sum_{l=1}^{k} d_{lj}\psi_l\right) = \sum_{l=1}^{k}\left(\sum_{j=1}^{k} d_{lj}c_{ji}\right)\psi_l.$$

From (13.12) and (13.15) we see that B is an eigenfunction of B for $B = b$ if

$$(13.16) \qquad \sum_{l=1}^{k}\left(\sum_{j=1}^{k} d_{lj}c_{ji}\right)\psi_l = b\sum_{l=1}^{k} c_{li}\psi_l.$$

Since the ψ_l are linearly independent, (13.16) implies that (see Problem 10.13)

$$(13.17) \qquad \sum_{j=1}^{k} d_{lj}c_{ji} = bc_{li}.$$

Here we have k homogeneous linear equations for the k c_{ji}, $j = 1, 2, \ldots, k$, i fixed. Nontrivial solutions exist only for those values of b for which the determinant of the coefficients of the c_{ji} vanishes, that is, for those values of b for which

$$(13.18) \qquad \Delta(b) \equiv |d_{lj} - b\delta_{lj}| = 0.$$

Since $\Delta(b)$ is a polynomial of degree k in b, (13.18) has k roots, not necessarily all distinct. For each nonrepeated root, say b_i, the system (13.17) may be solved for a set of numbers c_{ji}, not all zero, leading to a wave function (13.12) which is a simultaneous eigenfunction of A and B, for $A = a$

and for $B = b_i$. From the Hermiticity of B, it may also be shown that if any root, call it b_i, is of multiplicity m, there exist m sets of solutions of (13.17) leading to m linearly independent, simultaneous eigenfunctions of A and B, for $A = a$ and for $B = b_i$. By the Gram-Schmidt process, orthonormal eigenfunctions may be selected. We shall then have k orthonormal, simultaneous eigenfunctions of A and B.

The proof of the major theorem of this chapter may now be completed by a short proof of the converse of Theorem III.

THEOREM IV: Let A and B be two commuting Hermitean operators and let A possess a complete set of eigenfunctions. Then A and B possess a complete set of simultaneous orthonormal eigenfunctions.

Proof: By Lemma I, any eigenfunction of A belonging to a non-degenerate eigenvalue of A is also an eigenfunction of B. By Lemma II, any k linearly independent eigenfunctions of A belonging to a k-fold degenerate eigenvalue may be replaced by k linearly independent, simultaneous eigenfunctions of A and B. By this process we obtain a complete set of simultaneous eigenfunctions. An orthonormal set may be obtained by the Gram-Schmidt orthogonalization procedure.

Problem 13.3: Show that b in (13.17) is real if $d_{lj} = d_{jl}{}^*$, as when $d_{lj} = (\psi_l, B\psi_j)$, B Hermitean. (Hint: Multiply (13.17) by $c_{li}{}^*$, sum over l, and observe that b is the quotient of two real numbers.)

Problem 13.4: (a) Find the eigenvalues, their degeneracy, and independent real valued eigenfunctions of the operator $A = -\dfrac{d^2}{dx^2}$ in the linear manifold of functions $f(x)$ such that $f(x + 2\pi) = f(x)$. (b) Obtain simultaneous eigenfunctions of $A = -\dfrac{d^2}{dx^2}$ and $B = -i\dfrac{d}{dx}$ in the linear manifold of functions $f(x)$ such that $f(x + 2\pi) = f(x)$.

Problem 13.5: Show that the reflection operator R (see Problem 10.27) commutes with the operator A in Problem 13.4, but not with the operator B. Find the simultaneous eigenfunctions of A and R in the linear manifold of functions of x bounded for all real x. What other eigenfunctions of A are frequently used?

13.5. Sets of Compatible Constants of the Motion. If the expectation value of an observable A changes with time, repetitions of measurements of A would not be expected to give repetitious results. In the definition of compatible observables (Section 13.2), we avoid this complication by requiring that measurements be made in quick succession, i.e. "simultaneously." Obviously, this requirement is not necessary for constants of the motion, whose expectation values do not change as long as the system remains undisturbed.

Classically, an observable A is a constant of the motion if $dA/dt = 0$ for all possible motions. Quantum mechanically, an observable A is a constant of the motion if $d\langle A \rangle / dt = 0$ for all states. Although the classical and the quantum mechanical concepts of "constant of the motion" are not identical, we can be guided by our knowledge of classical constants of the motion in our search for quantum mechanical constants of the motion. In fact, from (8.37) and from the general commutation relation (7.13) we see that any classical constant of the motion is also a quantum mechanical constant of the motion. The converse of this statement is true for quantum mechanical observables which have classical counterparts. (For example, electron spin, which will be introduced in Section 14.8, has no classical counterpart and hence cannot be said to be a classical constant of the motion.)

When we consider a set of two or more quantum mechanical constants of the motion, we encounter a complication, not encountered in classical mechanics, due to the quantum mechanical uncertainty in the extent by which a system is disturbed by the measurement of an observable. Recall that (8.41) refers to time intervals during which the system is not disturbed. Now to say that A is a constant of the motion may be interpreted to imply that the expectation values of the results of two measurements of A, one subsequent to the other, are the same. But a measurement of another observable, B, intermediate between two measurements of A, disturbs the system in such a way that the uncertainty in a second measurement of A satisfies with the uncertainty in the measurement of B the general uncertainty relation (6.25). Unless A and B are compatible constants of the motion, we would not expect a sequence of measurements, such as $ABAABABBBA \ldots$, to give repetitious results. We are interested therefore in uniting constants of the motion into compatible sets, that is, into sets A, B, C, $\ldots$ such that any sequence of measurements of A, B, C, $\ldots$ gives repetitious results. Since observables are compatible only if the associated operators commute, we see that, if A and B do not commute, then both A and B cannot be members of the same set of compatible constants of the motion, even if A and B separately are constants of the motion.

The expression "good quantum number" is very frequently used for an eigenvalue of a constant of the motion.

Problem 13.6: Show that H, p_x, p_y, and p_z are good quantum numbers for a free particle (see (4.8) for H) and that these may be united into a compatible set of constants of the motion.

Problem 13.7: Show that H_x, H_y, H_z, and $H = H_x + H_y + H_z$, where

(13.19)
$$H_x = \frac{1}{2m} p_x{}^2 + \frac{1}{2} m\omega^2 x^2,$$

etc., are good quantum numbers for the harmonic oscillator in three-space dimensions and that these may be united into a compatible set of constants of the motion.

13.6. Complete Sets of Compatible Observables.   Classically, the initial state of a mechanical system is determined by precise measurements of the position coordinates and conjugate momenta. Since the quantum mechanical state is specified by a wave function ψ (Postulate I, Section 12.4), we are here interested in measurements which suffice to determine such a function uniquely.

The only possible results of a precise measurement of an observable A are the eigenvalues of the Hermitean operator associated with A (Postulate IV, Section 12.4). Let a precise measurement of A result in a certain eigenvalue of A, say a_j. Then the wave function describing the state of the system is an eigenfunction of A for $A = a_j$ (see Problem 12.7). If a_j is a nondegenerate eigenvalue of A, the wave function is uniquely determined except for arbitrary phase and normalization factors:

$$(13.20) \qquad \psi = ce^{i\delta}\psi_j, \qquad A\psi_j = a_j\psi_j.$$

If however a_j is a degenerate eigenvalue of A, say k fold, the wave function may be any linear combination of k linearly independent eigenfunctions (see Problem 10.9) and the measurement of A does not suffice to determine the wave function uniquely:

$$(13.21) \qquad \psi = \sum_{i=1}^{k} c_{ji}\psi_{ji}$$

where the k ψ_{ji} are linearly independent eigenfunctions of A for $A = a_j$ and the c_{ji} are undetermined by the measurement of A. Any number of additional measurements of A will not suffice to determine the c_{ji}.

Having measured A, we may measure a second observable B compatible with A. A sharp measurement of B can result only in $B = b_j'$, where b_j' is some eigenvalue of B. This reduces the wave function to the most general linear combination of the eigenfunctions ψ_{ji} in (13.21) which is a simultaneous eigenfunction of A and B, for $A = a_j$ and $B = b_j'$. This may or may not uniquely determine the wave function. If it does, A and B form a *complete set of compatible observables*. If it does not, that is, if there exists more than one simultaneous eigenfunction of A and B for $A = a_j$ and $B = b_j'$, we measure a third observable, C, compatible with both A and B. The process is continued until the wave function is reduced to a uniquely determined simultaneous eigenfunction of a *complete set of compatible observables*. Then we have a set of compatible observables $A, B, C, \ldots$, such that to any set of eigenvalues $a_j, b_j', c_j'', \ldots$ there exists exactly one simultaneous eigenfunction of $A, B, C, \ldots$ and the wave function can not be further reduced by additional measurements.

Such an observation is called *maximal* or *complete* and the corresponding set of observables with their operators is called a *complete set*.

Of necessity, the observables in a complete set are compatible and the associated operators commute in pairs. Of especial importance are *complete sets of constants of the motion*, whose expectation values do not change during time intervals in which the system is not disturbed.

In Section 13.7 two examples illustrating the preceding theory will be described in detail. In the first example the eigenvalues are degenerate of finite degrees. Simultaneous eigenfunctions of the observables forming a maximal set will be described in terms of the eigenvalues. The simultaneous eigenfunctions, which will be derived in Chapters 14 and 15, will be used to represent the most general square integrable wave function, then the successive reduction of this wave function to a unique wave function by a sequence of measurements of compatible constants of the motion will be described.

The second example illustrates how operators which do not depend on all of the coordinates of a system may have eigenvalues which are degenerate of infinite degree. This phenomenon is not restricted to such operators, however (see Problem 10.27).

13.7. Examples of Maximal Observations. As will be shown in Chapters 14 and 15, the observables H, M^2, and M_z, where H = the energy, M^2 = the squared angular momentum, and M_z = the component of $\mathbf{M}$ in an arbitrary direction, form a complete set of compatible constants of the motion for a structureless particle in a spherically symmetrical potential $V(r)$. For the Coulomb potential $V(r) = -Ze^2/r^2$ the eigenvalues of H, M^2, and M_z are

$$(13.22) \qquad E_n = -RchZ^2/n^2, \; M^2 = l(l+1)\hbar^2, \; M_z = m\hbar,$$

where R = the Rydberg constant, n = any positive integer, l = any integer from 0 to $n-1$, and m = any integer from $-l$ to $+l$. For given n, there are n values of l and for given l there are $2l+1$ values of m. Hence for given n there are n^2 pairs (l,m).

Let the symbol $\psi_{nl}{}^m$ represent a simultaneous eigenfunction of H, M^2, and M_z for $H = E_n$, $M^2 = l(l+1)\hbar^2$ and $M_z = m\hbar$, respectively. Any wave function ψ with finite norm may be represented in terms of the $\psi_{nl}{}^m$ in the form

$$(13.23) \qquad \psi = \sum_{n=1}^{\infty} \sum_{l=0}^{n=1} \sum_{m=-l}^{l} c_{nl}{}^m \psi_{nl}{}^m.$$

A sharp measurement of H giving $H = E_n$ reduces the wave function to

$$(13.24) \qquad \psi' = \sum_{l=0}^{n-1} \sum_{m=-l}^{l} c_{nl}{}^m \psi_{nl}{}^m$$

which contains n^2 undetermined $c_{nl}{}^m$. Any number of sharp measurements of H will not suffice to determine the $c_{nl}{}^m$ in (13.24). However, a sharp measurement of M^2, giving $M^2 = l(l + 1)\hbar^2$, where l is some integer between 0 and $n - 1$, reduces the wave function to

$$(13.25) \qquad \psi'' = \sum_{m=-l}^{l} c_{nl}{}^m \psi_{nl}{}^m$$

where the $2l + 1$ coefficients $c_{nl}{}^m$ remain undetermined. Any number of sharp measurements of M^2 (or of M^2 and H) will not suffice to determine them.

If the sharp measurements of H and M^2 are followed by a sharp measurement of M_z, then the wave function is reduced to

$$(13.26) \qquad \psi''' = c_{nl}{}^m \psi_{nl}{}^m$$

where $m\hbar$ is the result of the sharp measurement of M_z. Necessarily $-l \leq m \leq l$. Thus the wave function is uniquely determined, except for physically unimportant phase and normalization factors, by sharp measurements of H, M^2, and M_z, but not by sharp measurements of any two, or of any one, of this set of compatible constants of the motion. H, M^2, and M_z form a maximal set.

Consider next a free particle in three-space dimensions. The linear momentum $\mathbf{p}$ and the energy $E = p^2/2m$ are compatible constants of the motion (see Problem 13.6). Complete determination of the quantum mechanical state (and of the classical state) requires sharp measurements of the three components of $\mathbf{p}$. We proceed to give the details.

Let a sharp measurement of p_x give $p_x = p_1$. Then the wave function is an eigenfunction of p_x for $p_x = p_1$. In the position representation, we have

$$(13.27) \qquad -i\hbar \frac{\partial \psi}{\partial x} = p_1 \psi,$$

where, omitting the time factor, $\psi = \psi(x,y,z)$. From (13.27) we obtain

$$(13.28) \qquad \psi = e^{ip_1 x/\hbar} f(y,z).$$

The factor $f(y,z)$ cannot be determined by measurements of p_x.

If p_x and p_y are measured sharply, with $p_x = p_1$, $p_y = p_2$, then in addition to (13.27) and (13.28) we have

$$(13.29) \qquad -i\hbar \frac{\partial \psi}{\partial y} = p_2 \psi.$$

Substituting from (13.28) into (13.29), we find that

$$(13.30) \qquad\qquad -i\hbar \frac{\partial f}{\partial y} = p_2 f.$$

From (13.30) we obtain

$$(13.31) \qquad\qquad f = e^{ip_2 y/\hbar} g(z).$$

The factor $g(z)$ cannot be determined by measurements of p_x and p_y.

If p_x, p_y, and p_z are measured sharply, with $p_x = p_1$, $p_y = p_2$ and $p_z = p_3$, then in addition to the above we have

$$(13.32) \qquad\qquad -i\hbar \frac{\partial \psi}{\partial z} = p_3 \psi.$$

Substituting from (13.31), we obtain $g(z)$, then $\psi(x,y,z)$ which is now completely determined except for an arbitrary factor:

$$(13.33) \qquad\qquad \psi = c e^{i\mathbf{p}\cdot\mathbf{r}/\hbar}.$$

Since (13.33) is an eigenfunction of $H = p^2/2m$, the time factor may be inserted as in (9.4).

The eigenvalues of the components of $\mathbf{p}$ for a free particle are degenerate of infinite degrees. The eigenvalue spectra of p_x, p_y, and p_z each form the entire continuum $(-\infty, \infty)$. A modified version of Theorem IV, Section 13.4 applies: Any wave function with finite norm may be expressed as a superposition of a continuum of simultaneous eigenfunctions of the commuting operators p_x, p_y, and p_z. In fact, this is the Fourier integral theorem extended to three variables (see (5.52) and (5.53)).

Problem 13.8 (continuation of Problem 13.7): Obtain simultaneous eigenfunctions for H_x, H_y, H_z, and H. Any results in Chapter 11 may be used.

Problem 13.9: Show that if there exist two noncompatible constants of the motion, then there exist degenerate energy levels.

13.8. References for Supplementary Reading.

Section 13.1:   Kemble, 318–47; Mandl, 74–82.

Section 13.2:   Persico, 316–19, 340–42.

Section 13.4:   Frenkel, 60–62; Kemble, 281–8; Kramers, 139–41; Persico, 304–6.

Section 13.6:   Persico, 319–21.

CHAPTER 14

ANGULAR MOMENTUM

14.1. The Angular Momentum Operators. Classically, the angular momentum **M** of a particle, with respect to the origin in a chosen rectangular coordinate system, is the vector

(14.1) $$\mathbf{M} = \mathbf{r} \times \mathbf{p} = \mathbf{i}M_x + \mathbf{j}M_y + \mathbf{k}M_z, \text{ where}$$

$$
\begin{aligned}
\text{(a)} \quad & M_x = yp_z - zp_y, \\
\text{(14.2)} \qquad \text{(b)} \quad & M_y = zp_x - xp_z, \\
\text{(c)} \quad & M_z = xp_y - yp_x.
\end{aligned}
$$

The square of the magnitude of **M** is

(14.3) $$M^2 = M_x{}^2 + M_y{}^2 + M_z{}^2.$$

In working with relations involving components of **r**, **p**, and **M**, it is frequently advantageous to obtain additional relations by affecting cyclic permutations of the symbols x, y, z.

Quantum mechanically, with each component of **M** and with M^2 there are associated operators which are obtained by replacing in (14.1) and (14.2) the operators associated with the components of **r** and of **p**. For example, in the position representation, the operators for the components of **M** are

$$
\begin{aligned}
\text{(a)} \quad & M_x = -i\hbar\left(y\frac{\partial}{\partial z} - z\frac{\partial}{\partial y}\right), \\
\text{(14.4)} \qquad \text{(b)} \quad & M_y = -i\hbar\left(z\frac{\partial}{\partial x} - x\frac{\partial}{\partial z}\right), \\
\text{(c)} \quad & M_z = -i\hbar\left(x\frac{\partial}{\partial y} - y\frac{\partial}{\partial x}\right).
\end{aligned}
$$

The commutator of M_x and M_y is, by its definition and by use of some of the basic properties of commutators (see (6.22)):

$$
\begin{aligned}
(M_x, M_y) &= (yp_z - zp_y, zp_x - xp_z) \\
&= (yp_z, zp_x) - (yp_z, xp_z) - (zp_y, zp_x) + (zp_y, xp_z).
\end{aligned}
$$

The reduction is continued by use of (6.22c) and (6.22d). For example,

$$
\begin{aligned}
(yp_z, zp_x) &= y(p_z, zp_x) + (y, zp_x)p_z \\
&= yz(p_z, p_x) + y(p_z, z)p_x + z(y, p_x)p_z + (y, z)p_x p_z.
\end{aligned}
$$

Now, by means of the Heisenberg commutation relations (7.15) it is found that $(yp_z, zp_x) = -i\hbar y p_x$. In a similar manner it is found that $(yp_z, xp_z) = 0$, $(zp_y, zp_x) = 0$, and $(zp_y, xp_z) = i\hbar x p_y$. Hence $(M_x, M_y) = -i\hbar y p_x + i\hbar x p_y = i\hbar(x p_y - y p_x) = i\hbar M_z$. Cyclical permutations of x, y, and z give (M_y, M_z) and (M_z, M_x). Thus three important commutation relations are obtained:

(14.5) (a) $(M_x, M_y) = i\hbar M_z$, (b) $(M_y, M_z) = i\hbar M_x$,

(c) $(M_z, M_x) = i\hbar M_y$.

These may be written in the symbolic form

(14.6) $$\mathbf{M} \times \mathbf{M} = i\hbar \mathbf{M}.$$

We proceed now to evaluate the commutator $(M^2, \mathbf{M})$. Starting with (M^2, M_x), we have $(M^2, M_x) = (M_x^2 + M_y^2 + M_z^2, M_x) = (M_x^2, M_x) + (M_y^2, M_x) + (M_z^2, M_x)$. But $(M_x^2, M_x) = M_x^2 M_x - M_x M_x^2 = 0$, $(M_y^2, M_x) = M_y(M_y, M_x) + (M_y, M_x)M_y = M_y(-i\hbar M_z) + (-i\hbar M_z)M_y = -i\hbar(M_y M_z + M_z M_y)$. Also, $(M_z^2, M_x) = M_z(M_z, M_x) + (M_z, M_x)M_z = M_z(i\hbar M_y) + (i\hbar M_y)M_z = i\hbar(M_z M_y + M_y M_z)$. Combining the final expressions for (M_x^2, M_x), (M_y^2, M_x), and (M_z^2, M_x), we find that $(M^2, M_x) = 0$. We thus obtain

(14.7) (a) $(M^2, M_x) = 0$, (b) $(M^2, M_y) = 0$, (c) $(M^2, M_z) = 0$.

In combined form this is

(14.8) $$(M^2, \mathbf{M}) = 0.$$

M^2 commutes with each component of $\mathbf{M}$, but the components of $\mathbf{M}$ do not commute among themselves.

Problem 14.1: Using the Hermiticity of the components of $\mathbf{r}$ and of $\mathbf{p}$, and the Heisenberg commutation relations (7.15), show that the operators for the components of $\mathbf{M}$ are Hermitean. Then show that M^2 is Hermitean.

Problem 14.2: Show that any simultaneous eigenfunction of any two of M_x, M_y, and M_z is a simultaneous eigenfunction of all three, and that the three eigenvalues are zero.

Problem 14.3: The transformation from rectangular coordinates to spherical coordinates is effected by the equations

(14.9)
$$x = r \sin \theta \cos \varphi,$$
$$y = r \sin \theta \sin \varphi,$$
$$z = r \cos \theta.$$

Obtain the spherical coordinate representations

(14.10)
(a) $M_x = i\hbar \left(\cot \theta \cos \varphi \dfrac{\partial}{\partial \varphi} + \sin \varphi \dfrac{\partial}{\partial \theta} \right)$,

(b) $M_y = i\hbar \left(\cot \theta \sin \varphi \dfrac{\partial}{\partial \varphi} - \cos \varphi \dfrac{\partial}{\partial \theta} \right)$,

(c) $M_z = -i\hbar \dfrac{\partial}{\partial \varphi}$.

Problem 14.4: Show that

(14.11) $$(\mathbf{M}, f(r)) = 0,$$

where $f(r)$ is any differentiable function of $r = \sqrt{x^2 + y^2 + z^2}$.

Problem 14.5: Verify that

(14.12)
(a) $(M_i, x_i) = 0.$ $i = 1, 2,$ or $3;$
(b) $(M_i, x_i) = i\hbar x_k,$ $(i,j,k) = (1,2,3),\ (2,3,1)$ or $(3,1,2);$
(c) $(M_i, x_j) = -i\hbar x_k,$ $(i,j,k) = (3,2,1).\ (2,1,3)$ or $(1,3,2).$

Problem 14.6: Show that

(14.13)   (a) $\mathbf{M} \cdot \mathbf{r} = 0,$ (b) $\mathbf{r} \cdot \mathbf{M} = 0.$

Problem 14.7: Show that

(14.14)
(a) $(M^2, \mathbf{r}) = i\hbar(\mathbf{r} \times \mathbf{M} - \mathbf{M} \times \mathbf{r}),$
(b) $\mathbf{M} \times \mathbf{r} + \mathbf{r} \times \mathbf{M} = 2i\hbar\mathbf{r}.$

Problem 14.8: Show that

(14.15) $$(\mathbf{M}, f(p)) = 0,$$

where $f(p)$ is any differentiable function of $p = \sqrt{p_x^2 + p_y^2 + p_z^2}$.

Problem 14.9: Verify that

(14.16)
(a) $(M_i, p_i) = 0,$ $i = 1, 2,$ or $3;$
(b) $(M_i, p_j) = i\hbar p_k,$ $(i,j,k) = (1,2,3),\ (2,3,1)$ or $(3,1,2,)$
(c) $(M_i, p_j) = -i\hbar p_k,$ $(i,j,k) = (3,2,1),\ (2,1,3)$ or $(1,3,2).$

Problem 14.10: Show that

(14.17)   (a) $\mathbf{M} \cdot \mathbf{p} = 0,$ (b) $\mathbf{p} \cdot \mathbf{M} = 0.$

Problem 14.11: Show that

(14.18)
(a) $(M^2, \mathbf{p}) = i\hbar(\mathbf{p} \times \mathbf{M} - \mathbf{M} \times \mathbf{p}),$
(b) $\mathbf{M} \times \mathbf{p} + \mathbf{p} \times \mathbf{M} = 2i\hbar\mathbf{p}.$

14.2. The Operators M_+ and M_-. Very useful in the study of the quantum mechanical theory of angular momentum are two *shift* operators M_+ and M_- defined by

(14.19)   (a) $M_+ = M_x + iM_y,$ (b) $M_- = M_x - iM_y.$

These are adjoint operators (see Problem 6.33).

Problem 14.12: Show that

(14.20)
(a) $M_- M_+ = M^2 - M_z^2 - \hbar M_z,$
(b) $M_+ M_- = M^2 - M_z^2 + \hbar M_z.$

Problem 14.13: Show that

$$
(14.21) \quad
\begin{array}{ll}
\text{(a)} \quad (M_+, M_x) = \hbar M_z, & \text{(d)} \quad (M_-, M_x) = -\hbar M_z, \\
\text{(b)} \quad (M_+, M_y) = i\hbar M_z, & \text{(e)} \quad (M_-, M_y) = i\hbar M_z, \\
\text{(c)} \quad (M_+, M_z) = -\hbar M_+ & \text{(f)} \quad (M_-, M_z) = \hbar M_-, \\
\end{array}
$$

$$
\text{(g)} \quad (M_+, M_-) = 2\hbar M_z.
$$

Problem 14.14: Show that

$$
(14.22) \qquad \text{(a)} \quad (M^2, M_+) = 0, \qquad \text{(b)} \quad (M^2, M_-) = 0.
$$

Problem 14.15: Verify that

$$
(14.23) \quad
\begin{array}{ll}
\text{(a)} \quad (M_+, \xi) = 0, & \text{(e)} \quad (M_+, \eta) = 2\hbar z, \\
\text{(b)} \quad (M_-, \xi) = -2\hbar z, & \text{(f)} \quad (M_z, \eta) = -\hbar \eta, \\
\text{(c)} \quad (M_z, \xi) = \hbar \xi, & \text{(g)} \quad (M_+, z) = -\hbar \xi, \\
\text{(d)} \quad (M_-, \eta) = 0, & \text{(h)} \quad (M_-, z) = \hbar \eta.
\end{array}
$$

where $\xi = x + iy$, $\eta = x - iy$.

Problem 14.16: Obtain the spherical coordinate representations

$$
(14.24) \qquad M_\pm = \hbar e^{\pm i\varphi} \left(i \cot \theta \, \frac{\partial}{\partial \varphi} \pm \frac{\partial}{\partial \theta} \right).
$$

Problem 14.17: Obtain in spherical coordinates

$$
(14.25) \qquad M^2 = -\hbar^2 \left\{ \frac{1}{\sin \theta} \frac{\partial}{\partial \theta} \left(\sin \theta \frac{\partial}{\partial \theta} \right) + \frac{1}{\sin^2 \theta} \frac{\partial^2}{\partial \varphi^2} \right\}.
$$

(Hint: Use (14.20a) and (14.24).)

14.3. The Rotator with Space Fixed Axis. For a rigid rotator of moment of inertia I, the kinetic energy is

$$
(14.26) \qquad T = \tfrac{1}{2} I (\omega_x{}^2 + \omega_y{}^2 + \omega_z{}^2) = \tfrac{1}{2} I \omega^2.
$$

In the absence of external torque, the Lagrangian $L = T$. Then

$$
(14.27) \quad M_x = \frac{\partial L}{\partial \omega_x} = I\omega_x, M_y = \frac{\partial L}{\partial \omega_y} = I\omega_y, M_z = \frac{\partial L}{\partial \omega_z} = I\omega_z, \mathbf{M} = I\boldsymbol{\omega}.
$$

Proceeding according to classical methods (outlined in Section 4.1) we obtain the Hamiltonian

$$
(14.28) \qquad H = \frac{1}{2I} (M_x{}^2 + M_y{}^2 + M_z{}^2) = \frac{1}{2I} M^2.
$$

In this section we assume that the direction of the axis of rotation is known. Taking the z axis in this direction, we have $M_x = 0$, $M_y = 0$, $H = M_z{}^2/2I$. Then an eigenfunction of M_z for $M_z = \mu$ is an eigenfunction of H for $H = E = \mu^2/2I$.

From (14.10c) we write the eigenvalue equation for M_z:

$$(14.29) \qquad -i\hbar \frac{\partial \psi}{\partial \varphi} = \mu \psi$$

where φ is the azimuthal angle measured around the axis of rotation. Solving (14.29), we obtain

$$(14.30) \qquad \psi = ce^{i\mu\varphi/\hbar}.$$

We now require that ψ be a *single-valued function of position in space*, that is, that

$$(14.31) \qquad \psi(\varphi + 2\pi) = \psi(\varphi), \text{ all } \varphi.$$

Quite readily, we find that this condition is satisfied by (14.30) only if $\mu = m\hbar$ where $m =$ an integer. Hence the function

$$(14.32) \qquad \psi_m = ce^{im\varphi}, \; m = \text{an integer},$$

is an eigenfunction of M_z for the nondegenerate eigenvalue $M_z = m\hbar$.

The functions ψ_m and ψ_{-m} are eigenfunctions of H for $H = E_m = m^2\hbar^2/2I$. Since ψ_m and ψ_{-m} are linearly independent when $m \neq 0$, the energy eigenvalues, with the exception of E_0, are doubly degenerate. This double degeneracy corresponds to the two possible directions of rotation for given direction of the axis of rotation.

The formula for the energy levels, $E_m = m^2\hbar^2/2I$, which is known as the *Deslandre formula*, was discovered empirically before the advent of Wilson-Sommerfeld quantization (see Problem 4.8). This formula is not in agreement with observations on the band spectra of molecules. However, this is not criticism of the theory since such observations deal with rotators in space, the directions of their axes of rotation not being known. According to (14.28), correct energy levels should be calculable from eigenvalues of M^2, the direction of the axes of rotation being unspecified.

14.4. Eigenvalues and Eigenfunctions of M² and M_z. Since M^2 commutes with M_z, we look for simultaneous eigenfunctions of M^2 and M_z. Let Y be a simultaneous eigenfunction of M^2 and M_z for $M^2 = \lambda$ and $M_z = \mu$:

$$(14.33) \qquad \text{(a)} \quad M^2Y = \lambda Y, \qquad \text{(b)} \quad M_zY = \mu Y.$$

This implies that

$$(14.34) \qquad \text{(a)} \quad M_+(M^2Y) = \lambda M_+Y, \qquad \text{(b)} \quad M_+(M_zY) = \mu M_+Y.$$

From (14.21c) and (14.22a) we have

$$(14.35) \qquad \begin{array}{l} \text{(a)} \quad M_+(M^2Y) = M^2(M_+Y), \\ \text{(b)} \quad M_+(M_zY) = M_z(M_+Y) - \hbar M_zY. \end{array}$$

Substituting from (14.35) into (14.34), we find that (14.33) implies

(14.36)
$$\text{(a)} \quad M^2(M_+Y) = \lambda(M_+Y),$$
$$\text{(b)} \quad M_z(M_+Y) = (\mu + \hbar)(M_+Y).$$

From this we conclude that, if Y is a simultaneous eigenfunction of M^2 and M_z for $M^2 = \lambda$ and $M_z = \mu$, then either $M_+Y = 0$ or M_+Y is a simultaneous eigenfunction of M^2 and M_z for $M^2 = \lambda$ and $M_z = \mu + \hbar$.

From this, we find by repetition and/or induction that, if Y is a simultaneous eigenfunction of M^2 and M_z for $M^2 = \lambda$ and $M_z = \mu$, then either $(M_+)^k Y = 0$ or $(M_+)^k Y$ is a simultaneous eigenfunction of M^2 and M_z for $M^2 = \lambda$ and $M_z = (\mu + k\hbar)$, where k is any nonnegative integer.

In a similar manner, using M_- in place of M_+ in (14.34), it may be shown that, if Y is a simultaneous eigenfunction of M^2 and M_z for $M^2 = \lambda$ and $M_z = \mu$, then either $(M_-)^k Y = 0$ or $(M_-)^k Y$ is a simultaneous eigenfunction of M^2 and M_z for $M^2 = \lambda$ and $M_z = \mu - k\hbar$, where k is any nonnegative integer.

The next step in finding the eigenvalues and simultaneous eigenfunctions of M^2 and M_z is to show that, corresponding to any particular simultaneous eigenfunction Y, there exist nonnegative integers k_1 and k_2 such that

(14.37) $\quad$ (a) $\quad (M_+)^{k_1+1} Y = 0,$ $\quad$ (b) $\quad (M_-)^{k_2+1} Y = 0.$

To show this, we start with (14.3), which implies that

(14.38) $$\langle M^2 \rangle = \langle M_x^2 \rangle + \langle M_y^2 \rangle + \langle M_z^2 \rangle.$$

From (14.38) we readily see that, since $\langle M_x^2 \rangle$, $\langle M_y^2 \rangle$, and $\langle M_z^2 \rangle$ are nonnegative (see Problem 6.34),

$$\langle M^2 \rangle \geq \langle M_z^2 \rangle \geq 0.$$

For the simultaneous eigenfunctions $(M_+)^k Y$ and $(M_-)^k Y$ for which $M^2 = \lambda$ and $M_z = \mu \pm k\hbar$, this gives, respectively

(14.39) $\quad$ (a) $\quad \lambda \geq (\mu + k\hbar)^2 \geq 0,$ $\quad$ (b) $\quad \lambda \geq (\mu - k\hbar)^2 \geq 0.$

Let k_1 and k_2 be the greatest integers for which (14.39a) and (14.39b) respectively, are satisfied. Then (14.37) is satisfied, for otherwise we would have simultaneous eigenfunctions violating (14.39).

The next step is to obtain several relations between λ, μ, k_1 and k_2 which enable us to determine the eigenvalues λ and μ. From (14.20) we see that

(14.40)
$$\text{(a)} \quad M_-M_+(M_+{}^{k_1}Y) = M^2(M_+{}^{k_1}Y) - M_z{}^2(M_+{}^{k_1}Y)$$
$$- \hbar M_z(M_+{}^{k_1}Y),$$
$$\text{(b)} \quad M_+M_-(M_-{}^{k_2}Y) = M^2(M_-{}^{k_2}Y) - M_z{}^2(M_-{}^{k_2}Y)$$
$$+ \hbar M_z(M_-{}^{k_2}Y).$$

Using (14.37) and the eigenvalue relations

$$(14.41) \qquad \begin{array}{ll} \text{(a)} & M^2(M_\pm{}^k Y) = \lambda(M_\pm{}^k Y), \\ \text{(b)} & M_z(M_\pm{}^k Y) = (\mu \pm k\hbar)(M_\pm{}^k Y), \end{array}$$

we find from (14.40) that

$$(14.42) \qquad \begin{array}{ll} \text{(a)} & \lambda = (\mu + k_1\hbar)(\mu + k_1\hbar + \hbar), \\ \text{(b)} & \lambda = (\mu - k_2\hbar)(\mu - k_2\hbar - \hbar). \end{array}$$

Let $x = \mu + k_1\hbar$, $y = \mu - k_2\hbar$. Eliminating λ from the two expressions (14.42), we have $x(x + \hbar) = y(y - \hbar)$ or $x^2 - y^2 + (x + y)\hbar = 0$. Factoring, this gives $(x + y)(x - y + \hbar) = 0$. Hence either $x + y = 0$ or $x - y + \hbar = 0$. In the latter case, $(\mu + k_1\hbar) - (\mu - k_2\hbar) + \hbar = 0$, or $k_1 + k_2 + 1 = 0$. Since k_1 and k_2 are nonnegative, this case is ruled out. Hence $x + y = 0$, $(\mu + k_1\hbar) + (\mu - k_2\hbar) = 0$, or $\mu = (k_2 - k_1)\hbar/2$.

There are two cases to be distinguished: whether $k_2 - k_1$ is an odd integer, or whether $k_2 - k_1$ is an even integer. If $k_2 - k_1$ is an odd integer, the eigenvalues of M_z are half-integral multiples of $\hbar$. Experiment dictates the elimination of this possibility for orbital angular momentum. Hence we continue only with the other case, in which $k_2 - k_1$ is an even integer. In this case $k_2 + k_1$ is also an even integer, and we may let $k_2 - k_1 = 2k_0$, $k_2 + k_1 = 2l$, where k_0 and l are integers. Then $k_1 = l - k_0$, $k_2 = l + k_0$, and

$$(14.43) \qquad \begin{array}{ll} \text{(a)} & \mu = (k_2 - k_1)\hbar/2 = k_0\hbar, \\ \text{(b)} & \lambda = (\mu + k_1\hbar)(\mu + k_1\hbar + \hbar) = l(l + 1)\hbar^2. \end{array}$$

Of the four integers, k_0, k_1, k_2 and l, we may select any two consistent with the requirements that $k_1 + k_2$ is an even integer and that k_1 and k_2 are nonnegative. After choosing any two of the four integers, we determine the other two from the equations $k_1 = l - k_0$, $k_2 = l + k_0$. Two convenient choices are: (1) Pick any $l \geq 0$ and let $k_2 = 0$, then $k_0 = -l$, $k_1 = 2l$, and $\mu = -l\hbar$; (2) Pick any $l \geq 0$ and let $k_1 = 0$, then $k_0 = l$, $k_2 = 2l$, and $\mu = l\hbar$.

For the same l, the two choices lead to the same sequence of normalized eigenfunctions and sets of eigenvalues of M^2 and M_z. The first choice starts with $M_z = -l\hbar$ and by $2l$ application of M_+ leads to $M_z = l\hbar$. The second choice starts with $M_z = l\hbar$ and by $2l$ applications of M_- leads to $M_z = -l\hbar$. We describe the first choice in more detail, leaving detailed description of the second choice as a problem (Problem 14.18).

Choice 1: *Ascending the M_z scale:* Choose any $l \geq 0$ and let $k_2 = 0$. The system of equations

$$(14.44) \qquad \text{(a)} \quad M_z Y_l^{-l} = -l\hbar Y_l^{-l}, \qquad \text{(b)} \quad M_- Y_l^{-l} = 0,$$

determines a simultaneous eigenfunction Y_l^{-l} of M^2 and M_z for $M^2 = l(l + 1)\hbar^2$ and $M_z = -l\hbar$. Let Y_l^{-l} be normalized, inner products and norms being defined by integration over the surface of the unit sphere. Define Y_l^{-l+k} by

$$\text{(14.45)} \qquad d_l^k Y_l^{-l+k} = M_+^k Y_l^{-l}.$$

d_l^k being a numerical factor introduced to retain the normalization. Y_l^{-l+k}, where $0 \leq k \leq 2l$, is a simultaneous eigenfunction of M^2 and M_z for $M^2 = l(l + 1)\hbar^2$ and $M_z = (-l + k)\hbar$. Letting $-l + k = m$, for $0 \leq k \leq 2l$, we may write

$$\text{(14.46)} \qquad d_l^{l+m} Y_l^m = M_+^{l+m} Y_l^{-l}, \text{ for } -l \leq m \leq l.$$

Then

$$\text{(14.47)} \quad d_l^{l+m+1} Y_l^{m+1} = M_+^{l+m+1} Y_l^{-l} = M_+(M_+^{l+m} Y_l^{-l}) = M_+(d_l^{l+m} Y_l^m),$$

or

$$\text{(14.48)} \qquad c_l^m Y_l^{m+1} = M_+ Y_l^m, \text{ for } -l \leq m \leq l,$$

where $c_l^m = d_l^{l+m+1}/d_l^{l+m}$ may be determined to retain normalization. The Y_l^m thus determined in sequence, by (14.44) and (14.48), beginning with Y_l^{-l} and terminating with Y_l^l, are orthonormal simultaneous eigen-functions for $M^2 = l(l + 1)\hbar^2$ and $M_z = m\hbar$. The sequence terminates with Y_l^l since $M_+ Y_l^l = 0$.

In terms of spherical coordinates (r,θ,φ), (14.44) has the representation (see (14.10c) and (14.24))

$$\text{(14.49)} \quad \begin{array}{ll} \text{(a)} & -i\hbar \dfrac{\partial Y_l^{-l}}{\partial \varphi} = -l\hbar Y_l^{-l}, \\[2mm] \text{(b)} & \hbar e^{-i\varphi} \left\{ i \cot \theta \dfrac{\partial}{i \partial \varphi} - \dfrac{\partial}{\partial \theta} \right\} Y_l^{-l} = 0. \end{array}$$

Integrating (14.49a), we obtain

$$\text{(14.50)} \qquad Y_l^{-l} = e^{-il\varphi} g(\theta),$$

where $g(\theta)$ is to be determined by (14.49b). Thus:

$$\text{(14.51)} \qquad \left(l \cot \theta - \dfrac{\partial}{\partial \theta} \right) g(\theta) = 0.$$

Integrating (14.51), and substituting into (14.50), we have

$$\text{(14.52)} \qquad Y_l^{-l} = c(\sin \theta)^l \cdot e^{-il\varphi}.$$

where c is to be determined by the normalization:

$$(14.53) \quad N(Y_l{}^{-l}) = c^2 \int_0^{2\pi} d\varphi \int_0^\pi d\theta \sin \theta (Y_l{}^{-l})^* Y_l{}^{-l}$$

$$= c^2 \int_0^{2\pi} d\varphi \int_0^\pi d\theta (\sin \theta)^{2l+1} = 1.$$

We find

$$(14.54) \qquad c^2 = \Gamma(l + \tfrac{3}{2})/2\pi\Gamma(\tfrac{1}{2})\Gamma(l + 1).$$

With $Y_l{}^{-l}$ given by (14.52), successive $Y_l{}^m$ may be calculated by using (14.48) and (14.24), the $c_l{}^m$ being determined by normalization. The functions $Y_l{}^m$, $-l \leq m \leq l$, thus obtained form an orthonormal set of simultaneous eigenfunctions of M^2 and M_z for $M^2 = l(l + 1)\hbar^2$ and $M_z = m\hbar$. These functions, which are called *surface spherical harmonics*, are given explicitly by

$$(14.55) \quad Y_l{}^m = (-1)^m \left\{ \frac{(2l + 1)}{4\pi} \frac{(l - |m|)!}{(l + |m|)!} \right\}^{1/2} P_l{}^m(\cos \theta)e^{im\varphi},$$

where

$$(14.56) \quad P_l{}^m(x) = \frac{1}{2^l l!} (1 - x^2)^{\frac{|m|}{2}} \frac{d^{l+|m|}}{dx^{l+|m|}} (x^2 - 1)^l, \quad -l \leq m \leq l,$$

are the *associated Legendre functions*.

Problem 14.18: Write a detailed description of "Choice 2, Descending the M_z Scale," paralleling the preceding description of Choice 1.

Problem 14.19: Show that $Y_l{}^m$ is a simultaneous eigenfunction of M_-M_+ and M_+M_- for $M_-M_+ = (l - m)(l + m + 1)\hbar^2$ and $M_+M_- = (l + m)(l - m + 1)\hbar^2$.

Problem 14.20: Show that $Y_l{}^{m+1}$ is normalized if $Y_l{}^m$ is normalized and if

$$(14.57) \qquad |c_l{}^m|^2 = (l - m)(l + m + 1)\hbar^2.$$

For $c_l{}^m$, take the positive real root.

(Hint: Follow the method used in obtaining (11.55).)

Problem 14.21: Show that

$$(14.58) \qquad M_-Y_l{}^{m+1} = c_l{}^m Y_l{}^m.$$

Problem 14.22: Obtain $Y_l{}^{-l+1}$ and $Y_l{}^{l+1}$.

Problem 14.23: Obtain the normalized eigenfunctions $Y_1{}^{-1}$, $Y_1{}^0$ and $Y_1{}^1$. Answers:

$$(14.59) \qquad Y_1{}^{\pm 1} = \sqrt{\frac{3}{8\pi}} \sin \theta e^{\pm i\varphi} = \sqrt{\frac{3}{8\pi}} \frac{(x \pm iy)}{r},$$

$$Y_1{}^0 = \sqrt{\frac{3}{4\pi}} \cos \theta = \sqrt{\frac{3}{4\pi}} \cdot \frac{z}{r}.$$

14.5. Angular Momentum and Magnetic Moment. Picture an electron as a particle of mass m_0, charge e (numerically negative), bound to a fixed nucleus by a central force arising from a Coulomb potential $V(r)$. The orbit of the electron is a circle if there is equilibrium between the centripetal force $m_0 r \omega^2$ and the Coulombic attraction Ze^2/r^2. From the equality between these two forces we derive an expression for the classical frequency of orbital motion

$$(14.60) \qquad \nu = \frac{\omega}{2\pi} = \frac{1}{2\pi} \sqrt{Ze^2/m_0 r^3}.$$

The mean electric current due to the motion of the electron in its orbit is $J = e/T$ where $T = 1/\nu$ is the period of the motion. According to the laws of electrodynamics, a closed stream J is equivalent in external effects to a magnetic moment $\mathbf{\mu}_M$ of magnitude

$$(14.61) \qquad \mu_M = |J|A/c = A|e|/cT,$$

where A is the area enclosed by the stream, c is the velocity of light. We wish to find the relation between the magnetic moment $\mathbf{\mu}_M$ and the angular momentum $\mathbf{M}$. According to classical mechanics, $\mathbf{M}$, which is perpendicular to the plane of the motion, is a constant of the motion, in particular, $M = m_0 r^2 \dot{\varphi} = $ a constant. Hence

$$(14.62) \quad A = \frac{1}{2} \int_0^{2\pi} r^2 \, d\varphi = \frac{1}{2} \int_0^T r^2 \dot{\varphi} \, dt = \frac{1}{2} \int_0^T \left(\frac{M}{m_0} \right) dt = \frac{MT}{2m_0}.$$

Elimination of A from (14.61) and (14.62) gives the proportionality between μ_M and M. Then, since $\mathbf{\mu}_M$ is anti-parallel to $\mathbf{M}$, we may write

$$(14.63) \qquad \mathbf{\mu}_M = e\mathbf{M}/2m_0 c.$$

A magnetic field $\mathbf{H}$ (more properly, magnetic induction $\mathbf{B}$), interacting with a magnetic dipole of moment $\mathbf{\mu}_M$ produces on it a torque $\mathbf{L} = \mathbf{\mu}_M \times \mathbf{H}$. The torque causes the angular momentum $\mathbf{M}$ to change at a rate

$$(14.64) \qquad \frac{d}{dt} \mathbf{M} = \mathbf{L} = \mathbf{\mu}_M \times \mathbf{H} = \left(\frac{e}{2m_0 c} \right) \mathbf{M} \times \mathbf{H}.$$

From the final expression in (14.64), which was obtained by substituting from (14.63), we see that $d\mathbf{M}/dt$ is perpendicular to both $\mathbf{M}$ and $\mathbf{H}$. In the presence of a magnetic field $\mathbf{H}$ the angular momentum vector $\mathbf{M}$ precesses around the direction of $\mathbf{H}$ with an angular velocity ω_L ($\nu_L = \omega_L/2\pi = $ the "Larmor frequency") which we proceed to determine. Letting θ be the angle formed by $\mathbf{M}$ and $\mathbf{H}$ (see Fig. 14.1), we have

$$(14.65) \qquad \left| \frac{d\mathbf{M}}{dt} \right| = \omega_L |M \sin \theta|.$$

Comparison of (14.64) and (14.65) and the fact that ω_L is anti-parallel to **H** leads to

$$(14.66) \qquad \omega_L = \left(\frac{e}{2m_0c}\right)\mathbf{H}.$$

The direction of the precession of **M** around **H** (*the Larmor precession*) is independent of the direction of rotation and of the orientation of the plane of the motion, even of the shape and size of the orbit. Hence all electrons in an atom and in various atoms undergo the same precessional motion.

Classically, θ, the angle between the directions of **M** and **H**, may have any value, $0 \leq \theta \leq \pi$. Quantum mechanically, the only observable values of M^2 and M_z are the eigenvalues $M^2 = l(l+1)\hbar^2$ and $M_z = m\hbar$.

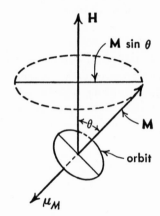

Fig. 14.1. Angular momentum, magnetic moment, and the Larmor precession in a magnetic field.

From these eigenvalues a discrete set of $2l + 1$ values of θ is calculable from the formula

$$(14.67) \qquad \cos\theta = M_z/M = m/\sqrt{l(l+1)}, \quad -l \leq m \leq l.$$

This is *spatial quantization* (see Fig. 4.4).

Both classically and quantum mechanically, we picture **M** as precessing around **H** with the Larmor frequency (14.66). The expectation values of M_x and M_y, components of **M** perpendicular to the direction of **H**, vanish classically and quantum mechanically for any state in which M^2 and M_z are sharp (i.e. a state described by a simultaneous eigenfunction of M^2 and M_z).

The ratio of the magnitude of the magnetic moment and the magnitude of the angular momentum is called the *gyromagnetic ratio*. From (14.63) we find the *gyromagnetic ratio for orbital motion* to be

(14.68) $$G = |e|/2m_0c.$$

The quantity $|e|\hbar/2m_0c$, which is the natural unit of magnetic moment, is called the *Bohr magneton*. The quantum number m, which is directly observable, as in the Stern-Gerlach experiment, is called the *magnetic quantum number*.

Problem 14.24: Show that $\langle M_x \rangle = 0$ and $\langle M_y \rangle = 0$ for a state described by an eigenfunction of M_z. (Hint: Use (14.5b) and (14.5c).)

Problem 14.25: Show that $(\Delta M_x)(\Delta M_y) \geq m\hbar^2/2$ when $M_z = m\hbar$. (Hint: Let $A = M_x$, $B = M_y$ in the general uncertainty relation (6.26).)

Problem 14.26: Calculate the classical frequency of circular orbital motion of an electron in a hydrogen atom ($r = 10^{-8}$ cm). Show that the result corresponds to light of wavelength $\lambda = c/\nu \cong 3 \times 10^{-6}$ cm which is in the ultra-violet and near visible range. Since atoms when forced to radiate in an electric discharge emit light in this range, it is reasonable to ascribe this radiation to the outermost or *optical* electrons of the atoms.

Problem 14.27: Calculate the Larmor frequency. Compare it with the frequency of orbital motion (Problem 14.26), for a field of 10^4 Gausses. Answer: $\nu_L = 1.41 \times 10^6 B$ Gausses.

14.6. The Stern-Gerlach Experiment. In the Stern-Gerlach experiment[1] (proposed by O. Stern in 1921, performed by Stern and Gerlach in 1922) a spatially inhomogeneous magnetic field serves to separate atoms for which values of M_z for the valence electrons differ. The experiment is important as a direct observation of spatial quantization. Anomalous observations, which will be described in Section 14.8, have had far-reaching consequences in leading Uhlenbeck and Goudsmit to the hypothesis of the spinning electron (1925).

The potential energy of a magnetic dipole of moment $\mathbf{\mu}$ in a magnetic field $\mathbf{H}$ is

(14.69) $$W = -\mathbf{\mu} \cdot \mathbf{H}.$$

In an inhomogeneous field the dipole experiences a force

(14.70) $$\mathbf{F} = -\text{grad } W = \text{grad } (\mathbf{\mu} \cdot \mathbf{H}).$$

To avoid considering the rapid variation of $\mathbf{F}$ as $\mathbf{\mu}$ precesses around $\mathbf{H}$, we take the mean value of $\mathbf{F}$. Since the mean value of $\mathbf{\mu}$ is antiparallel to $\mathbf{H}$ (see (14.63) and Problem 14.24), we obtain

(14.71) $$\mathbf{F} = \text{grad } (\mu_z H) = \mu_z \text{ grad } H,$$

---

[1] O. Stern and W. Gerlach, *Ann. Physik*, **74**, 673 (1924).

when we replace $\mathbf{F}$ in (14.70) by its mean value. Here μ_z is the component of $\mathbf{u}$ in the direction of $\mathbf{H}$. Finally, from (14.63) and (14.71) we find that the mean force on an atom due to the interaction between $\mathbf{H}$ and the magnetic dipole produced by an orbital electron is

$$(14.72) \qquad\qquad \mathbf{F} = \frac{e}{2m_0 c}\, M_z\, \mathrm{grad}\, H$$

where M_z is the component of the orbital angular momentum $\mathbf{M}$ in the direction of $\mathbf{H}$.

In the Stern-Gerlach experiment, pole pieces are arranged to give a magnetic field $\mathbf{H}$ which varies rapidly in the direction of $\mathbf{H}$ (Fig. 14.2). In a typical arrangement, $\partial H/\partial z \cong 250{,}000$ Gausses/cm. Particles in-

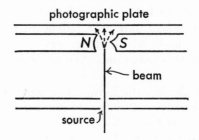

Fig. 14.2. Schema for the Stern-Gerlach experiment.

jected transversally to $\mathbf{H}$ are deflected by a force whose component parallel to $\mathbf{H}$ is

$$(14.73) \qquad\qquad F_z = K M_z$$

where $K = (e/2m_0 c)\, \partial H/\partial z$. From (14.73) we find, by integrating twice, that

$$(14.74) \qquad\qquad z = K M_z t^2/2m_0,$$

where z is the deflection in the direction of $\mathbf{H}$ and t is the time required for an atom to traverse the field.

Classically, M_z and therefore the deflection z may have any value in a continuum. Hence a spreading out of the beam toward each side, with a gradual decrease in intensity from the maximum at the center, might be expected. This broadening into a single wide beam is not observed, rather there is observed a splitting into a definite number of distinct beams, the number depending upon the atomic species and its state of excitation (see Fig. 14.5). Quantum mechanically, M_z has only discrete values, $M_z = m\hbar$, $m =$ an integer. The number of beams into which the original beam is split gives the number of possible values of m. Further,

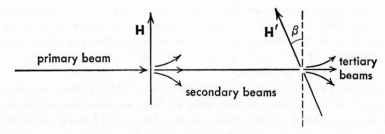

Fig. 14.3. The double Stern-Gerlach experiment.

the magnitude of the magnetic moment of orbital electrons can be calculated from the magnitude of the splitting and the constants of the apparatus.

Proper interpretation of the Stern-Gerlach experiment contributes to a good understanding of quantum mechanics. It may be pointed out, for example, that the Stern-Gerlach experiment does not determine the direction of the magnetic moment, nor its z component, before the atom enters the magnetic field. These are undetermined, and hence undefined. Interaction between the atom and the magnetic field disturbs the atom in a way, not described by quantum mechanics, such that after passing through the field the component of the angular momentum of the orbital electron in the direction of the magnetic field is an integral multiple of $\hbar$.

14.7. The Double Stern-Gerlach Experiment. A primary beam is split by an inhomogeneous field **H** into secondary beams according to values of M_z, where M_z is the component of **M** in the direction of **H**. A selected secondary beam is then split by a second inhomogeneous magnetic field **H′** into tertiary beams according to values of $M_{z'}$, where $M_{z'}$ is the component of **M** in the direction of **H′** (see Fig. 14.3). We wish to compute the relative intensities of the tertiary beams, for a given angle β between the directions of **H** and **H′**.

Since M_z is known for atoms in the selected secondary beam, the

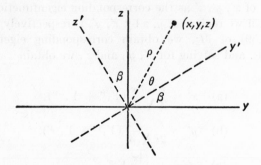

Fig. 14.4. Rotation of axes.

wave function representing the state of these atoms is an eigenfunction of M_z for which $M_z = m\hbar$, m a known integer. To be more specific, let us assume that M^2 is known also. Then the wave function is a simultaneous eigenfunction of M^2 and M_z: $\psi = Y_l^m$, $M^2 = l(l+1)\hbar^2$, $M_z = m\hbar$, $-l \le m \le l$, l and m known.

Postulate IV, Section 12.4 (see in particular (12.22)) gives the relative intensities of the tertiary beams, once we have an expansion of the wave function in terms of eigenfunctions of $M_{z'}$. Of several known methods for obtaining this expansion, we choose the most elementary: transformation of coordinates determined by a rotation of the coordinate system.

Place the z and z' axes parallel to $\mathbf{H}$ and $\mathbf{H'}$, respectively, and place y and y' axes in the plane of $\mathbf{H}$ and $\mathbf{H'}$, the y axis perpendicular to $\mathbf{H}$, the y' axis perpendicular to $\mathbf{H'}$. We readily express the original coordinates x, y, z in terms of new coordinates x', y', z':

$$(14.75) \quad \begin{aligned} &\text{(a)} \quad x = x', \\ &\text{(b)} \quad y = \rho \cos(\theta + \beta) = \rho \cos\theta \cos\beta - \rho \sin\theta \sin\beta \\ &\qquad\quad = y' \cos\beta - z' \sin\beta, \\ &\text{(c)} \quad z = \rho \sin(\theta + \beta) = \rho \sin\theta \cos\beta + \rho \cos\theta \sin\beta \\ &\qquad\quad = y' \sin\beta + z' \cos\beta, \\ &\text{(d)} \quad r = \sqrt{x^2 + y^2 + z^2} = \sqrt{x'^2 + y'^2 + z'^2}. \end{aligned}$$

The procedure is to express $\psi(x,y,z)$ as a function of x', y', z', and then rearrange terms as necessary to express the resulting function of x', y', z' in terms of eigenfunctions of $M_{z'}$. For the purpose of illustrating the method, let us suppose that $l = 1$ and $m = -1$ for the selected secondary beam. Then, from (14.59) and (14.75), we write

$$(14.76) \quad \psi = Y_1^{-1} = \sqrt{\frac{3}{8\pi}}\left(\frac{x - iy}{r}\right) = \sqrt{\frac{3}{8\pi}}\left(\frac{x' - iy'\cos\beta + iz'\sin\beta}{r}\right).$$

Quite evidently, an eigenfunction of $M_{z'}$ for a given value of M^2 is the same function of x', y', z' as the corresponding eigenfunction of M_z is of x, y, z. Hence, if we replace x, y, z by x', y', z' respectively, in the eigenfunctions (14.59) of M_z, we obtain corresponding eigenfunctions of $M_{z'}$. Doing this, and solving for x', y', and z', we obtain

$$(14.77) \quad \begin{aligned} &\text{(a)} \quad x' = \frac{r}{2}\sqrt{\frac{8\pi}{3}}\,(Y_1^{1'} + Y_1^{-1'}), \\ &\text{(b)} \quad y' = \frac{r}{2i}\sqrt{\frac{8\pi}{3}}\,(Y_1^{1'} - Y_1^{-1'}), \\ &\text{(c)} \quad z' = r\sqrt{\frac{4\pi}{3}}\,Y_1^{0'}. \end{aligned}$$

Using (14.77) to eliminate x', y', z' from (14.76), we obtain, after a little simplification

$$(14.78) \quad \psi = \left(\cos^2 \frac{\beta}{2}\right) Y_1^{-1'} + \frac{i}{\sqrt{2}} (\sin \beta) Y_1^{0'} + \left(\sin^2 \frac{\beta}{2}\right) Y_1^{1'}.$$

Finally, from (12.22), we find from (14.78) that the three tertiary beams have relative intensities:

$$\begin{aligned}
&\text{(a)} \quad I_1^{-1'} = P(M_{z'} = -\hbar) = \cos^4 (\beta/2), \\
(14.79) \quad &\text{(b)} \quad I_1^{0'} = P(M_{z'} = 0) = \tfrac{1}{2} \sin^2 \beta, \\
&\text{(c)} \quad I_1^{1'} = P(M_{z'} = \hbar) = \sin^4 (\beta/2).
\end{aligned}$$

It may be readily verified that $I_1^{-1'} + I_1^{0'} + I_1^{1'} = 1$, as implied by the normalization of ψ.

Problem 14.28: Find the relative intensities of the beams into which a beam for which $M^2 = 2\hbar^2$, $M_z = 0$ are split by an inhomogeneous field making an angle of 30° with the z axis. (Answers: $I_1^{-1} = \frac{1}{8}$, $I_1^0 = \frac{3}{4}$, $I_1^1 = \frac{1}{8}$.)

Problem 14.29: Work Problem 14.28 for an angle of 90°. (Answers: $I_1^{-1} = \frac{1}{2}$, $I_1^0 = 0$, $I_1^1 = \frac{1}{2}$.)

14.8. Stern-Gerlach Patterns and Electron Spin. As stated in Section 14.6, according to the theory developed to that point the number of components to be expected in a Stern-Gerlach pattern is equal to the number of possible values of the magnetic quantum number m. For orbital angular momentum $\mathbf{M}$ for which $M^2 = l(l + 1)\hbar^2$, the number of possible values of m is $2l + 1$, *an odd integer.* Thus, according to this rather elementary theory, a Stern-Gerlach pattern should always have an odd number of components and should always contain an undeflected component (for which $m = 0$). However, for many elements, in particular for H, Ag, and the alkalis, there appear an even number of components and no undeflected component (see Fig. 14.5).

To account for the observed Stern-Gerlach patterns and for the observed splitting of excited energy levels by a magnetic field (the anomalous Zeeman effect, see Section 18.5), Uhlenbeck and Goudsmit were led in 1925 to propose that the "point electron" model should be replaced by a "spinning electron" model. Analogous to the orbital angular momentum $\mathbf{M}$ for which $M^2 = l(l + 1)\hbar^2$, they proposed that an electron should be pictured as possessing a *spin angular momentum* $\mathbf{s}$. for which $|s|^2 = s(s + 1)\hbar^2$. (Note the vertical bars used to distinguish the magnitude of the spin angular momentum $\mathbf{s}$ from the spin quantum number s.) What value, or values, should be assigned to the spin quantum number s?

The $2l + 1$ values of M_z led us to expect an odd number of Stern-Gerlach components. For H, Ag, or for an alkali in the ground state, for which $n = 1$, $l = 0$, $m = 0$ (see Section 13.7), we would expect 1 undisplaced component. However, two displaced components are observed. These two components must be explained entirely in terms of electron spin. Corresponding to the $2l + 1$ values of M_z, let us suppose that there are $2s + 1$ values of s_z, each of which accounts for one of the components in the Stern-Gerlach pattern for H, Ag, or an alkali, in the ground state. Since there are observed two components, we write $2s + 1 = 2$ and find $s = \frac{1}{2}$. Then

$$(14.80) \qquad \begin{array}{ll} \text{(a)} & |s|^2 = s(s + 1)\hbar^2 = (\frac{3}{4})\hbar^2, \\ \text{(b)} & s_z = \pm s\hbar = \pm(\frac{1}{2})\hbar. \end{array}$$

Measurement of the deflection of the components in a Stern-Gerlach pattern leads to the numerical value of the magnetic moment to be

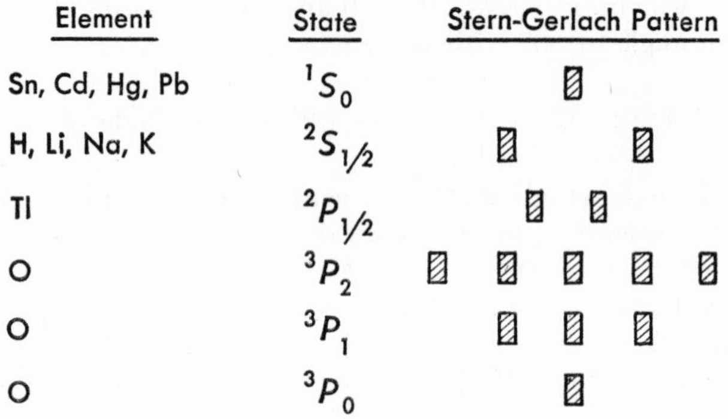

Element	State	Stern-Gerlach Pattern
Sn, Cd, Hg, Pb	$^1S_0$	
H, Li, Na, K	$^2S_{1/2}$	
Tl	$^2P_{1/2}$	
O	$^3P_2$	
O	$^3P_1$	
O	$^3P_0$	

Fig. 14.5. Representative Stern-Gerlach patterns.

associated with the spin angular momentum. This is found to be equal to the magnetic moment associated with the orbital angular momentum. (A slight but important difference was observed in 1947 in very precise measurements by Lamb,[2] the *Lamb shift*.) Since the unit of spin angular momentum, $\hbar/2$, is only one-half the unit of orbital angular momentum, $\hbar$, the spin gyromagnetic ratio G_s is twice as great as the orbital gyromagnetic ratio G (14.68):

$$(14.81) \qquad \begin{array}{ll} \text{(a)} & G = \dfrac{\text{orbital magnetic moment}}{\text{orbital angular momentum}} = \dfrac{(|e|\hbar/2m_0c)}{\hbar} = \dfrac{|e|}{2m_0c}, \\[2ex] \text{(b)} & G_s = \dfrac{\text{spin magnetic moment}}{\text{spin angular momentum}} = \dfrac{(|e|\hbar/2m_0c)}{\frac{1}{2}\hbar} = \dfrac{|e|}{m_0c} \end{array}$$

[2] W. E. Lamb and R. C. Retherford, *Phys. Rev.*, **72**, 241 (1947); W. E. Lamb, *Reports on Progress in Physics*, **14**, 19 (1951); also see R. S. Shankland, *Atomic and Nuclear Physics*, Macmillan, 1955, pp. 99–107.

14.9. References for Supplementary Reading.

Section 14.1: Bohm, 310–14; Born, 141–4, 358–9; Dirac, 140–44; Frenkel, 51–2, 58–60; Kemble, 224–30; Kramers, 168–9; Mandl, 54–6, 104–9; McConnell, 78–81; Pauling and Wilson, 425–8; Persico, 351–5; Schaefer, 389–96; Schiff, 69–76, 141–3; Sherwin, 148–51, 359–61.

Section 14.3: Finkelnburg, 217–19; Landé, 51–2; Schaefer, 270–71.

Section 14.4: Bohm, 314–26; Dirac, 144–9; Frenkel, 52–4; Houston, 278–80; Kemble, 143–52, 583–4; Kramers, 169–79; Landé, 57–60; Mandl, 47–57; Mott and Sneddon, 60–63, 85–7, 380–88; Schaefer, 270–79; Schiff, 143–9; Sherwin, 152–60.

Section 14.5: Eldridge, 222–31; French, 321–33; Peaslee and Mueller, 51–3; Persico, 258–61; Shankland, 78–87.

Section 14.6: Bohm, 326–7; Born, 182–5; Eldridge, 231–6; Finkelnburg, 152–62; Peaslee and Mueller, 62–71, 74.

Section 14.7: Bohm, 327–32.

Section 14.8: French, 210–14; Pauling and Wilson, 207–10; Schaefer, 145–63; Shankland, 52–4, 99–107.

CHAPTER 15

THE HYDROGEN ATOM

15.1. Classical Treatment of the Two-Body Problem. Consider two particles, masses m_1 and m_2, whose positions in space are described by two vectors $\mathbf{r}_1 = (x_1, y_1, z_1)$ and $\mathbf{r}_2 = (x_2, y_2, z_2)$. The center of mass is located by the vector $\mathbf{R} = (X, Y, Z) = (m_1\mathbf{r}_1 + m_2\mathbf{r}_2)/M_0$, where $M_0 = m_1 + m_2$, and the position of the second particle relative to that of the first particle by the vector $\mathbf{r} = (x, y, z) = \mathbf{r}_1 - \mathbf{r}_2$. We shall call X, Y, and Z the *external coordinates* and x, y, and z the *internal coordinates*. The velocities of the two particles are $\mathbf{v}_1 = \dot{\mathbf{r}}_1$ and $\mathbf{v}_2 = \dot{\mathbf{r}}_2$. The velocity of the center of mass is $\mathbf{w} = \dot{\mathbf{R}}$, and the relative velocity is $\mathbf{v} = \dot{\mathbf{r}}$.

We wish to describe the motion in terms of internal and external coordinates and velocities. From the defining equations it is readily found that

(15.1)   (a) $\mathbf{r}_1 = \mathbf{R} + (m_2/M_0)\mathbf{r}$,   (b) $\mathbf{r}_2 = \mathbf{R} - (m_1/M_0)\mathbf{r}$.

Hence

(15.2)   (a) $\mathbf{v}_1 = \mathbf{w} + (m_2/M_0)\mathbf{v}$,   (b) $\mathbf{v}_2 = \mathbf{w} - (m_1/M_0)\mathbf{v}$.

For the kinetic energy T we obtain

(15.3) $T = \frac{1}{2}m_1v_1^2 + \frac{1}{2}m_2v_2^2 = \frac{1}{2}M_0w^2 + \frac{1}{2}m_0v^2$,

where $m_0 = m_1m_2/M_0$ is the *reduced mass*. Here the kinetic energy is expressed as a sum of the *translational kinetic energy* $T_{tr} = M_0w^2/2$ and the *internal kinetic energy* $T_{in} = m_0v^2/2$.

Let there be a potential V which is a function of r only, $V = V(r)$. From the Lagrangian function

(15.4) $L = T - V = \frac{1}{2}M_0w^2 + \frac{1}{2}m_0v^2$

we obtain linear momenta vectors $\mathbf{P}$ and $\mathbf{p}$ conjugate to $\mathbf{R}$ and $\mathbf{r}$, respectively,

(15.5)   (a) $\mathbf{P} = \dfrac{\partial L}{\partial \mathbf{w}} = M_0\mathbf{w}$,   (b) $\mathbf{p} = \dfrac{\partial L}{\partial \mathbf{v}} = m_0\mathbf{v}$.

From this, we obtain the Hamiltonian in terms of internal and external variables:

(15.6) $\qquad H = T + V = P^2/2M_0 + p^2/2m_0 + V.$

In order to make a transformation to internal spherical coordinates, we express the internal linear momentum $\mathbf{p}$ in terms of its *radial component* p_r and the *internal angular momentum* $\mathbf{M} = \mathbf{r} \times \mathbf{p}$. Letting $\mathbf{A} = \mathbf{C} = \mathbf{r}$, $\mathbf{B} = \mathbf{D} = \mathbf{p}$ in the vector identity

(15.7) $\quad (\mathbf{A} \times \mathbf{B}) \cdot (\mathbf{C} \times \mathbf{D}) = (\mathbf{A} \cdot \mathbf{C})(\mathbf{B} \cdot \mathbf{D}) - (\mathbf{A} \cdot \mathbf{D})(\mathbf{B} \cdot \mathbf{C}),$

we find that

(15.8) $\qquad M^2 = r^2 p^2 - (\mathbf{r} \cdot \mathbf{p})(\mathbf{p} \cdot \mathbf{r}).$

Since $\mathbf{r} \cdot \mathbf{p} = \mathbf{p} \cdot \mathbf{r} = r p_r$, we obtain, upon using (15.8) to eliminate p^2 from (15.6), that

(15.9) $\qquad H = P^2/2M_0 + p_r{}^2/2m_0 + M^2/2m_0 r^2 + V.$

When V is a function of r only, the external linear momentum $\mathbf{P}$, the internal angular momentum $\mathbf{M}$, the translational energy $E_{tr} = T_{tr} = M_0 w^2/2$, and the internal energy $E_{in} = T_{in} + V = p^2/2m_0 + V$ are classical constants of the motion. The Hamiltonian splits very naturally into the two parts

(15.10) (a) $H_{tr} = P^2/2M_0,$
$\qquad$ (b) $H_{in} = p^2/2m_0 + V = p_r{}^2/2m_0 + M^2/2m_0 r^2 + V(r).$

We turn now to the quantum mechanical two-body problem.

15.2. A Complete Set of Compatible Constants of the Motion. Quite evidently, H is a quantum mechanical constant of the motion, since $(H,H) = 0$ and $\partial H/\partial t = 0$. We proceed to show that $\mathbf{P}$, $\mathbf{M}$, H_{tr}, and H_{in} are also constants of the motion.

In the position representation, in the coordinate system of Section 15.1,

(15.11) $\quad$ (a) $\mathbf{P} = -i\hbar\, \mathrm{grad}_R,$ $\qquad$ (b) $\mathbf{p} = -i\hbar\, \mathrm{grad}_r.$

When V is a function of r only, H does not depend on $\mathbf{R}$ (see (15.9). Hence $\mathbf{P}$ commutes with H; $\mathbf{P}$ is a quantum mechanical constant of the motion. Quite readily then, $H_{tr} = P^2/2M_0$ is also a constant of the motion. Further, H_{in} is also a constant since $H_{in} = H - H_{tr}$ is the difference of two constants of the motion.

To show that $\mathbf{M}$ commutes with H, we observe first that $\mathbf{M}$ commutes with $P^2/2M_0$, since $\mathbf{M}$ operates only on the internal coordinates (x,y,z) and $\mathbf{P}$ operates only on the external coordinates (X,Y,Z). Observing from (14.11) and (14.15) that $\mathbf{M}$ commutes with $V(r)$ and with p^2, we readily see that $\mathbf{M}$ commutes with $H = P^2/2M_0 + p^2/2m_0 + V(r)$.

Hence $\mathbf{M}$ is a constant of the motion. Evidently, M^2 is also a constant of the motion.

Corresponding to the six independent classical constants of the motion (viz. the three components of $\mathbf{P}$ and the three components of $\mathbf{M}$), we look for a set of six compatible quantum mechanical constants of the motion. From the 10 operators $\mathbf{P}$, $\mathbf{M}$, M^2, H_{tr}, H_{in}, and H we desire to choose six such that (a) every pair of the six commutes and (b) no one of the six is a function of the other five. Among these six there may be included only one component of $\mathbf{M}$. Calling it M_z, we readily select the six operators $\mathbf{P}$, M_z, M^2, and H_{in} as a set with the desired properties. We proceed to look for simultaneous eigenfunctions of these six operators.

15.3. The External Momentum and Energy. In terms of the external coordinates (X,Y,Z), the components of $\mathbf{R}$, the system of three equations

$$(15.12) \qquad\qquad \mathbf{P}\Psi = \mathbf{P}_0\Psi,$$

for simultaneous eigenfunctions of the components of $\mathbf{P}$ has the representation

$$(15.13) \qquad\qquad -i\hbar \, \text{grad}_{\mathbf{R}}\Psi = \hbar\mathbf{K}\Psi,$$

where $\hbar\mathbf{K} = \mathbf{P}_0$. By the method given in Section 13.7, we find a solution finite for all $(X,Y,Z) = \mathbf{R}$ to be

$$(15.14) \qquad\qquad \Psi = e^{i\mathbf{K}\cdot\mathbf{R}}\psi(\mathbf{r})$$

where $\psi(\mathbf{r})$ is a function of the internal coordinates $(x,y,z) = \mathbf{r}$ only.

For a free two-particle system, there are no further conditions to fix the components of $\mathbf{K}$. Hence $\mathbf{P}_0 = \hbar\mathbf{K}$ may be any vector with real components. The momentum $\mathbf{P}_0$ and the translational energy $E_{\text{tr}} = P_0^2/2M_0$, which are associated with the motion of the center of mass, are not quantized.

Problem 15.1: Show that a simultaneous eigenfunction of $\mathbf{P}$ and of H_{in} is also an eigenfunction of $H = P^2/2M_0 + H_{\text{in}}$.

15.4. The Internal Angular Momentum. The wave function (15.14), which is a simultaneous eigenfunction of the three components of $\mathbf{P}$, is also a simultaneous eigenfunction of M_z, M^2, and H_{in} if $\psi(\mathbf{r})$ is a simultaneous eigenfunction of M_z, M^2, and H_{in}. That such is the case follows from the fact that these three operators operate on $\mathbf{r}$ only, not on $\mathbf{R}$.

In order to obtain simultaneous eigenfunctions $\psi(\mathbf{r})$ of M_z, M^2, and H_{in}, we introduce internal spherical coordinates (r,θ,φ) with polar axis in the preferred direction parallel to which we place the z axis. In terms of these coordinates, $\mathbf{M}$ and M^2 have the representations (14.10) and (14.25), respectively. Noting from (14.10c) and (14.25) that M_z and M^2 operate on θ and φ only, not on r, we see from results obtained in Section 14.4 that the functions

(15.15) $$\psi_l{}^m(\mathbf{r}) = e^{im\varphi}P_l{}^m(\cos\theta)g(r),$$

where $g(r)$ is any function of r, $l =$ any nonnegative integer, and $m =$ any integer such that $-l \le m \le l$, are simultaneous eigenfunctions of M_z and M^2 for $M_z = m\hbar$, $M^2 = l(l + 1)\hbar^2$. The factor $g(r)$ in (15.15) remains to be determined so that $\psi_l{}^m(\mathbf{r})$ will also be an eigenfunction of H_{in}. Then the wave function

(15.16) $$\Psi = e^{i\mathbf{K}\cdot\mathbf{R}+im\varphi}P_l{}^m(\cos\theta)g(r)$$

will be a simultaneous eigenfunction of $\mathbf{P}$, M_z, M^2, and H_{in}, and of H.

15.5. The Radial Equation. Elimination of p^2 from $H_{\text{in}} = p^2/2m_0 + V(r)$ by means of (15.8) will give a representation of H_{in} in terms of the spherical coordinates (r,θ,φ). Now we must be more careful about the order in which the operators involved are written, since $\mathbf{r}\cdot\mathbf{p} \ne \mathbf{p}\cdot\mathbf{r}$. In (15.8), we carefully kept the order implied by the vector identity (15.7). We shall assume without verification that we have the proper order of operators when we write

(15.17) $$M^2 = r^2p^2 - rp_r{}^2r,$$

as suggested by (15.8).

We may solve (15.17) for p^2 by multiplying from the left by $1/r^2$. Since M^2 and $1/r^2$ commute (see (14.11)), we may write the result in the form

(15.18) $$p^2 = M^2/r^2 + (1/r^2)(rp_r{}^2r).$$

Finally, upon eliminating p^2 from (15.10b) by means of (15.18), we obtain

(15.19) $$H_{\text{in}} = \frac{M^2}{2m_0r^2} + \frac{1}{2m_0r^2}(rp_r{}^2r) + V(r).$$

Since (15.15) is an eigenfunction of M_z and of M^2 for $M_z = m\hbar$, $M^2 = l(l + 1)\hbar^2$, we see from (15.19) that (15.15) will also be an eigenfunction of H_{in}, for $H_{\text{in}} = E_{\text{in}}$, if $g(r)$ satisfies the equation

(15.20) $$\left\{\frac{l(l + 1)\hbar^2}{2m_0r^2} + \frac{1}{2m_0r^2}(rp_r{}^2r) + V(r)\right\}g(r) = E_{\text{in}}g(r).$$

Substituting

(15.21) $$p_r = -i\hbar\frac{\partial}{\partial r},$$

we obtain from (15.20) the second-order ordinary differential equation for $g(r)$:

(15.22) $$-\frac{\hbar^2}{2m_0}r\frac{d^2}{dr^2}(rg) + \left\{\frac{l(l + 1)\hbar^2}{2m_0} + r^2V - r^2E_{\text{in}}\right\}g = 0.$$

This is called the *radial equation*, a solution $g(r)$ is called the *radial factor*.

Problem 15.2: From the equation $r^2 = x^2 + y^2 + z^2$ obtain the classical relation

$$(15.23) \qquad rp_r = xp_x + yp_y + zp_z,$$

where $p_r = m\dot{r}$, $p_x = m\dot{x}$, etc. Then, using the position representations of p_x, p_y, and p_z, justify (15.21).

15.6. Asymptotic Solution for a Coulomb Potential. For a Coulomb potential $V(r) = -Ze^2/r$,* the radial equation is

$$(15.24) \qquad -\frac{\hbar^2}{2m_0}\frac{d^2G}{dr^2} + \left(\frac{l(l+1)\hbar^2}{2m_0r^2} - \frac{Ze^2}{r} - E_{in}\right)G = 0,$$

where $G(r) = r \cdot g(r)$. Limiting forms of the solutions are readily found, as $r \to \infty$, by neglecting the two terms with r in the denominators. We consider separately the two cases $E_{in} > 0$ and $E_{in} < 0$.

Case 1: E_{in} *positive:* As $r \to \infty$,

$$(15.25) \qquad g(r) = G(r)/r \to \frac{1}{r}\{A\cos(br) + B\sin(br)\}$$

where

$$(15.26) \qquad b = (2m_0E_{in})^{\frac{1}{2}}/\hbar.$$

The solution is bounded for any positive values of E_{in}. In fact, $g(r) \to 0$ as $r \to \infty$, although, as may be shown, its norm is not finite. The solutions for $E_{in} > 0$ correspond roughly to the hyperbolic orbits in the classical theory (see Section 4.2).

Case 2: E_{in} *negative:* In this case, as $r \to \infty$,

$$(15.27) \qquad g(r) = G(r)/r \to \frac{1}{r}\{Ae^{-br} + Be^{br}\}$$

where

$$(15.28) \qquad b = (-2m_0E_{in})^{\frac{1}{2}}/\hbar.$$

The solution remains bounded as $r \to \infty$ only if $B = 0$. This suggests that, for this case, we attempt to obtain an exact solution of the form $g(r) = G(r)/r = (A/r)e^{-br}v(r)$ where $v(r)$ remains finite as $r \to \infty$. We shall find that such solutions exist only for certain values of E_{in}, the energy eigenvalues for the internal motion.

15.7. Solution of the Radial Equation, for Negative Energies. Making change of both independent and dependent variables from r and $G(r)$ to s and $f(s)$ by means of the relations

$$(15.29) \qquad \text{(a)} \quad r = s/b, \qquad \text{(b)} \quad G(r) = e^{-s}f(s),$$

_____

* $Z = 1, 2, 3, \ldots$ for H, He^+, Li^{++}, $\ldots$, respectively.

we obtain from (15.24) the equation

(15.30) $s^2f'' - 2s^2f' + 2\lambda sf - l(l + 1)f = 0$

where

(15.31) $\lambda = m_0 Z e^2 / \hbar^2 b.$

Here the value of b is to be taken from (15.28).

We try to obtain a series solution

(15.32) $f = s^p \sum_{k=0}^{\infty} c_k s^k, \ c_0 \neq 0,$

where p and the c_k are to be determined. Substituting from (15.32) into (15.30), we find that we must have

(15.33) $\sum_{k=0}^{\infty} c_k (k + p + l)(k + p - l - 1)s^k$

$$+ \sum_{k=0}^{\infty} 2c_k (\lambda - k - p)s^{k+1} = 0.$$

Picking out from (15.33) the coefficients of the various powers of s, we find that (15.32) satisfies (15.30) only if

(15.34)   (a) $c_0(p + l)(p - l - 1) = 0,$
          (b) $c_{k+1}(k + p + l + 1)(k + p - l) + 2c_k(\lambda - k - p) = 0,$

for $k = 0, 1, 2, \ldots$. From (15.34a) we see that either $p = -l$ or $p = l + 1$, since $c_0 \neq 0$. To avoid negative exponents, we rule out $p = -l$ and take $p = l + 1$. Then from (15.34b) we obtain

(15.35) $c_{k+1} = 2c_k(k + l + 1 - \lambda)/(k + 2l + 2)(k + 1).$

From this *recurrence relation* we may determine all the coefficients c_k in terms of c_0. Before doing this, we discuss the conditions under which the series solution (15.32) yields a wave function with finite norm. Two cases are to be distinguished: (1) the solution (15.32) reduces to a polynomial, and (2) the solution (15.32) does not reduce to a polynomial.

From (15.32) and (15.35) we see that (15.32) represents a polynomial of degree $N + p = N + l + 1$ if and only if $c_{N+1} = 0$, $c_N \neq 0$, and that this can happen only for $\lambda = N + l + 1$. Hence if $\lambda =$ an integer $n \geq l + 1$, $f(s)$ is a polynomial of degree n and $g(r) = (1/r)e^{-br}f(br)$ is equal to e^{-br} times a polynomial of degree $n - 1$, where $n - 1 \geq l \geq 0$.

The function $g(r) \rightarrow 0$ as $r \rightarrow \infty$ and in fact has a finite norm, the norm being defined by

$$(15.36) \qquad N(g) = (g,g) = \int_0^\infty |g(r)|^2 r^2 \, dr.$$

When λ is not equal to a positive integer $n \geq l + 1$, the series (15.32) does not terminate, but is an infinite series. Then $c_{k+1} \cong 2c_k/(k + 1)$ when k is large. Noting that

$$(15.37) \qquad e^{2br} = \sum_{k=0}^\infty d_k(br)^k, \; d_k = \frac{2^k}{k!}, \; d_{k+1} = \frac{2}{k+1} d_k,$$

we see that $g(r)$ behaves like $b(br)^l \cdot e^{-br} \cdot e^{2br} = b(br)^l \cdot e^{br}$ when r is large. Hence when $\lambda \neq n \geq l + 1$, the radial equation has no solution with finite norm.

Only for $\lambda = n \geq l + 1$ does the radial equation (15.22) have a solution with finite norm, defined by (15.36). For each integer $l \geq 0$ and for each integer $n \geq l + 1$ there exists a normalizable radial eigenfunction $g_{nl}(r)$:

$$(15.38) \qquad g_{nl}(r) = e^{-br} L_n{}^l(br)$$

where $L_n{}^l(br)$ is a polynomial of degree $n - 1$, called a *Laguerre polynomial*, and where, according to (15.31) and the condition $\lambda = n$,

$$(15.39) \qquad b = m_0 Z e^2/n\hbar^2.$$

We may observe that $b = 1/nr_1$ where r_1 is the radius of the first Bohr orbit (see (3.18)).

The eigenvalues for the internal energy E_{in} are obtained by eliminating b from (15.28) and (15.39). Designating them by the symbol E_n, we find

$$(15.40) \qquad E_n = -Z^2 Rch/n^2$$

where R is the Rydberg constant (3.20). This is in complete agreement with Bohr's formula (3.19) since, for hydrogen, $Z = 1$.

15.8. The Hydrogen Eigenfunctions and Quantum Symbols. In Sections 15.5 and 15.7 we have found simultaneous eigenfunctions of M_z, M^2, and H_{in} of the form

$$(15.41) \qquad \psi_{nl}{}^m = e^{-br} L_n{}^l(br) P_l{}^m(\cos \theta) e^{im\varphi},$$

for $M_z = m\hbar$, $M^2 = l(l + 1)\hbar^2$, and $H_{in} = -Rch/n^2$, where n, l, and m are integers subject to the restrictions $0 \leq l \leq n - 1$, $-l \leq m \leq l$.

Normalized eigenfunctions for the ground state and for the first excited states are given in the accompanying table. In the table, $s = br$ and $B = (b^3/\pi)^{1/2}$.

Table of Normalized Eigenfunctions $\psi_{nl}{}^m$

n	l	m	$\psi_{nl}{}^m$
1	0	0	Be^{-s}
2	0	0	$Be^{-s}(1 - s)$
2	1	-1	$Be^{-s} s \sin \theta\, e^{-i\varphi}$
2	1	0	$Be^{-s} s \cos \theta$
2	1	1	$Be^{-s} s \sin \theta\, e^{i\varphi}$

Electron quantum states are frequently designated by alphabetical letters according to the convention:

l	0	1	2	3	4		$\|m\|$	0	1	2	3
Symbol	s	p	d	f	g		Symbol	σ	π	δ	φ

Electrons for which $l = 0$ are called "s electrons," those for which $l = 1$ are called "p electrons," etc. A "$3d\pi$ electron" is one for which $n = 3$, $l = 2$, and $m = \pm 1$.

Problem 15.3: Verify the correctness of the preceding table of Normalized Eigenfunctions $\psi_{nl}{}^m$. The inner product is

$$(15.42) \qquad (\psi_i, \psi_j) = \int_0^\infty \int_0^\pi \int_0^{2\pi} \psi_i{}^* \psi_j r^2 \sin \theta\, d\varphi\, d\theta\, dr.$$

15.9. Solution by the Factorization Method. The *Schroedinger factorization method*[1] for the solution of eigenvalue problems, of which the harmonic oscillator (Sections 11.4 and 11.5) and the rigid rotator (Section 14.4) provide relatively simple examples, has been applied by Infeld and Hull[2] to practically all of the solvable eigenvalue problems of mathematical physics. In this section we apply this method to the problem of obtaining square integrable solutions $G(r) = rg(r)$ of (15.24) which vanish at $r = 0$. The method leads again to the energy eigenvalues (15.40).

First we note from (15.36) that, since $G(r) = rg(r)$, inner products for functions $G(r)$ which vanish sufficiently rapidly at $r = 0$ and at $r = \infty$ are to be defined by

$$(15.43) \qquad (G_1, G_2) = \int_0^\infty G_1{}^* G_2\, dr.$$

It is readily verified that the operator p_r defined in (15.21) is Hermitean over the inner product space thus defined.

[1] E. Schroedinger, *Proc. Roy. Irish Acad.*, **A46**, 9 (1940).
[2] L. Infeld and T. E. Hull, *Revs. of Modern Phys.*, **23**, 21 (1951).

Using (15.21), we may write (15.24) in the form

$$(15.44) \qquad H_l G = EG,$$

where

$$(15.45) \qquad H_l = \frac{1}{2m_0} p_r{}^2 + \frac{l(l+1)\hbar^2}{2m_0 r^2} - \frac{Ze^2}{r}, \; E = E_{\text{in}}.$$

Next we seek to determine a function $A_l(r)$ and a constant B such that the operators

$$(15.46) \qquad \text{(a)} \quad L_+{}^{(l)} = p_r + iA_l, \qquad \text{(b)} \quad L_-{}^{(l)} = p_r - iA_l,$$

satisfy the relations

$$(15.47) \qquad \begin{array}{l} \text{(a)} \quad L_+{}^{(l)} L_-{}^{(l)} = 2m_0 H_l + B_l, \\ \text{(b)} \quad L_-{}^{(l)} L_+{}^{(l)} = 2m_0 H_{l-1} + B_l, \; l > 0. \end{array}$$

Since

$$(15.48) \qquad (A_l, p_r) = i\hbar \frac{\partial A_l}{\partial r},$$

(see (8.44a)), we find from (15.46) that

$$(15.49) \qquad \begin{array}{l} \text{(a)} \quad L_+{}^{(l)} L_-{}^{(l)} = p_r{}^2 + A_l{}^2 - \hbar \dfrac{\partial A_l}{\partial r}, \\[2mm] \text{(b)} \quad L_-{}^{(l)} L_+{}^{(l)} = p_r{}^2 + A_l{}^2 + \hbar \dfrac{\partial A_l}{\partial r}. \end{array}$$

By means of (15.45) and (15.49) we find that (15.47) is satisfied provided

$$(15.50) \qquad \begin{array}{l} \text{(a)} \quad \dfrac{\partial A_l}{\partial r} = -\dfrac{l\hbar}{r^2}, \\[3mm] \text{(b)} \quad A_l{}^2 = \dfrac{l^2\hbar^2}{r^2} - \dfrac{2m_0 Ze^2}{r} + B_l. \end{array}$$

From (15.50a) we find

$$(15.51) \qquad A_l = \frac{l\hbar}{r} + C_l,$$

where C_l is a constant. Next, substituting from (15.51) into (15.50b), we find

$$(15.52) \quad \text{(a)} \quad C_l = -m_0 Ze^2/l\hbar, \qquad \text{(b)} \quad B_l = C_l{}^2 = \frac{m_0{}^2 Z^2 e^4}{l^2 \hbar^2}, \; l > 0.$$

Using the associative property of operator multiplication, expressed in the equations

$$(15.53) \qquad \begin{array}{l} \text{(a)} \quad L_+{}^{(l)}(L_-{}^{(l)} L_+{}^{(l)}) = (L_+{}^{(l)} L_-{}^{(l)}) L_+{}^{(l)}, \\ \text{(b)} \quad L_-{}^{(l)}(L_+{}^{(l)} L_-{}^{(l)}) = (L_-{}^{(l)} L_+{}^{(l)}) L_-{}^{(l)}, \end{array}$$

we find by means of (15.47) that

(15.54) (a) $L_+^{(l)}H_{l-1} = H_l L_+^{(l)}$,   (b) $L_-^{(l)}H_l = H_{l-1}L_-^{(l)}$, $l > 0$.

Then, letting $G_n{}^l$ be an eigenfunction of H_l for $H_l = E_{nl}$, we find by means of (15.54b) that either $L_-^{(l)}G_n{}^l = 0$ or $L_-^{(l)}G_n{}^l$ is an eigenfunction of H_{l-1} for $H_{l-1} = E_{nl}$, $l > 0$. From this it follows that E_{nl} does not depend on l. Call the eigenvalue E_n.

For any eigenfunction of H_l for which $H_l = E_n$, $\langle H_l \rangle = E_n$. Since $L_+^{(l)}$ and $L_-^{(l)}$ are adjoint operators in the inner product space defined above, $\langle L_+^{(l)}L_-^{(l)} \rangle \geq 0$ for all functions in this inner product space (see Problems 6.33 and 6.34), we find from (15.47a) that

(15.55) $$2m_0 E_n + B_l \geq 0.$$

Using (15.52b), we then find from (15.55) that

(15.56) $$l^2 \leq m_0 Z^2 e^4 / (-2\hbar^2 E_n).$$

Corresponding to any particular energy eigenvalue E_n this determines a maximum value of l. Identifying n with the maximum value of l, which we call n, we find from (15.56) the energy eigenvalue (15.40). It is to be noted, however, that this maximum value of l, called n, does not give a maximum value of $M^2 = l(l + 1)\hbar^2$, rather it leads to a key function $G_n{}^{n-1}$ by means of the equation

(15.57) $$L_+^{(n)}G_n{}^{n-1} = 0,$$

which, when satisfied, leads to equalities in (15.55) and (15.56). From (15.47b) we see that $G_n{}^{n-1}$ is an eigenfunction of H_{n-1} for $H_{n-1} = -B_n/2m_0 = E_n$.

To find $G_n{}^{n-1}$, we use (15.21), (15.46a), and (15.52a) to write (15.57) in the explicit form

(15.58) $$L_+^{(n)}G_n{}^{n-1} = -i\hbar \left(\frac{\partial}{\partial r} - \frac{n}{r} + \frac{m_0 Z e^2}{n\hbar^2} \right) G_n{}^{n-1} = 0$$

From this we readily find

(15.59) $$G_n{}^{n-1} = C r^n e^{-br}$$

where b is given by (15.39) and where C may be determined by normalization.

Since $G_n{}^{l-1}$ is an eigenfunction of H_{l-1} for $H_{l-1} = E_n$ if $G_n{}^l$ is an eigenfunction of H_l for $H_l = E_n$, the operator $L_-^{(l)}$ provides a means of generating from $G_n{}^{n-1}$ eigenfunctions of H_l, $l = n - 2, \ldots, 2, 1, 0$.

For a comprehensive review of the factorization method, the reader is referred to the paper by Infeld and Hull.[2]

Problem 15.4:   Show that the operator $p_r = -i\hbar \dfrac{\partial}{\partial r}$ is Hermitean over the inner product space defined in (15.43) for functions $G(r)$ which vanish at $r = 0$ and at $r = \infty$, but is not Hermitean when the inner product is that leading to the norm (15.36).

Problem 15.5:   Find C in (15.59) so that $N(G_n{}^{n-1}) = 1$. Answer:

(15.60) $$|C|^2 = \frac{(2b)^{2n+1}}{(2n)!}.$$

Problem 15.6:   Writing

(15.61) $$L_-^{(l)}G_n{}^{(l)} = C_n{}^l G_n{}^{l+1},$$

find $C_n{}^l$ so that $N(G_n{}^l) = N(G_n{}^{l-1}) = N(G_n{}^{n-1}) = 1$. Answer: Take

(15.62) $$C_n{}^l = -\frac{i\hbar b}{l}\sqrt{n^2 - l^2}.$$

Problem 15.7:   For given n, we find from (15.46), (15.51), and (15.52) that

(15.63) $$L_\pm^{(l)} = -i\hbar b\left(\frac{\partial}{\partial s} \mp \frac{l}{s} \pm \frac{n}{l}\right), \quad s = br,$$

where b is given in (15.39). Solve the equation $L_+^{(3)}G = 0$ for $n = 3$, obtaining $G_3{}^2$ which may be normalized as in Problem 15.5. Then, using (15.61) and (15.63), obtain the normalized functions $G_3{}^1$ and $G_3{}^0$. Compare the results with the $3d$, $3p$, and $3s$ radial eigenfunctions given in Section 15.7.

15.10. Semiclassical Theory of Radiation.   According to classical electromagnetic theory, a vibrating dipole radiates energy at a rate

(15.64) $$S = (2/3c^3)|\ddot{\mathbf{D}}|^2$$

where $\mathbf{D} = e\mathbf{r}$ is the dipole moment. The direction of polarization lies in the plane containing the direction of observation and the direction of the dipole moment.

According to this theory, the Rutherford atom (Section 3.3) should continuously radiate its energy away. To account for spontaneous transitions actually observed. Bohr assumed (see Section 3.5) that an electron in an atom moves in certain privileged orbits, called "stationary orbits," or "stable states." Radiation occurs only when the electron drops from an excited state to a state of lower energy.

In Schroedinger's interpretation of the wave function (see Section 8.2), an electron is pictured as a cloud with density proportional to $\psi^*\psi$. Then, when ψ is normalized, the dipole moment is

(15.65) $$\mathbf{D} = e(\psi, \mathbf{r}\psi).$$

It is readily verified that $\dot{\mathbf{D}}$ and $\ddot{\mathbf{D}}$ vanish when the electron is in a stationary state (8.33). Thus the energy eigenfunctions correspond to the stable states of Bohr's theory.

To account for radiation, we assume spontaneous transitions between stable states, i.e. between energy eigenstates. Consider a transition from an energy eigenstate $|n\rangle$ to an energy eigenstate $|n'\rangle$ where

$$(15.66) \qquad |n\rangle = \psi_n(\mathbf{r})e^{-iE_nt/\hbar}.$$

From the *transition dipole moment*

$$(15.67) \qquad \mathbf{D}_{nn'} = e\langle n|\mathbf{r}|n'\rangle e^{-i\omega_{nn'}t},$$

where

$$(15.68) \qquad \omega_{nn'} = (E_n - E_{n'})/\hbar,$$

we calculate

$$(15.69) \qquad \ddot{\mathbf{D}}_{nn'} = -e\omega_{nn'}^2\langle n|\mathbf{r}|n'\rangle e^{-i\omega_{nn'}t}.$$

This is a vector whose components may be complex numbers when they do not vanish.

To obtain the rate of radiation by transitions between the energy states $|n\rangle$ and $|n'\rangle$, we substitute from (15.68) into (15.64). Averaging over a period, we obtain

$$(15.70) \qquad \bar{S} = \frac{2e^2}{3c^3}\,\omega_{nn'}^4|\mathbf{r}_{nn'}|^2 = \frac{2e^2}{3c^3}\,\omega_{nn'}^4(|x_{nn'}|^2 + |y_{nn'}|^2 + |z_{nn'}|^2).$$

If a matrix element $\mathbf{r}_{nn'}$ vanishes, transitions between the $|n\rangle$ and $|n'\rangle$ stationary states are forbidden, in the dipole approximation. Thus we are led to selection rules. For example, in Section 11.7 we found that, for the harmonic oscillator in one-space dimension, $x_{nn'} = 0$ unless $n = n' \pm 1$. This *selection rule* implies that quantum mechanical harmonic oscillators make transitions only between adjacent states.

Calculation of $\mathbf{r}_{nn'}$ for a system in three dimensions gives (1) selection rules for forbidden transitions, (2) information about relative intensities of lines emitted in unforbidden transitions, and (3) information about polarization of lines emitted.

15.11. Selection Rules for the Hydrogen Atom. Since stationary states of the electron in a hydrogen atom may be specified by the three quantum numbers n, l, and m (neglecting the electron spin), of interest are the matrix elements $\langle nlm|\mathbf{r}|n'l'm'\rangle$. It may be shown that there is no selection rule for n. Hence, in obtaining selection rules for l and m we need not specify n. Selection rules for l and m are as follows:

$$
(15.71) \quad
\begin{array}{ll}
\text{(a)} & \langle lm|x|l'm'\rangle = 0 \text{ unless } m' = m \pm 1 \text{ and } l' = l \pm 1, \\
\text{(b)} & \langle lm|y|l'm'\rangle = 0 \text{ unless } m' = m \pm 1 \text{ and } l' = l \pm 1, \\
\text{(c)} & \langle lm|z|l'm'\rangle = 0 \text{ unless } m' = m \text{ and } l' = l \pm 1.
\end{array}
$$

Further, matrix elements of $\mathbf{r}$ between s states vanish.

The selection rules for x and y follow readily from

$$
(15.72) \quad
\begin{array}{ll}
\text{(a)} & \langle lm|\xi|l'm'\rangle = 0 \text{ unless } m' = m - 1 \text{ and } l' = l \pm 1, \\
\text{(b)} & \langle lm|\eta|l'm'\rangle = 0 \text{ unless } m' = m + 1 \text{ and } l' = l \pm 1,
\end{array}
$$

where $\xi = x + iy$, $\eta = x - iy$.

In obtaining the selection rules for l we need not specify m and in obtaining the rules for m we need not specify l.

The selection rules for l follow from two forms for the second commutator $\mathbf{C} = (M^2, (M^2, \mathbf{r}))$:

$$
(15.73) \quad
\begin{array}{ll}
\text{(a)} & \mathbf{C} = M^4\mathbf{r} - 2M^2\mathbf{r}M^2 + \mathbf{r}M^4, \\
\text{(b)} & \mathbf{C} = 2\hbar^2(M^2\mathbf{r} + \mathbf{r}M^2).
\end{array}
$$

Form (a) follows readily by repeated application of (6.21) and form (b) may be obtained by rather lengthy manipulations using commutation relations from Section 14.1 (Problems 15.8 and 15.9 below).

Since

$$
(15.74) \quad
\begin{array}{ll}
\text{(a)} & \langle l|M^2 = l(l + 1)\hbar^2 \langle l|, \\
\text{(b)} & M^2|l'\rangle = l'(l' + 1)\hbar^2|l'\rangle,
\end{array}
$$

we obtain, by means of (15.73),

$$
(15.75) \quad
\begin{array}{ll}
\text{(a)} & \langle l|\mathbf{C}|l'\rangle = \hbar^4(l + l' + 1)^2(l - l')^2\langle l|\mathbf{r}|l'\rangle, \\
\text{(b)} & \langle l|\mathbf{C}|l'\rangle = 2\hbar^4\{l(l + 1) + l'(l' + 1)\}\langle l|\mathbf{r}|l'\rangle.
\end{array}
$$

Equality of these two expressions for $\langle l|\mathbf{C}|l'\rangle$ may be expressed in the form (Problem 15.12)

$$
(15.76) \quad (l - l' + 1)(l - l' - 1)(l + l')(l + l' + 2)\langle l|\mathbf{r}|l'\rangle = 0.
$$

Since l and l' are nonnegative integers, this implies that $\langle l|\mathbf{r}|l'\rangle = 0$ unless $l' = l \pm 1$ or $l = l' = 0$. That $\langle l|\mathbf{r}|l'\rangle = 0$ for $l = l' = 0$ follows from the spherical symmetry of s states (see Section 15.8).

Selection rules for m are to be derived in Problem 15.13.

Problem 15.8:   Obtain (15.73a) from the definition of $\mathbf{C}$ and (6.21).[3]

Problem 15.9:   Obtain (15.73b).[3]

---

[3] See R. H. Atkin, *Mathematics and Wave Mechanics*, Wiley, 1957, pp. 337–9, or W. V. Houston, *Principles of Quantum Mechanics*, Dover, 1959, pp. 168–9.

Problem 15.10: From (15.73a) and (15.74), obtain (15.75a).

Problem 15.11: From (15.73b) and (15.74), obtain (15.75b).

Problem 15.12: Obtain (15.76) from (15.75). (Hint: Let $x = l + l' + 1$, $y = l - l'$. Eliminating l and l', obtain $x^2 y^2 - x^2 - y^2 - 1 = 0$ or $\langle l|\mathbf{r}|l'\rangle = 0$. Easy factorization leads to (15.76).)

Problem 15.13: Show that

(15.77)
$$
\begin{aligned}
&\text{(a)} \quad \langle m|\xi|m'\rangle = 0 \text{ unless } m' = m - 1,\\
&\text{(b)} \quad \langle m|\eta|m'\rangle = 0 \text{ unless } m' = m + 1,\\
&\text{(c)} \quad \langle m|z|m'\rangle = 0 \text{ unless } m' = m.
\end{aligned}
$$

Hint: Use (14.23c), (14.23f), and the eigenvalue relations

(15.78) (a) $\; < m|M_z = m\hbar < m|,$ (b) $\; M_z|m'> = m'\hbar|m'>.$

Problem 15.14: Show by direct integration that $\langle l0|\mathbf{r}|l'0\rangle = 0$ unless $l' = l \pm 1$, given the orthogonality of the Legendre polynomials $P_l(\cos\theta)$ over the interval $(0,\pi)$ and the recurrence relation

(15.79) $\qquad (2l + 1)x P_l(x) = (l + 1)P_{l+1}(x) + l P_{l-1}(x).$

Problem 15.15: Suppose that there exists an algebraic relation between an operator A and an operator B, linear in A, of the form

(15.80)
$$
\sum_{j=1}^{k} f_j(B)A g_j(B) = 0,
$$

A and B being Hermitean. Let A_{mn} be the matrix element of A between the eigenfunctions ψ_m and ψ_n of B, for which $B = b_m$, $B = b_n$, respectively. Show that $A_{mn} = 0$ unless[3]

(15.81)
$$
\sum_{j=1}^{k} f_j(b_m) g_j(b_n) = 0.
$$

Problem 15.16: Show that if a linear operator A commutes with $\mathbf{M}$, then the matrix elements $\langle nlm|A|n'lm\rangle$ do not depend on m. In particular, the matrix elements $\langle nlm|H|n'lm\rangle$ do not depend on m. (Hint: Starting with $\langle nlm|AM_+|n'lm'\rangle = \langle nlm|M_+A|n'lm'\rangle$, show, by means of (14.48) and (14.58), that $\langle nlm|A|n'lm\rangle = \langle nlm'|A|n'lm'\rangle$ when $m' = m - 1$.)

15.12. The Normal Zeeman Effect. On the basis of classical theory, we expect that the frequencies of spectral lines correspond to frequencies of rotation of electrons in their orbits (see Problem 14.26). As we shall see, these frequencies are affected by magnetic fields. The frequency shifts of spectral lines by a magnetic field constitute the

---

[3] See R. H. Atkin, *Mathematics and Wave Mechanics*, Wiley, 1957, pp.337-9, or W. V. Houston, *Principles of Quantum Mechanics*, Dover, 1959, pp. 168-9.

Zeeman effect.[4] In the *normal Zeeman effect*, the observed shifts are in full agreement with classical theory and with the Schroedinger wave theory as developed to this point. However, in by far the greater number of cases, an *anomalous* effect, which can be accurately predicted only by the Uhlenbeck-Goudsmit spinning electron hypothesis (see Section 14.8) and/or by Dirac's relativistic wave equation, is observed.

In the normal Zeeman effect, which was discovered by Zeeman in 1896, the spectral lines when observed transversally (magnetic field at right

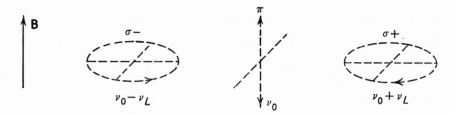

Fig. 15.1. The normal Zeeman effect.

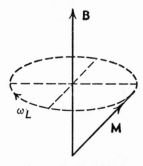

Fig. 15.2. Precession of **M** around **B**.

angles to the direction of observation) are split into three lines, the middle undisplaced line being polarized parallel to the field and the outer lines being polarized perpendicularly to the field. When observed longitudinally (magnetic field parallel to the direction of observation) the spectral lines are split into two displaced lines, one left circularly polarized and the other right circularly polarized (see Fig. 15.1). For a line in the visible region, of wavelength 6000 Ångstroms, the separation of the Zeeman lines in a field of 10,000 Gausses is 0.17 Å, observable in a very good spectrograph.

The Dutch physicist and Nobel prize winner H. A. Lorentz (1853–1928) showed that a classical oscillator in a magnetic field may be expected to

[4] P. Zeeman, *Phil. Mag.*, **43**, 226 (1897).

show these phenomena. We have seen (Section 14.5) that the effect of the magnetic field $\mathbf{B}$ is to cause $\mathbf{M}$ to precess around $\mathbf{B}$ with angular velocity $\omega_L = eB/2m_0c$ (see (14.66)), in a clockwise sense as seen from the direction of the field, independently of the direction in which the electron rotates around the nucleus. Let the motion of the electron be resolved into a linear motion parallel to $\mathbf{B}$ (π motion) and into two opposite circular motions at right angles to $\mathbf{B}$ (σ_+ and σ_- motions), the frequencies of the three motions being $\nu_0 = \omega_0/2\pi$ (see Problem 15.16). Then, by the action of $\mathbf{B}$, the frequency of the π motion is not affected, that of one of the σ motions is increased by $\nu_L = \omega_L/2\pi$ and that of the other σ motion is decreased by ν_L. This fully accounts for the normal Zeeman effect, since components of motion parallel to the direction of observation do not emit radiation toward the observer.

A quantum mechanical explanation of the normal Zeeman effect may be obtained by introducing the vector potential

$$(15.82) \qquad \mathbf{A} = (-By/2, Bx/2, 0)$$

which represents a uniform magnetic field

$$(15.83) \qquad \mathbf{B} = \mathrm{Curl}\ \mathbf{A} = (0, 0, B)$$

parallel to the z axis, into the Schroedinger wave equation, using the Hamiltonian (7.42). Since

$$(15.84) \qquad \text{(a)} \quad ei\hbar\mathbf{A} \cdot \mathrm{grad} = i\hbar B \left(x\,\frac{\partial}{\partial y} - y\,\frac{\partial}{\partial x} \right) = -BM_z,$$

$$\text{(b)} \quad \mathrm{div}\ \mathbf{A} = 0,$$

the Hamiltonian (7.43), when the term in A^2 is neglected, may be written in the form

$$(15.85) \qquad H = H_0 + GBM_z$$

where

$$(15.86) \qquad H_0 = p^2/2m_0 + eV$$

is the Hamiltonian in the absence of the field and $G = -e/2m_0c$ (see (14.68)). Here we are again using m_0 for the mass of the electron, to avoid confusion with the magnetic quantum number m.

Now let $|nlm>$ be a simultaneous eigenfunction of H_0, M^2, and M_z for $H_0 = E_n$, $M^2 = l(l+1)\hbar^2$ and $M_z = m\hbar$. Then

$$(15.87) \quad H|nlm> = H_0|nlm> + GBM_z|nlm> = (E_n + GBm\hbar)|nlm>.$$

This states that $|nlm>$ is an eigenfunction of H for $H =$

$$(15.88) \qquad E_{nm} = E_n + GBm\hbar.$$

Since for given l there are $2l + 1$ values of m, each energy level (with the exception of s states, for which $l = 0$, $m = 0$) is split by the magnetic field into $2l + 1$ levels. In a transition between the states $|nlm>$ and $|n'l'm'>$ the energy of an emitted or absorbed photon is

$$(15.89) \qquad h\nu = |E_{n'm'} - E_{nm}| = |E_{n'} - E_n + GB(m' - m)\hbar|.$$

From the selection rule (15.71) we have that only transitions for which $m' - m = 0$, ± 1 occur. Thus a line of frequency $\nu_0 = \nu_{nn'} = |(E_{n'} - E_n)/h|$ which appears in the absence of a magnetic field is split by a field into three lines, of frequencies

$$(15.90) \qquad \nu_0, \; \nu_+ = \nu_0 + GB/2\pi, \; \nu_- = \nu_0 - GB/2\pi,$$

as predicted by classical theory. Polarizations of the lines are predicted by refinement of the selection rule as may be deduced from (15.72).

The displacement of the energy levels by a magnetic field from E_n to E_{nm} is in agreement with classical theory according to which a magnetic dipole of magnetic moment $\mathbf{\mu}$ in a magnetic field $\mathbf{B}$ has a potential energy $W = -\mathbf{\mu} \cdot \mathbf{B}$ (see (14.69)). Writing $\mathbf{\mu} = -G\mathbf{M}$ (see (14.63)), and orienting the z axis parallel to the magnetic field, we find that $W = GBM_z$. Complete agreement ensues since the quantum mechanically allowed values of M_z are $m\hbar$. Needed also are the selection rules for m.

Problem 15.17: Show that the equations

$$(15.91) \qquad x = x_1 + x_2 + x_3, \; y = y_1 + y_2 + y_3, \; z = z_1 + z_2 + z_3,$$

where

$$(15.92) \qquad x_1 + iy_1 = (A/2)e^{i(\gamma - \omega t)}, \; x_2 + iy_2 = (A/2)e^{i(\gamma + \omega t)}$$
$$z_1 = 0, \; z_2 = 0, \; z_3 = A \sin(\omega t),$$

represent a resolution of circular motion in the plane $x \cos \gamma = y \sin \gamma$ into a linear motion parallel to the z axis and oppositely polarized circular motions in the x-y plane.

15.13. References for Supplementary Reading.

Section 15.1:   Bohm, 334–8; Houston, 74–5; Schiff, 80–82; Sherwin, 347–52.

Section 15.2:   Kemble, 291–3.

Section 15.4:   Houston, 75–8; McConnell, 81–3; Pauling and Wilson, 117–20; Persico, 203–12; Schaefer, 282–4; Sherwin, 72–87, 353–5.

Section 15.6:   Schaefer, 291–4; Schiff, 82–3.

Section 15.7:   Bohm, 345–9; Born, 353–8; French, 338–40; Houston, 79–82; Kemble, 158–61; Kramers, 180–87; Landé, 60–66; McConnell, 38–44; Mott and Sneddon, 54–9; Pauling and Wilson, 121–5; Peaslee and

Mueller, 230–39; Persico, 212–23; Schaefer, 284–91; Schiff, 83–5; Sherwin, 87–94.

Section 15.8: Bohm, 349–51; Finkelnburg, 221–8; French, 206–10, 214–15; Houston, 117–20; Kemble, 585–7; March, 62–75; Mott and Sneddon, 379–88; Pauling and Wilson, 125–50, 448–52; Schiff, 85–7; Shankland, 65–78, 87; Sherwin, 94–96, 356–8; Sproull, 160–66; White, 56–76.

Section 15.10: Born, 147–50; Finkelnburg, 212–17; French, 228–33; Landé, 69–72; March, 76–9; Peaslee and Mueller 243–7; Persico, 162–4; Schaefer, 412–24; Shankland, 88–90.

Section 15.11: Bohm, 433–43; Born, 363–8; Dirac, 159–65; Houston, 168–9; Kemble, 470–73; Landé, 72–5; March, 77–82; Pauling and Wilson, 21–4, 306–8; Peaslee and Mueller, 247–51; Persico, 223–6, 270–73; Schaefer, 99–106; Sproull, 166–70.

Section 15.12: Bohm, 359–60, 443–6; Born, 120–23; Dirac, 165–6; Eldridge, 228–31; French, 46–9; Houston, 120–23; Landé, 67–9; McConnell, 83–4; Mott and Sneddon, 87–9; Peaslee and Mueller, 75–86; Schaefer, 107–13, 294–300; Shankland, 123–6; White, 149–62.

CHAPTER 16

TIME INDEPENDENT PERTURBATION THEORY

16.1. Introductory Remarks. There are many problems in quantum mechanics for which the Schroedinger wave equation is not solvable. When the potential V in the Hamiltonian function depends explicitly on the time, as in the case of a sinusoidally varying external electric field, the time factor cannot be separated (see Section 8.3) and the wave function cannot be represented in terms of energy eigenfunctions. Only rarely is some other method of obtaining an exact solution available. Fortunately, significant approximate results for such problems may usually be obtained by Dirac's time-dependent perturbation theory, which was developed briefly in Section 12.5 in the discussion of transition probabilities. An extensive discussion of this method with special applications to cases in which the perturbing potential U in (12.42)

(a) is initiated abruptly at $t = t_0$,

(b) oscillates trigonometrically with time,

(c) is turned on very slowly with time,

is given by Bohm.[1] Applications of a more advanced nature, requiring the relativistic wave mechanics (Chapter 19), frequently appear in the literature. Among more important applications of the time-dependent perturbation theory are those to the emission and absorption of photons (photoelectric effect and Compton effect), and to pair production and annihilation. These and other problems of this nature have recently been very lucidly presented by McConnell,[2] at a level available to the reader of this text.

In addition to wave equations with time dependent potentials, there are many wave equations with time independent potentials which are not exactly solvable. Classical among these are the problems for the anharmonic oscillator, the hydrogen atom in an electric field (Stark effect), the helium atom, the hydrogen molecule, and many-particle systems.[3] Important also are problems in scattering and diffraction, leading to the calculation of scattering cross sections, for example.

[1] D. Bohm, *Quantum Theory*, Prentice-Hall, 1951, Part IV.

[2] J. McConnell, *Quantum Particle Dynamics*, Interscience, 1958.

[3] See E. M. Corson, *Perturbation Methods in the Quantum Mechanics of n-Electron Systems*, Hafner, 1950.

16.2. The Schroedinger Perturbation Method. The Schroedinger perturbation method[4] depends upon the assumption that the Schroedinger time independent wave equation (8.4) is exactly solvable for a Hamiltonian H^0, where H^0 does not differ greatly from the Hamiltonian H for a given problem. Writing $H = H^0 + \lambda H^1$, where the "perturbation parameter" λ is introduced to aid in distinguishing orders of magnitude, the eigenvalue equation to be solved is

$$(16.1) \qquad H\psi \equiv (H^0 + \lambda H^1)\psi = E\psi.$$

It is assumed that the eigenvalues $E_k{}^0$ and eigenfunctions $\psi_k{}^0$ of H^0 are known.

When $\lambda = 0$, (16.1) is satisfied by any eigenfunction $\psi_k{}^0$ of H^0, for $E = E_k{}^0$. It is quite reasonable to expect that, when $\lambda \neq 0$, (16.1) has a solution ψ_k belonging to an eigenvalue $E = E_k$ which does not differ greatly from $E_k{}^0$. We therefore write

$$(16.2) \qquad
\begin{aligned}
&\text{(a)} \quad \psi_k = \psi_k{}^0 + \lambda\psi_k{}' + \lambda^2\psi_k{}'' + \cdots, \\
&\text{(b)} \quad E_k = E_k{}^0 + \lambda E_k{}' + \lambda^2 E_k{}'' + \cdots,
\end{aligned}$$

assuming that $\psi_k \cong \psi_k{}^0$ when λ is sufficiently small.

Substituting from (16.2) into (16.1), and equating coefficients of corresponding powers of λ, we obtain, up to the coefficients of λ^2:

$$(16.3) \qquad
\begin{aligned}
&\text{(a)} \quad H^0\psi_k{}^0 = E_k{}^0\psi_k{}^0, \\
&\text{(b)} \quad H^0\psi_k{}' + H'\psi_k{}^0 = E_k{}^0\psi_k{}' + E_k{}'\psi_k{}^0, \\
&\text{(c)} \quad H^0\psi_k{}'' + H'\psi_k{}' = E_k{}^0\psi_k{}'' + E_k{}'\psi_k{}' + E_k{}''\psi_k{}^0.
\end{aligned}$$

By hypothesis, (16.3a) is satisfied. From (16.3b) we obtain, by forming the inner product of each term with $\psi_k{}^0$:

$$(16.4) \qquad (\psi_k{}^0, H^0\psi_k{}') + (\psi_k{}^0, H'\psi_k{}^0) = E_k{}^0(\psi_k{}^0, \psi_k{}') + E_k{}'(\psi_k{}^0, \psi_k{}^0).$$

The unperturbed Hamiltonian H^0 is assumed to be Hermitean. From this property of H^0 we find, by using (16.3a), that the first term in the left-hand member of (16.4) is equal to the first term in the right-hand member. Assuming without loss of generality that the known unperturbed eigenfunction $\psi_k{}^0$ has been normalized, we thus obtain

$$(16.5) \qquad E_k{}' = H_{kk}{}' \equiv (\psi_k{}^0, H'\psi_k{}^0).$$

This states that $E_k{}'$ is the expectation value of H' over the unperturbed energy eigenstate $\psi_k{}^0$.

When $E_k{}^0$ is a nondegenerate eigenvalue of H^0, the normalized eigenfunction $\psi_k{}^0$ is uniquely determined except for an arbitrary phase factor which has no effect on the value of $E_k{}'$ calculated from (16.5). When $E_k{}^0$ is

---

[4] E. Schroedinger, *Ann. Physik*, **80**, 437 (1926).

a degenerate eigenvalue of H^0, it is not apparent that ψ_k is close to $\psi_k{}^0$ unless $\psi_k{}^0$ is properly chosen from the linear manifold of eigenfunctions of H^0 belonging to the eigenvalue $E_k{}^0$. The appropriate unperturbed eigenfunction $\psi_k{}^0$ is some unknown linear combination

$$(16.6) \qquad \psi_k{}^0 = \sum_{j=1}^{n} c_j \psi_{kj}{}^0$$

of n linearly independent functions $\psi_{kj}{}^0$, each an eigenfunction of H^0 for $H^0 = E_k{}^0$.

Substitution of a linear combination (16.6) into (16.3b) leads to the condition

$$(16.7) \qquad H_0 \psi_k{}' + \sum_{j=1}^{n} c_j H' \psi_{kj}{}^0 = E_k{}^0 \psi_k{}' + E_k{}' \sum_{j=1}^{n} c_j \psi_{kj}{}^0.$$

For simplicity and without loss of generality, we assume that orthonormal unperturbed eigenfunctions $\psi_{kj}{}^0$ have been selected. Then, upon forming the inner product of each term in (16.7) with $\psi_{kl}{}^0$, and using the Hermiticity of H^0 and the eigenvalue relation $H^0 \psi_{kl}{}^0 = E_k{}^0 \psi_{kl}{}^0$, we obtain

$$(16.8) \qquad \sum_{j=1}^{n} H'_{kl,kj} c_j = E_k{}' C_l, \; l = 1, 2, \ldots, n.$$

This is a system of n linear homogeneous equation for the n coefficients c_j, similar to that which was obtained in Section 13.4 (see (13.17)). The system is consistent only for those values of $E_k{}'$ for which

$$(16.9) \qquad |H'_{kl,kj} - E_k{}' \delta_{lj}| = 0.$$

When (16.9) has n distinct solutions, the degeneracy is completely removed by the perturbation. On the other hand, a multiple solution of (16.9) indicates only partial removal of degeneracy.

To obtain $\psi_k{}'$, we assume that the unperturbed eigenfunctions $\psi_k{}^0$ form a complete orthonormal set and write

$$(16.10) \qquad \begin{aligned} &\text{(a)} \quad \psi_k{}' = \Sigma_j A_j \psi_j{}^0, \\ &\text{(b)} \quad H' \psi_k{}^0 = \Sigma_j H_{jk}{}' \psi_j{}^0. \end{aligned}$$

For simplicity of notation, we assume absence of degeneracy, for the present. Substituting from (16.10) into (16.3b), we readily obtain, from the linear independence of the $\psi_j{}^0$,

$$(16.11) \qquad a_j = \frac{H_{jk}{}'}{E_k{}^0 - E_j{}^0}, \; j \neq k.$$

Normalization of $\psi_k{}'$ to first-order terms in λ gives $a_k = 0$.

The solution out to second order terms in λ may be obtained from (16.3c), using methods illustrated above. For the energy correction there is found

$$(16.12) \qquad E_k'' = \sum_j{}' \frac{H_{kj}' H_{jk}'}{E_k^0 - E_j^0}$$

where the prime on Σ indicates that the term $j = k$ is omitted. If a state ψ_k^0 is degenerate and the first order perturbation calculation has removed the degeneracy, the appropriate unperturbed eigenfunctions (16.6), found by solving (16.8) are to be used.

Problem 16.1: Derive (16.12).

16.3. The Normal Zeeman Effect. A simple application of perturbation theory is to the normal Zeeman effect, for which results can be compared with the exact solution obtained in Section 15.12.

The perturbing potential is $H' = GBM_z$ (see (15.85)). We use as eigenfunctions for the unperturbed Hamiltonian the normalized hydrogen atom eigenfunctions $\psi_{nl}{}^m$ (see (15.41)). For a given unperturbed energy level, $E_n^0 = -Rch/n^2$, there is n^2-fold degeneracy. The perturbation theory for degenerate levels is to be applied.

Since the $\psi_{nl}{}^m$ are orthonormal eigenfunctions of M_z for $M_z = m\hbar$, we readily find

$$(16.13) \qquad H'_{nlm,\,n'l'm'} = GBm\hbar\, \delta_{nn'}\delta_{ll'}\delta_{mm'}.$$

The determinant (16.9) has nonzero elements only along the principal diagonal, each diagonal element being $GBm\hbar - E_n'$. Hence $E_n' = GBm\hbar$ appears as a solution of multiplicity n^2. The perturbation calculation has failed to remove the degeneracy. The results of these simple calculations are in full agreement with the results of Section 15.12.

16.4. The Stark Effect for the Plane Rotator. The potential energy of a rigid rotator of moment of inertia I and electric moment μ, constrained to rotate about an axis perpendicular to a uniform electric field $\mathbf{F}$ is $U = -\mu F \cos \theta$, where θ is the polar axis measured from the direction of $\mathbf{F}$. There is double degeneracy in the absence of the field (except for the ground state) since each of the two functions

$$(16.14) \qquad \psi_{\pm k}^0 = \frac{1}{\sqrt{2\pi}} e^{\pm ik\varphi}$$

is a (normalized) eigenfunction of $H^0 = M^2/2I$ for $H^0 = E_k^0 = k^2\hbar^2/2I$. (see Section 14.3). The existence of two energy eigenfunctions for the same energy level corresponds to the two possible directions of rotation. However, it is not necessary to consider this degeneracy since for a sufficiently weak field there should exist an energy eigenfunction ψ_k representing rotation in a definite direction and not differing greatly from $\psi_k{}^0$. In agreement with this observation, it may be shown that the degeneracy is not removed in either the first or the second order perturbation calculation.

Taking $H' = -\mu F \cos \theta$, we readily calculate

$$(16.15) \qquad \begin{aligned} H_{kj}' &= -\frac{\mu F}{2\pi} \int_0^{2\pi} e^{-ik\varphi} \cos \varphi \, e^{ij\varphi} \, d\varphi \\ &= -\frac{\mu F}{2}, \qquad j = k \pm 1, \\ &= 0, \qquad j \neq k \pm 1. \end{aligned}$$

Then, substituting from (16.15) into (16.5) and (16.12) and using the above expression for the unperturbed energy eigenvalue $E_k{}^0$, we obtain

$$(16.16) \qquad \begin{aligned} &\text{(a)} \quad E_k' = 0, \\ &\text{(b)} \quad E_k'' = \mu^2 F^2 I / \hbar^2 (4k^2 - 1). \end{aligned}$$

Thus, second-order perturbation theory is needed to account for the displacement of the energy levels, which increases quadratically as the field strength increases.

Problem 16.2: Prove that the degeneracy is not removed in the first order perturbation calculations.

16.5. The Stark Effect for Hydrogen. The potential energy of a charge Ze in a uniform electric field $\mathbf{F}$, parallel to which we orient the z axis, is $U = eFz$. Considering U as a perturbation from the Coulomb potential $V(r) = -Ze^2/r$, we may use as eigenfunctions of the unperturbed Hamiltonian $H^0 = H_{\text{in}}$ the functions $\psi_{nl}{}^m$ which are simultaneous eigenfunctions of M_z, M^2, and H_{in} (see (15.10b) and (15.42)).

Taking $H = U = eFz$, we have, in Dirac's notation,

$$(16.17) \qquad H'_{nlm,n'l'm'} = eF\langle nlm|z|n'l'm'\rangle.$$

There are n^2 eigenfunctions $\psi_{nl}{}^m$ belonging to the unperturbed energy level $E_n{}^0 = -Rch/n^2$. The determinant (16.9) has n^2 rows and n^2 columns. Only the ground state, for which $n = 1$, is nondegenerate. For this state we find, by glancing at (15.71c), that $H_{100,100}' = 0$. Hence the ground state is not displaced in the first order perturbation calculation. This is an immediate consequence of the spherical symmetry of the ground state.

For the first excited state, $n = 2$, we need the matrix elements of H' between the normalized energy eigenstates $\psi_a = \psi_{200}$, $\psi_b = \psi_{21\bar{1}}$, $\psi_c = \psi_{210}$, and $\psi_d = \psi_{211}$, which are given explicitly in Section 15.8. From (15.71c) we find that the only nonvanishing matrix elements of H' between pairs of these states are the two elements $\langle a|z|c\rangle$ and $\langle c|z|a\rangle$. By elementary, direct integrations we find that

(16.18) $$H_{ac}' = H_{ca}' = -3\hbar^2 F/m_0 Ze.$$

The secular equation (16.9), for the first order perturbation in the energy level E_2^0 is

(16.19) $$\begin{vmatrix} -E_2' & 0 & H_{ac}' & 0 \\ 0 & -E_2' & 0 & 0 \\ H_{ac}' & 0 & -E_2' & 0 \\ 0 & 0 & 0 & -E_2' \end{vmatrix} = 0.$$

This equation has H_{ac}' and $-H_{ac}'$ as simple roots, 0 as a double root. Since there are only three distinct roots, E_2^0 splits into a triplet in the first order perturbation calculation.

The degeneracy is completely removed in the second order perturbation calculation. To obtain the appropriate eigenfunctions for use in the second order perturbation calculations, we solve (16.8), first using H_{ac}' for E_2', then $-H_{ac}'$, and finally, 0. The appropriate eigenfunctions are then given by (16.6). These, when normalized, are

(16.20)

(a) $\quad \psi_+ = \dfrac{1}{\sqrt{2}} (\psi_{200} + \psi_{210})$, for $E_2' = H_{ac}'$,

(b) $\quad \psi_- = \dfrac{1}{\sqrt{2}} (\psi_{200} - \psi_{210})$, for $E_2' = -H_{ac}'$,

(c) $\quad \psi_b = \psi_{21\bar{1}}$, $\qquad\qquad$ for $E_2' = 0$,

(d) $\quad \psi_d = \psi_{211}$, $\qquad\qquad$ for $E_2' = 0$.

The undisplaced level remains degenerate.

A hydrogen atom in the state $\psi_\pm$ behaves as though it has a permanent electric dipole moment of magnitude $-3\hbar^2/m_0 Ze$, parallel or anti-parallel to the external field. An atom in any state dependent on ψ_b and ψ_d has a dipole moment perpendicular to the field.

The unperturbed level E_3^0 has ninefold degeneracy and yields a quintet in first order perturbation calculation.[5]

The complexity of the calculations following this procedure increases rapidly with n. Schroedinger[6] discovered that when the problem is solved in parabolic coordinates, the complicated handling of degenerate systems can be avoided. The perturbation calculations have been effected to the third order.[7] The calculated displacements agree excellently with observa-

[5] A. Landé, *Quantum Mechanics*, Pitman, 1951.

[6] E. Schroedinger, *Ann. Physik*, **80**, 437 (1926); P. S. Epstein, *Phys. Rev.*, **28**, 695 (1926); C. Schaefer, *Einführung in die theoretischen Physik*, Walter de Gruyter, B. III, T. II, 1937, S. 311–18.

[7] See L. Pauling and E. B. Wilson, *Introduction to Quantum Mechanics*, McGraw-Hill, 1935, p. 179 for references.

tions,[8] proportionality between the field strength and the displacements of spectral lines being observed even up to a value of $F = 100,000$ volt/cm.

Problem 16.3:   Check the calculations of this section.

Problem 16.4:   A harmonic oscillator performs free oscillations in a gravitational field, in a line parallel to the field. Calculate the first and second order energy perturbations. (Hint: Use (11.67).) Answers:

$$(16.21) \qquad \text{(a)} \quad E_n' = 0, \qquad \text{(b)} \quad E_n'' = -mg^2/2\omega^2.$$

16.6. References for Supplementary Reading.

Section 16.2:   Bohm, 453–8; 462–70; Dirac, 168—72; Houston, 90–93; Kemble, 380–94; Kramers, 188–98; Landé, 81–8; Mandl, 131–5; March, 127–35; Mott and Sneddon, 71–83; Pauling and Wilson, 156–60, 165–72; Persico, 370–83; Schaefer, 305–11; Schiff, 151–8; Sherwin, 162–204.

Section 16.3:   Kemble, 398–403; Mandl, 140–41.

Section 16.4:   Kemble, 403–8; Pauling and Wilson, 177–9; also see M. Schwartz and M. Martin, *Am. J. Phys.*, **26,** 639 (1858).

Section 16.5:   Bohm, 459–61, 470–72; Finkelnburg, 162–64; Landé, 65–6, 88–90; Schaefer, 117–29, 311–19; Schiff, 87–90, 158–60; Shankland, 119–23, 167–73; White, 401–12.

[8] C. Schaefer, op. cit. S. 125, 318; for detailed description of the Stark effect and further references see H. E. White, *Introduction to Atomic Spectra*, McGraw-Hill, 1934, Ch. XX, and G. Herzberg, *Atomic Spectra and Atomic Structure*, Dover, 1944, pp. 115–18.

CHAPTER 17

MATRIX REPRESENTATIONS

17.1. Finite Dimensional Linear Manifolds. Let $f_1, f_2, \ldots, f_n$ be a set of n linearly independent functions in a linear manifold M having the property that, given any f in M, there exist n constants $c_1, c_2, \ldots,$ c_n, real or complex, such that

$$(17.1) \qquad f = \sum_{i=1}^{n} c_i f_i.$$

The c_i, which are determined by f and the particular set of functions $f_1, f_2, \ldots, f_n$ in M, are called the *components of f relative to the basis* $f_1, f_2, \ldots, f_n$. Since the components of f relative to a given basis fully specify f, and vice versa, we may consider the c_i as providing a matrix *representation* of f and write

$$(17.2) \qquad f \leftrightarrow c = \begin{pmatrix} c_1 \\ c_2 \\ - \\ c_n \end{pmatrix}.$$

The representation (17.2) is frequently called a *column vector*, or, occasionally, a *vector representation* of f, without referring to the particular basis unless required for clarity.

A linear manifold M is said to be *finite dimensional* if there exists a finite number of functions $f_1, f_2, \ldots, f_n$ in M such that a representation (17.1) exists for every f in M. The number of linearly independent functions f_i required in order to obtain representations of the form (17.1) for all functions f in M is called the *dimensionality* of M. The dimensionality of a finite dimensional linear manifold does not depend on the particular functions selected in forming a basis. When M is a finite dimensional inner product space, an orthonormal basis (for example, by Gram-Schmidt orthogonalization) may be chosen. Then, in (17.1) and (17.2),

$$(17.3) \quad \text{(a)} \quad (f_i, f_j) = \delta_{ij}, \quad \text{(b)} \quad c_i = (f_i, f), \quad \text{(c)} \quad c_i^* = (f, f_i).$$

When f has the representation (17.1), its complex conjugate, f^*, has the representation

(17.4)
$$f^* = \sum_{i=1}^{n} c_i^* f_i^*.$$

Writing

(17.5)
$$f^* \leftrightarrow c' = (c_1^*, c_2^*, c_3^*, \ldots, c_n^*)$$

we regard the *row vector* as providing a representation of f^* in a *dual linear manifold* M^* whose functions f^* are the complex conjugate gates of the functions f in M. Thus we do not imply that f^* belongs to M when f belongs to M. In particular, it is not true that $f^* \leftrightarrow c^*$ unless the basis functions f_i are real valued. Additional reasons for carefully distinguishing between column vectors (17.2) and row vectors (17.5) appear when full use is made of matrix notations.

Problem 17.1: Let $f \leftrightarrow c$ and $g \leftrightarrow d$. Define $\alpha c + \beta d$, where α and β are real or complex numbers, in such a way that $\alpha f + \beta g \leftrightarrow \alpha c + \beta d$. Answer:

(17.6)
$$(\alpha c + \beta d)_i = \alpha c_i + \beta d_i.$$

Problem 17.2: Let M be a finite dimensional inner product space. Define (c,d) in such a way that

(17.7)
$$(f,g) = (c,d)$$

wherever $f \leftrightarrow c$ and $g \leftrightarrow d$ relative to an orthonormal basis in M. Answer:

(17.8)
$$(c,d) = \sum_{i=1}^{n} c_i^* d_i.$$

Problem 17.3: Obtain a basis for the linear manifold of all functions $f(x)$ which satisfy $d^2f/dx^2 + 4f = 0$.

Problem 17.4: Obtain an orthonormal basis for the linear manifold of all eigenfunctions of the squared angular momentum operator M^2 for $M^2 = l(l + 1)\hbar^2$, l fixed. (Hint: See Section 14.4.)

17.2. Matrix Representations of Operators. Let A be a linear operator on a finite dimensional linear manifold M, such that Af belongs to M whenever f belongs to M. Letting $f_1, f_2, \ldots, f_n$ be a basis for M, we may obtain a representation of the form (17.1) for any f in M. In particular, since Af_j belongs to M, there exists a representation of the form (17.1) for Af_j:

(17.9)
$$Af_j = \sum_{i=1}^{n} a_{ij} f_i, \quad j = 1, 2, \ldots n.$$

The sequence of numbers a_{ij}, $i = 1, 2, \ldots, n$, j fixed, provides a representation of Af_j as a column vector

$$(17.10) \qquad Af_j \leftrightarrow a_j = \begin{pmatrix} a_{1j} \\ a_{2j} \\ - \\ - \\ a_{nj} \end{pmatrix}.$$

Further, the sequence of column vectors, $\mathcal{Q} = (a_1, a_2, \ldots, a_n)$, which we exhibit as a rectangular array of n rows and n columns,

$$(17.11) \qquad \mathcal{Q} = \begin{pmatrix} a_{11} & a_{12} & \cdots & a_{1n} \\ a_{21} & a_{22} & \cdots & a_{2n} \\ a_{31} & a_{32} & \cdots & a_{3n} \\ - & - & \cdots & - \\ - & - & \cdots & - \\ a_{n1} & a_{n2} & \cdots & a_{nn} \end{pmatrix},$$

provides a matrix representation of the operator A relative to the basis $f_1, f_2, \ldots, f_n$. For brevity, we frequently write $A \leftrightarrow \mathcal{Q}$ and mention the basis only when necessary for clarity. When M is an inner product space and the f_i are orthonormal,

$$(17.12) \qquad a_{ij} = (f_i, Af_j).$$

However, (17.9) is more general and frequently more readily applicable in obtaining the elements a_{ij} in the matrix representation (17.11). We observe that the first subscript on a_{ij} labels a row of the matrix representation (17.11), the second subscript labels a column.

A matrix $\mathcal{Q}$ in which $a_{ij} = 0$ when $i \neq j$ is called a *diagonal matrix*. It may be observed, from (17.9), that the matrix representation of an operator A relative to a basis $f_1, f_2, \ldots, f_n$ is diagonal if and only if the f_i are eigenfunctions of A.

Problem 17.5: Let $A \leftrightarrow \mathcal{Q}$ and $B \leftrightarrow \mathcal{B}$. Show that $A = B$ over M if and only if $a_{ij} = b_{ij}$ for each i and j. We then write $\mathcal{Q} = \mathcal{B}$.

Problem 17.6: Let $A = k$. Show that $a_{ij} = k\delta_{ij}$. When $k = 0$, we write $\mathcal{Q} = 0$, the *zero matrix;* when $k = 1$, we write $\mathcal{Q} = I$, the *identity;* when $k \neq 0$, $\mathcal{Q} = kI$ is a *scalar matrix.*

Problem 17.7: Let $A \leftrightarrow \mathcal{Q}$ and $B \leftrightarrow \mathcal{B}$. Define $\alpha\mathcal{Q} + \beta\mathcal{B}$ in such a way that $\alpha A + \beta B \leftrightarrow \alpha\mathcal{Q} + \beta\mathcal{B}$. Answer: $\alpha\mathcal{Q} + \beta\mathcal{B} = C$ where

$$(17.13) \qquad c_{ij} = \alpha a_{ij} + \beta b_{ij}.$$

Problem 17.8: Let $A \leftrightarrow \mathcal{Q}$ and $f \leftrightarrow c$. Define $\mathcal{Q}c$ in such a way that $Af \leftrightarrow \mathcal{Q}c$. Answer: $\mathcal{Q}c = d$ where

$$(17.14) \qquad d_i = \sum_{j=1}^{n} a_{ij}c_j.$$

Problem 17.9:   Let $A \leftrightarrow \mathfrak{A}$ and $B \leftrightarrow \mathfrak{B}$. Define $\mathfrak{A}\mathfrak{B}$ in such a way that $AB \leftrightarrow \mathfrak{A}\mathfrak{B}$. When is $\mathfrak{A}\mathfrak{B} = \mathfrak{B}\mathfrak{A}$? How is $\mathfrak{A}\mathfrak{B}$ obtained from $\mathfrak{B}$ when $A = k$? How is $\mathfrak{A}\mathfrak{B}$ obtained from $\mathfrak{A}$ when $B = k$? Answer: $\mathfrak{A}\mathfrak{B} = C$ where

$$(17.15) \qquad\qquad c_{ij} = \sum_{k=1}^{n} a_{ik}b_{kj}.$$

Problem 17.10:   Let $A \leftrightarrow \mathfrak{A}$, $f \leftrightarrow c$ and $g \leftrightarrow d$ relative to an orthonormal basis in an inner product space M. Define $(c,\mathfrak{A} d)$ in such a way that $(f,Ag) = (c,\mathfrak{A}d)$. Answer:

$$(17.16) \qquad\qquad (c,\mathfrak{A}d) = \sum_{i=1}^{n} \sum_{j=1}^{n} c_i{}^* a_{ij} d_j.$$

Problem 17.11:   Let $A \leftrightarrow \mathfrak{A}$ and $f \leftrightarrow c$ relative to an orthonormal basis in an inner product space M. Define $\langle \mathfrak{A} \rangle$ in such a way that $\langle A \rangle = \langle \mathfrak{A} \rangle$ where $\langle A \rangle = (f,Af)/(f,f)$. Answer:

$$(17.17) \qquad\qquad \langle \mathfrak{A} \rangle = (c,\mathfrak{A}c)/(c,c)$$

where $(c,\mathfrak{A}c)$ and (c,c) are defined by (17.16).

Problem 17.12:   Let $A \leftrightarrow \mathfrak{A}$ relative to an orthonormal basis in an inner product space M. Show that, if A is Hermitean over M, then $a_{ij} = a_{ji}{}^*$. Conversely, show that if $a_{ij} = a_{ji}{}^*$, then A is Hermitean over M.

Problem 17.13:   Obtain matrix representations $\mathfrak{A}$ and $\mathfrak{B}$ of $A = \dfrac{d}{dx}$ and $B = \dfrac{d^2}{dx^2}$ over the linear manifold M determined by functions $f(x)$ which satisfy $d^2f/dx^2 + m^2f = 0$, relative to (a) $f_1 = \dfrac{1}{\sqrt{\pi}} \cos(mx)$, $f_2 = \dfrac{1}{\sqrt{\pi}} \sin(mx)$ as basis, and (b) $f_1 = \dfrac{1}{\sqrt{2\pi}} e^{imx}$, $f_2 = \dfrac{1}{\sqrt{2\pi}} e^{-imx}$ as basis. Verify that $\mathfrak{B} = \mathfrak{A}^2 = -m^2 I$ when restricted to M. (Hint: See the remarks following (17.12).) Answers:

$$(17.18) \quad \begin{array}{ll} \text{(a)} & \mathfrak{A} = \begin{pmatrix} 0 & m \\ -m & 0 \end{pmatrix}, \qquad \mathfrak{B} = \begin{pmatrix} -m^2 & 0 \\ 0 & -m^2 \end{pmatrix}, \\[3mm] \text{(b)} & \mathfrak{A} = \begin{pmatrix} im & 0 \\ 0 & -im \end{pmatrix}, \qquad \mathfrak{B} = \begin{pmatrix} -m^2 & 0 \\ 0 & -m^2 \end{pmatrix}. \end{array}$$

Problem 17.14:   Obtain vector representations c and d of $f = e^{imx}$ and $g = e^{-imx}$, respectively, relative to the basis (a) of Problem 17.13. Calculate $(c,\mathfrak{A}d)$ and $(c,\mathfrak{B}d)$ and compare the results with (f,Ag) and (f,Bg), where $(f,g) = \displaystyle\int_0^{2\pi} f^*g \, dx$.

Problem 17.15: Using the simultaneous eigenfunctions $Y_l^m(\theta,\varphi)$ of M^2 and M_z, obtain matrix representations of M_+, M_-, M_x, M_y, M_z, and M^2 when restricted to the linear manifold of functions for which $M_z = 2\hbar^2$ ($l = 1$). (Hint: Use (14,19), (14.48), (14.57), (14.58), (17.12), and the eigenvalue relations for M^2 and M_z.) Answer:

$$M_+ = \hbar\sqrt{2}\begin{pmatrix}0 & 1 & 0\\0 & 0 & 1\\0 & 0 & 0\end{pmatrix}, \qquad M_- = \hbar\sqrt{2}\begin{pmatrix}0 & 0 & 0\\1 & 0 & 0\\0 & 1 & 0\end{pmatrix},$$

$$M_x = \frac{\hbar}{\sqrt{2}}\begin{pmatrix}0 & 1 & 0\\1 & 0 & 1\\0 & 1 & 0\end{pmatrix},$$

(17.19)

$$M_y = \frac{i\hbar}{\sqrt{2}}\begin{pmatrix}0 & -1 & 0\\1 & 0 & -1\\0 & 1 & 0\end{pmatrix}, \qquad M_z = \hbar\begin{pmatrix}1 & 0 & 0\\0 & 0 & 0\\0 & 0 & -1\end{pmatrix},$$

$$M^2 = 2\hbar^2\begin{pmatrix}1 & 0 & 0\\0 & 1 & 0\\0 & 0 & 1\end{pmatrix},$$

where rows and columns are labeled successively with values of m in the order 1, 0, −1.

Problem 17.16: Verify that the matrix representations (17.19) satisfy (14.3), (14.5), (14.7), (14.20), (14.21), and (14.22).

Problem 17.17: The relations (14.19), (14.48), (14.57), and (14.58) remain valid for half-odd-integral values of l when the surface spherical harmonics Y_l^m in (14.48) and (14.58) are replaced by orthonormal spin functions S_l^m, $m = -l, -l+1, -l+2, \ldots, l-1, l$ which are simultaneous eigenfunctions of M^2 and M_z for $M^2 = l(l+1)\hbar^2$ and $M_z = m\hbar$. Obtain matrix representations of M_+, M_-, M_x, M_y, M_z, and M^2 when restricted to the linear manifold of spin functions for which $l = \frac{1}{2}$. Answer: Multiply the Pauli spin matrices (18.28) by $\hbar/2$ to obtain M_x, M_y, and M_z. In addition,

(17.20) $M_+ = \hbar\begin{pmatrix}0 & 1\\0 & 0\end{pmatrix}, M_- = \hbar\begin{pmatrix}0 & 0\\1 & 0\end{pmatrix}, M^2 = \frac{3\hbar^2}{4}\begin{pmatrix}1 & 0\\0 & 1\end{pmatrix}$

where rows and columns are labeled successively with values of m in the order $\frac{1}{2}$, $-\frac{1}{2}$.

17.3. Eigenvalues and Eigenvectors. A vector u such that $\alpha u = au$ for some scalar a is called an eigenvector of α for $\alpha = a$ (see Section 10.1). When α is a square matrix of order n, the eigenvalue equation $\alpha u = \lambda u$ has meaning and is equivalent to a system of n linear homogeneous equations for the n components of u. This system is consistent only for certain values of λ, those for which det $(\alpha - \lambda I) = 0$.

The values of λ for which this system is consistent are the eigenvalues of $\mathfrak{a}$. Corresponding to any eigenvalue, call it a, there exists at least one vector u such that $\mathfrak{a}u = au$. It is almost trivial that any matrix $\mathfrak{a}$ of order n having n distinct eigenvalues has n linearly independent eigenvectors. It may be shown that, when $\mathfrak{a}$ is Hermitean, there exist n linearly independent eigenvectors, regardless of multiplicity of eigenvalues. The eigenvectors belonging to distinct eigenvalues of a Hermitean matrix are orthogonal (see Problem 6.17). Since the Gram-Schmidt orthogonalization procedure (Section 10.3) may be applied to eigenvectors belonging to the same eigenvalue, any Hermitean matrix of order n has n mutually orthogonal, linearly independent eigenvectors which, if desired, may be normalized.

An example of the matrix eigenvalue problem appears in (13.14)-(13.18). The explanation there should be reviewed at this point. The reader should be able, without difficulty, to interpret previously deduced properties of linear operators, in particular of Hermitean operators, in terms of matrices.

Problem 17.18: Obtain the eigenvalues and the eigenvectors of the matrix $\mathfrak{a}$ in (17.18a). Show that the normalized eigenvectors are vector representations of the basis functions used in part (b) of Problem 17.13.

Problem 17.19: Obtain a matrix representation $\mathfrak{a}$ of $A = \dfrac{d}{dx}$ using $f_1 = \cos x$, $f_2 = \sin x$, $f_3 = \cosh x$, $f_4 = \sinh x$. Then obtain the eigenvalues and eigenvectors of $\mathfrak{a}$. Show that, depending upon choice of undetermined factors, the eigenvectors of $\mathfrak{a}$ provide vector representations of the functions e^{ix}, e^{-ix}, e^x, and e^{-x}. These are eigenfunctions of A.

17.4. The Hilbert Space H_0. Let f_1, f_2, f_3, . . . be a complete orthonormal set in the linear manifold M of all square integrable functions. Then given any f in M, there exist m constants c_1, c_2, c_3, . . . c_m such that

$$(17.21) \qquad f = \sum_{i=1}^{m} c_i f_i, \qquad c_i = (f_i, f), \qquad 1 \le i \le m,$$

or there exists an infinite sequence of constants c_1, c_2, c_3, . . . such that

$$(17.22) \qquad f = \lim_{n \to \infty} \sum_{i=1}^{n} c_i f_i, \qquad c_i = (f_i, f), \qquad i \ge 1$$

(see Section 10.6). By taking $c_i = 0$ when $i > m$, we may consider (17.21) as being a special case of (17.22) (see Problem 10.22). The c_i, which are determined by f and the particular set of orthonormal functions f_1, f_2, f_3, . . . are called the *components* of f *relative to the basis* f_1, f_2, f_3, ... The components of f relative to a given basis fully specify f. Conversely, it may be shown that a complete orthonormal set $f_1, f_2, f_3, \ldots$ and any infinite sequence of constants $c_1, c_2, c_3, \ldots$ having the property that

$$(17.23) \qquad c^2 = \lim_{n \to \infty} \sum_{i=1}^{n} c_i{}^* c_i$$

exists uniquely determine, by means of (17.22), a square integrable function f. We may therefore write

$$(17.24) \qquad f \leftrightarrow c = \begin{pmatrix} c_1 \\ c_2 \\ c_3 \\ \overline{} \end{pmatrix}$$

and consider c as providing a representation of f, or, conversely, consider f as providing a representation of c. The representation (17.24) is called a *column vector*.

The set of all column vectors c such that c^2, defined by (17.23), exists is called the *Hilbert space* H_0. Foregoing statements imply that there is a one-one correspondence between vectors in Hilbert space H_0 and functions in the linear manifold M of all square integrable functions, relative to a preselected orthonormal basis in M.

It is almost trivial that if $f \leftrightarrow c$ and $g \leftrightarrow d$, where f and g are two square integrable functions and c and d are their representations in H_0, then $\alpha f + \beta g \leftrightarrow \alpha c + \beta d$, where $(\alpha c + \beta d)_i = \alpha c_i + \beta d_i$. The reader is also reminded of (10.42) and (10.44) and more generally of the methods and results of Sections 10.5 and 10.6.

Let A be a linear operator defined on the linear manifold M of all square integrable functions such that Af is square integrable whenever f is square integrable. Then, for any f_j in an orthonormal basis $f_1, f_2, f_3, \ldots$,

$$(17.25) \qquad Af_j = \lim_{n \to \infty} \sum_{i=1}^{n} a_{ij} f_i, \qquad a_{ij} = (f_i, Af_j).$$

The column vector

$$(17.26) \qquad a_j = \begin{pmatrix} a_{1j} \\ a_{2j} \\ a_{3j} \\ \overline{} \end{pmatrix}$$

provides a representation of Af_j in the Hilbert space H_0 relative to the orthonormal basis $f_1, f_2, f_3, \ldots$. Further, the sequence $\mathcal{A} = (a_1, a_2,$

$a_3,$ . . .) of column vectors, which we exhibit as a rectangular array

$$(17.27) \qquad \mathcal{Q} = \begin{pmatrix} a_{11} & a_{12} & a_{13} & \cdots \\ a_{21} & a_{22} & a_{23} & \cdots \\ a_{31} & a_{32} & a_{33} & \cdots \\ - & - & - & \cdots \\ - & - & - & \cdots \end{pmatrix}$$

containing an infinite number of rows and columns, provides a *matrix representation* of the linear operator A relative to the basis $f_1, f_2, f_3, \ldots$. For brevity, we write $A \leftrightarrow \mathcal{Q}$ and refer to the basis only when necessary for clarity.

Problem 17.20: Extend the results of Problems 17.5–17.12 to the linear manifold of all square integrable functions, waiving questions of convergence.

Problem 17.21: Obtain a vector representation of $f(x) = x, 0 \le x \le a$, relative to the basis formed by the orthonormal energy eigenfunctions (9.52) for a particle in a box. What integrals must be evaluated in obtaining a matrix representation of the operator $A = x \cdot$? Answer: $f(x) \leftrightarrow c$ where $c_n = (-1)^{n+1} \sqrt{2a^3}/n\pi$.

Problem 17.22: Obtain matrix representations of the operators L_+ and L_- (see (11.32)), relative to the orthonormal basis formed by the harmonic oscillator energy eigenfunctions (11.57). (Hint: Using (11.51), (11.58), and the orthonormality of the ψ_n, obtain the matrix elements

$$(17.28) \quad \begin{aligned} \text{(a)} \quad & (L_+)_{mn} = \langle m|L_+|n\rangle = c_{n+1}\langle m|n+1\rangle = c_m\delta_{m,n+1}, \\ \text{(b)} \quad & (L_-)_{mn} = \langle m|L_-|n\rangle = -c_n\langle m|n-1\rangle = -c_n\delta_{m,n-1}, \end{aligned}$$

where c_n is given by (11.56).) Answer:

$$L_+ = \frac{i\hbar}{\alpha} \begin{pmatrix} 0 & 0 & 0 & 0 & 0 & 0 & \cdots \\ 2 & 0 & 0 & 0 & 0 & 0 & \cdots \\ 0 & 4 & 0 & 0 & 0 & 0 & \cdots \\ 0 & 0 & 6 & 0 & 0 & 0 & \cdots \\ 0 & 0 & 0 & 8 & 0 & 0 & \cdots \\ & & & & & & \end{pmatrix},$$

$$(17.29)$$

$$L_- = -\frac{i\hbar}{\alpha} \begin{pmatrix} 0 & 2 & 0 & 0 & 0 & 0 & \cdots \\ 0 & 0 & 4 & 0 & 0 & 0 & \cdots \\ 0 & 0 & 0 & 6 & 0 & 0 & \cdots \\ 0 & 0 & 0 & 0 & 8 & 0 & \cdots \\ 0 & 0 & 0 & 0 & 0 & 10 & \cdots \\ & & & & & & \end{pmatrix}.$$

Problem 17.23: Obtain matrix representations of the operators $A = x$ and $B = p$, relative to the orthonormal basis formed by the harmonic oscillator eigenfunctions (11.57). (Hint: Use (11.67) and (11.68), or use (11.32) and (17.29).)

Problem 17.24: Obtain a matrix representation of the Hamiltonian operator (11.5) for a harmonic oscillator, using as basis the energy eigenfunctions (11.57). Answer: A diagonal matrix with elements $H_{mn} = E_n \delta_{nm}$ where E_n is given by (11.50).

Problem 17.25: Let a linear operator A possess a complete set of orthonormal eigenfunctions in an inner product space M. Show that the only nonzero elements in the matrix representation of A, or of any power of A, relative to the set of orthonormal eigenfunctions of A as basis, are the diagonal elements. Show also that the diagonal elements in the matrix representation of A^n are the n-th powers of the eigenvalues of A, $n = 1, 2, 3, \ldots$.

17.5. Change of Basis. In order to simplify the exposition of this section, it is written in terms of orthonormal bases in a finite dimensional inner product space. Waiving questions of convergence, the results are readily extended to orthonormal bases in the linear manifold of all square integrable functions.

Each of the functions f_i of an orthonormal basis $f_1, f_2, \ldots, f_n$ in a finite dimensional inner product space M may be expressed in terms of the functions g_j of another orthonormal basis $g_1, g_2, \ldots, g_n$:

$$(17.30) \qquad f_i = \sum_{j=1}^n T_{ji} g_j, \qquad T_{ji} = (g_j, f_i).$$

Upon substituting from (17.30) into (17.1), we obtain for a function f in M:

$$(17.31) \qquad f = \sum_{j=1}^n \left(\sum_{i=1}^n T_{ji} c_i \right) g_j.$$

However,

$$(17.32) \qquad f = \sum_{j=1}^n d_j g_j, \qquad d_j = (g_j, f).$$

Hence, since the g_j are mutually orthogonal (see Problem 10.12),

$$(17.33) \qquad d_j = \sum_{i=1}^n T_{ji} c_i.$$

We see that the transformation from a vector representation c, relative to an orthonormal basis $f_1, f_2, \ldots, f_n$, to a vector representation d, relative to an orthonormal basis $g_1, g_2, \ldots, g_n$, is accomplished by a linear transformation. The coefficients T_{ji} of the transformation may be exhibited as a *transformation matrix* T with T_{ji} appearing in the j-th row and i-th column. We then write (17.33) in the symbolic form

$$(17.34) \qquad\qquad d = Tc.$$

Since $(f_i, g_j) = (g_j, f_i)^* = T_{ji}^*$, we may also write

$$(17.35) \qquad\qquad g_j = \sum_{i=1}^{n} T_{ji}^* f_i,$$

Upon substituting from (17.35) into (17.32) we obtain

$$(17.36) \qquad\qquad f = \sum_{i=1}^{n} \left(\sum_{j=1}^{n} T_{ji} d_j \right) f_i.$$

Comparing (17.1) and (17.36), we see that

$$(17.37) \qquad\qquad c_i = \sum_{j=1}^{n} T_{ji}^* d_j$$

since the f_i are mutually orthonormal (see Problem 10.12). The matrix $T\dagger$ for transforming from d to c is the *transposed conjugate* of the matrix T for transforming from c to d. We may write

$$(17.38) \qquad\qquad c = T\dagger d$$

where $(T\dagger)_{ij} = T_{ji}^*$.

In (17.33) we may replace the index of summation i by k. Then, substituting into (17.37), we have

$$(17.39) \qquad\qquad c_i = \sum_{k=1}^{n} \left(\sum_{j=1}^{n} T_{ji}^* T_{jk} \right) c_k.$$

Since the T_{ji} do not depend on the c_i which are arbitrary, we conclude that

$$(17.40) \qquad\qquad \sum_{j=1}^{n} (T\dagger)_{ij} T_{jk} = \delta_i^k.$$

This shows that $(T\dagger)T = I_n$, the $n \times n$ unit matrix. Similarly, $T(T\dagger) = I_n$. A matrix having this property is called *unitary*. A transformation from one orthonormal basis to another orthonormal basis is a *unitary transformation*.

Problem 17.26: Show that, when $c \leftrightarrow d$ under a unitary transformation, $c^2 = d^2$.

Problem 17.27: Let a linear operator L defined on a finite dimensional inner product space M have representations $\mathfrak{a}$ and $\mathfrak{B}$ relative to orthonormal bases $f_1, f_2, \ldots, f_n$ and $g_1, g_2, \ldots, g_n$, respectively. The matrix elements of α and $\mathfrak{B}$ are, respectively, $a_{ij} = (f_i, Lf_j)$ and $b_{ij} = (g_i, Lg_j)$, (see (17.12)). Show that

(17.41)
$$
\text{(a)} \quad a_{ij} = \sum_{k=1}^{n} \sum_{l=1}^{n} (T\dagger)_{ik} b_{kl} T_{lj},
$$

$$
\text{(b)} \quad b_{ij} = \sum_{k=1}^{n} \sum_{l=1}^{n} T_{ik} a_{kl} (T\dagger)_{lj}
$$

where $(T\dagger)_{ji}{}^* = T_{ij} = (f_i, g_j)$. In matrix notation,

(17.42)   (a) $\alpha = T\dagger \mathfrak{B} T$,   (b) $\mathfrak{B} = T\alpha T\dagger$.

Problem 17.28: (continuation of Problem 17.27.) Show that

(17.43)   (a) $\alpha^n = T\dagger \mathfrak{B}^n T$,   (b) $\mathfrak{B}^n = T\alpha^n T\dagger$.

Problem 17.29: Show that $(c, \alpha c) = (d, \mathfrak{B}d)$ when $c \leftrightarrow d$ and $\alpha \leftrightarrow \mathfrak{B}$ under a unitary transformation. As a special case, $c^2 = d^2$ (see Problem 17.26).

17.6. Matrix Representation of the Schroedinger Equation. Any square integrable wave function $\psi(\mathbf{r}, t)$ may be represented in the form

(17.44)
$$
\psi(\mathbf{r}, t) = \lim_{n \to \infty} \sum_{j=1}^{n} c_j(t) f_j(\mathbf{r}),
$$

where $f_1, f_2, f_3, \ldots$ is an arbitrarily selected complete orthonormal set in the linear manifold of all square integrable functions (see Section 17.3). Substituting from (17.44) into both members of the STDWE (8.3) we readily obtain, if we waive discussion of mathematical fine points,

(17.45)
$$
\lim_{m \to \infty} \sum_{j=1}^{n} c_j H f_j = i\hbar \lim_{n \to \infty} \sum_{j=1}^{n} f_j \frac{\partial c_j}{\partial t},
$$

for functions (17.44) which satisfy (8.3). As a consequence of the mutual orthogonality of the f_j this implies

(17.46)
$$
\sum_{j=1}^{\infty} H_{ij} c_j = i\hbar \frac{\partial c_i}{\partial t}
$$

where $H_{ij} = (f_i, Hf_j)$ is the element in the i-th row and j-th column of the matrix representation $\mathfrak{IC}$ of the Hamiltonian operator H, relative to $f_1, f_2, f_3, \ldots$ as basis. From (17.46) we obtain

(17.47)
$$
\mathfrak{IC}c = i\hbar \frac{\partial c}{\partial t}.
$$

This is the matrix representation of the STDWE (8.3) relative to f_1, f_2, f_3, . . . as basis. The matrix representation

$$(17.48) \qquad \qquad \mathfrak{IC}c = Ec$$

of the STIWE (8.4) is frequently the starting point for obtaining approximations to the energy eigenvalues of a system.

17.7. Transformation from the Schroedinger to the Heisenberg Picture. In this book we concentrate on the Schroedinger wave mechanics rather than on the Heisenberg matrix mechanics because of the greater flexibility and applicability of the former in the solution of problems of appreciable complexity, such as that of the hydrogen atom. This is not to minimize the importance of the Heisenberg matrix mechanics whose theory should be well understood by every student of quantum mechanics. Although we take the solution of any special problem using the Heisenberg method to be beyond the objectives of this book, we stress its importance by giving further consideration (see Section 8.5) to the connection between it and the Schroedinger method.

It was by emphasizing the importance of observables in physical theory that Heisenberg[1] was led to the discovery of matrix mechanics early in 1925, slightly before Schroedinger's discovery of the wave mechanics. Hence in the matrix formulation of the quantum theory, which was developed by Heisenberg in collaboration with M. Born and P. Jordan,[2] matrices were dealt with independently of any relation to a wave equation or a wave function. The introduction of a vector representation of the wave function, on which the Heisenberg matrices operate, is necessitated in order to obtain complete mathematical equivalence between the Heisenberg matrix mechanics and the Schroedinger wave mechanics. This equivalence was established by Schroedinger in 1926.

In the Schroedinger picture, the development in time of a mechanical system is borne by a wave function whose vector representation, relative to any complete set of time independent, orthonormal functions, has time dependent components. Taking, for example, the time independent energy eigenfunctions $\psi_j(\mathbf{r})$ as basis, we have (see (10.20)),

$$(17.49) \qquad \psi(\mathbf{r},t) \leftrightarrow c^S = \begin{pmatrix} c_0 e^{-iE_0 t/\hbar} \\ c_1 e^{-iE_1 t/\hbar} \\ c_2 e^{-iE_2 t/\hbar} \\ \cdot \cdot \cdot \\ \cdot \cdot \cdot \\ \cdot \cdot \cdot \end{pmatrix}.$$

---

[1] W. Heisenberg, *Z. Physik*, **33**, 879 (1925).

[2] M. Born, P. Jordon, and W. Heisenberg, *Z. Physik*, **34**, 858 (1925); **35**, 557 (1925).

Schroedinger operators, such as the Hamiltonian and the operators for the position coordinates and the components of linear and angular momentum are in general time independent.

In the Heisenberg picture, the time development of a mechanical system is borne by matrices whose elements, as Heisenberg stressed, correspond to physical observables. The vectors on which the matrices operate have time independent components which are of secondary importance, so long as we stay in the Heisenberg picture. Their importance is enhanced when we relate the Heisenberg picture to the Schroedinger picture. This we readily do by using the time dependent energy eigenfunctions $\psi_j(\mathbf{r},t)$ $= e^{-iE_jt/\hbar}$ as orthonormal basis for a vector representation of the wave function. By referring to (10.20) we see that, with this basis,

$$(17.50) \qquad \psi(\mathbf{r},t) \leftrightarrow c^H = \begin{pmatrix} c_0 \\ c_1 \\ c_2 \\ \underline{} \\ \underline{} \end{pmatrix}$$

where the c's are the same as in (17.49). As in Section 8.5, superscripts S and H distinguish representatives in the Schroedinger and in the Heisenberg pictures, respectively.

Comparison of (17.49) and (17.50) yields

$$(17.51) \qquad (c^H) = e_j^{iE_jt/\hbar}(c^S)_j$$

or

$$(17.52) \qquad c^H = e^{i\mathfrak{IC}t/\hbar}c^S$$

where $\mathfrak{IC}$ is the matrix representation of the Hamiltonian relative to the set of its orthonormal eigenfunctions as basis. In this representation, both $\mathfrak{IC}$ and $e^{i\mathfrak{IC}t/\hbar}$ are diagonal, the diagonal elements being E_j and $e^{iE_jt/\hbar}$, respectively (see Problem 17.25).

The result (17.52) may seem to be very special in that it was obtained by using the energy eigenfunctions as basis. To demonstrate that it is quite general, let T be the matrix for transforming from the energy eigenfunctions as basis to any other complete orthonormal set as basis. Then, according to (17.38)

$$(17.53) \qquad \text{(a)} \quad c^S = T^\dagger d^S, \qquad \text{(b)} \quad c^H = T^\dagger d^H,$$

where d^S and d^H are vector representations of the wave function in the Schroedinger and Heisenberg pictures, respectively, relative to the new basis. Substituting from (17.53) into (17.52), we readily obtain, since T is unitary,

(17.54) $d^H = e^{i\mathcal{3C}'t/\hbar}d^S$,

where

(17.55)   (a) $\mathcal{3C}' = T\mathcal{3C}T\dagger$,   (b) $e^{i\mathcal{3C}'t/\hbar} = Te^{i\mathcal{3C}t/\hbar}T\dagger$.

Since (17.54) and (17.52) are of the same form, the result (17.52) does not depend on use of the energy eigenfunctions as basis.

To relate matrix representations of operators in the Heisenberg picture with their matrix representations in the Schroedinger picture, we write, for any operator A and vector $\mathbf{c}$,

(17.56)   (a) $(Ac)^H = A^Hc^H$,   (b) $(Ac)^S = A^Sc^S$.

However, according to (17.52),

(17.57) $(Ac)^H = e^{i\mathcal{3C}t/\hbar}(Ac)^S$.

Hence

(17.58) $A^Hc^H = e^{i\mathcal{3C}t/\hbar}A^Sc^S$.

Eliminating c^H by using (17.52), we have

(17.59) $A^He^{i\mathcal{3C}t/\hbar}c^S = e^{i\mathcal{3C}t/\hbar}A^Sc^S$.

Since c^S is arbitrary, this implies

(17.60) $A^H = e^{i\mathcal{3C}t/\hbar}A^Se^{-i\mathcal{3C}t/\hbar}$.

These results are readily observed to be consistent with those of Section 8.5.

Problem 17.30:   Using (8.51) and the unitarity of T, obtain (17.55b) from (17.55a).

Problem 17.31:   Transform the matrix representations (17.29) of the operators L_+ and L_-, and of the operators $A = x$ and $B = p$ (see Problem 17.21), from the Schroedinger picture to the Heisenberg picture. The orthonormal harmonic oscillator energy eigenfunctions (11.57) are to be retained as basis.

Problem 17.32:   Transform the vector representation of $f(x) = x$, $0 < x < a$, obtained in Problem 17.21, to the Heisenberg picture. The orthonormal energy eigenfunctions (9.52) for a particle in a box are to be retained as basis.

Problem 17.33:   Let A^S be a time independent Schroedinger operator. Show that any eigenvalue of A^S is also an eigenvalue of A^H.

17.8. References for Supplementary Reading.

Section 17.1: Mandl, 1–5; Persico, 277–9.

Section 17.2: Bohm, 361–70; Born, 346–9, 380–87; Dirac, 67–72; Kemble, 348–55; March, 83–108; McConnell, 52–65; Mott and Sneddon, 363–71; Pauling and Wilson, 416–25; Persico, 283–93; Schiff, 122–7.

Section 17.3: Bohm, 370–71; Kemble, 359–66; Kramers, 131–41.

Section 17.4: Mandl, 5–14; Persico, 279–83.

Section 17.5: Bohm, 371–7; Kemble, 355–9; Persico, 293–308.

Section 17.6: Bohm, 378–9; McConnell, 65–8.

Section 17.7: Bohm, 379–83; Born, 128–30; Kemble, 366–70; McConnell, 68–77; Schaefer, 396–405.

CHAPTER 18

PAULI'S THEORY OF ELECTRON SPIN

18.1. Spin Wave Functions and Spin Operators. Experimental facts requiring the electron spin hypothesis (see Section 14.8) include (1) the anomalous Zeeman effect, (2) results of the Stern-Gerlach experiment, (3) the existence of doublets in the spectra of alkalis, and (4) the gyromagnetic effect. In this text we perforce concentrate on the mathematical theory.

The mathematical formalism for the treatment of the vector representing electron spin has been developed by proper modification of the mathematical relations for orbital angular momentum as required by the experimental phenomena which are to be explained in terms of electron spin. This must be done in the general framework of the already existing quantum mechanical formalism. Particular attention is paid to the interpretative postulates of quantum mechanics (Section 12.4).

The Pauli theory of electron spin[1] is of importance because of (1) its historical place, intermediate between the Schroedinger nonrelativistic one-component wave theory and the Dirac relativistic four-component wave theory, and (2) the introduction it provides to the study of multicomponent theories, including the Dirac theory.

Wave functions describing electron spin may be introduced in various ways. Assuming that our knowledge of the state of an electron includes information about the position of the electron and about s_z, the component of the spin vector **s** in some specified direction, we write

$$(18.1) \qquad \psi = \psi(x,y,z,\sigma_z)$$

where $\sigma_z = (2/\hbar)s_z$. We have seen in Section 14.8 that s_z is to be allowed the values $\pm\hbar/2$. Hence σ_z has the values ± 1. Since σ_z is restricted to two values, we find it convenient to introduce the *two*-component wave function

$$(18.2) \qquad \psi = \begin{pmatrix} \psi_+(xyz) \\ \psi_-(xyz) \end{pmatrix},$$

where

$$(18.3) \qquad \psi_\pm(xyz) = \psi(x,y,z, \pm 1)$$

[1] W. Pauli, *Z. Physik,* **43,** 601 (1927).

The wave functions $\begin{pmatrix} \psi_+ \\ 0 \end{pmatrix}$ and $\begin{pmatrix} 0 \\ \psi_- \end{pmatrix}$ are to be interpreted that σ_z is certainly $+1$, or certainly -1, respectively. More generally, when there is a probability distribution for σ_z, we may normalize so that

$$(18.4) \qquad N(\psi) = \int_\infty (\psi_+{}^*\psi_+ + \psi_-{}^*\psi_-)\, d\mathbf{r} = 1.$$

Then $\int_\infty \psi_+{}^*\psi_+\, d\mathbf{r}$ gives the probability that $\sigma_z = +1$ and $\int_\infty \psi_-{}^*\psi_-\, d\mathbf{r}$ gives the probability that $\sigma_z = -1$.

If the spin is independent of position, then $\psi_+(xyz)$ and $\psi_-(xyz)$ will vary in the same way. Then the two-component wave function (18.2) assumes the simpler form

$$(18.5) \qquad \psi = \begin{pmatrix} c_+\psi(xyz) \\ c_-\psi(xyz) \end{pmatrix} = \psi(xyz) \cdot \begin{pmatrix} c_+ \\ c_- \end{pmatrix}.$$

Effecting normalization by making

$$(18.6) \qquad \begin{aligned} &\text{(a)} \quad |c_+|^2 + |c_-|^2 = 1, \\ &\text{(b)} \quad \int_\infty |\psi(xyz)|^2\, d\mathbf{r} = 1, \end{aligned}$$

we then have that $|c_+|^2$ gives the probability that $\sigma_z = +1$ and $|c_-|^2$ gives the probability that $\sigma_z = -1$.

By Postulate II (Section 12.4), Hermitean operators with complete sets of orthonormal eigenfunctions are to be assigned to spin observables, which we take to include s^2 and any component of $\mathbf{s}$, say s_z. By Postulate IV', the eigenvalues of the operator s_z are the observed values $\pm\hbar/2$. Hence the eigenvalues of the operator $\sigma_z \equiv (2/\hbar)s_z$ are the integers $+1$ and -1. Taking the states $\begin{pmatrix} 1 \\ 0 \end{pmatrix}$ and $\begin{pmatrix} 0 \\ 1 \end{pmatrix}$ to be those in which σ_z is certainly $+1$ and certainly -1, respectively, we must have

$$(18.7) \qquad \sigma_z \begin{pmatrix} 1 \\ 0 \end{pmatrix} = \begin{pmatrix} 1 \\ 0 \end{pmatrix}, \qquad \sigma_z \begin{pmatrix} 0 \\ 1 \end{pmatrix} = -1 \cdot \begin{pmatrix} 0 \\ 1 \end{pmatrix} = \begin{pmatrix} 0 \\ -1 \end{pmatrix}.$$

Quite evidently, in the two-component wave function formalism, σ_z is to be represented by a 2×2 matrix:

$$(18.8) \qquad \sigma_z = \begin{pmatrix} p & r \\ q & s \end{pmatrix}.$$

Substituting the representation (18.8) of σ_z into (18.7), we find, using standard matrix multiplication (see (17.14)), that

$$(18.9) \qquad \sigma_z \begin{pmatrix} 1 \\ 0 \end{pmatrix} = \begin{pmatrix} p & r \\ q & s \end{pmatrix} \begin{pmatrix} 1 \\ 0 \end{pmatrix} = \begin{pmatrix} p \\ q \end{pmatrix} = \begin{pmatrix} 1 \\ 0 \end{pmatrix},$$

$$\sigma_z \begin{pmatrix} 0 \\ 1 \end{pmatrix} = \begin{pmatrix} p & r \\ q & s \end{pmatrix} \begin{pmatrix} 0 \\ 1 \end{pmatrix} = \begin{pmatrix} r \\ s \end{pmatrix} = \begin{pmatrix} 0 \\ -1 \end{pmatrix}.$$

Hence $p = 1$, $q = 0$, $r = 0$, $s = -1$. Then

$$(18.10) \qquad (a) \quad \sigma_z = \begin{pmatrix} 1 & 0 \\ 0 & -1 \end{pmatrix},$$

$$(b) \quad \sigma_z{}^2 = \begin{pmatrix} 1 & 0 \\ 0 & -1 \end{pmatrix} \begin{pmatrix} 1 & 0 \\ 0 & -1 \end{pmatrix} = \begin{pmatrix} 1 & 0 \\ 0 & 1 \end{pmatrix} = 1.$$

The matrix (18.10a) representing σ_z was obtained by taking the vectors $\begin{pmatrix} 1 \\ 0 \end{pmatrix}$ and $\begin{pmatrix} 0 \\ 1 \end{pmatrix}$ as representations of states in which σ_z is certainly $+1$ and σ_z is certainly -1, respectively. However, the relation (18.10b), $\sigma_z{}^2 = 1$, is independent of any representation and therefore holds for all representations since, writing for any state vector

$$(18.11) \qquad \psi = \begin{pmatrix} \psi_+ \\ \psi_- \end{pmatrix} = \psi_+ \begin{pmatrix} 1 \\ 0 \end{pmatrix} + \psi_- \begin{pmatrix} 0 \\ 1 \end{pmatrix},$$

we find

$$(18.12) \qquad \sigma_z \begin{pmatrix} \psi_+ \\ \psi_- \end{pmatrix} = \psi_+ \begin{pmatrix} 1 \\ 0 \end{pmatrix} + \psi_- \begin{pmatrix} 0 \\ -1 \end{pmatrix},$$

$$\sigma_z{}^2 \begin{pmatrix} \psi_+ \\ \psi_- \end{pmatrix} = \psi_+ \begin{pmatrix} 1 \\ 0 \end{pmatrix} + \psi_- \begin{pmatrix} 0 \\ 1 \end{pmatrix} = \begin{pmatrix} \psi_+ \\ \psi_- \end{pmatrix} = \psi.$$

We may therefore write

$$(18.13) \qquad \sigma_{z'}{}^2 = \begin{pmatrix} 1 & 0 \\ 0 & 1 \end{pmatrix} = 1,$$

where $\sigma_{z'}$ is the component of $\mathfrak{d} = (2/\hbar)\mathbf{s}$ in any arbitrary direction, here designated as z'.

Taking now α, β, γ as the direction cosines of a z' axis referred to an xyz coordinate system, we have

$$(18.14) \qquad \sigma_{z'} = \alpha\sigma_x + \beta\sigma_y + \gamma\sigma_z.$$

Then

$$(18.15) \quad \sigma_{z'}{}^2 = \alpha^2\sigma_x{}^2 + \beta^2\sigma_y{}^2 + \gamma^2\sigma_z{}^2 + \alpha\beta(\sigma_x\sigma_y + \sigma_y\sigma_x) + \\ \beta\gamma(\sigma_y\sigma_z + \sigma_z\sigma_y) + \gamma\alpha(\sigma_z\sigma_x + \sigma_x\sigma_z).$$

Quite readily, we see from (18.15) that the condition (18.13) for all directions of the z' axis, that is, for all direction cosines γ, β, and γ which satisfy

$$(18.16) \qquad\qquad \alpha^2 + \beta^2 + \gamma^2 = 1,$$

implies that

$$(18.17) \quad \begin{array}{ll} \text{(a)} & \sigma_x{}^2 = 1, \qquad \sigma_y{}^2 = 1, \qquad \sigma_z{}^2 = 1 \\ \text{(b)} & \sigma_x\sigma_y + \sigma_y\sigma_x = 0, \qquad \sigma_y\sigma_z + \sigma_z\sigma_y = 0, \qquad \sigma_z\sigma_x + \sigma_x\sigma_z = 0. \end{array}$$

Thus the components of $\mathbf{\sigma}$, and therefore those of $\mathbf{s}$, *anticommute*. We find quite readily from (18.17a) that

$$(18.18) \quad \text{(a)} \quad \sigma^2 \equiv \sigma_x{}^2 + \sigma_y{}^2 + \sigma_z{}^2 = 3, \qquad \text{(b)} \quad s^2 \equiv \left(\frac{\hbar}{2}\sigma\right)^2 = \frac{3}{4}\hbar^2.$$

In analogy with the relation $\mathbf{M} \times \mathbf{M} = i\hbar\mathbf{M}$ satisfied by orbital angular momentum operators let it be assumed that the spin angular momentum operator $\mathbf{s}$ satisfies the relation

$$(18.19) \qquad\qquad \mathbf{s} \times \mathbf{s} = i\hbar\mathbf{s}.$$

Since $\mathbf{s} = (\hbar/2)\mathbf{\sigma}$. in terms of $\mathbf{\sigma}$ this relation is

$$(18.20) \qquad\qquad \mathbf{\sigma} \times \mathbf{\sigma} = 2i\mathbf{\sigma}.$$

That is

$$(18.21) \quad \begin{array}{ll} \text{(a)} & \sigma_x\sigma_y - \sigma_y\sigma_x = 2i\sigma_z, \\ \text{(b)} & \sigma_y\sigma_z - \sigma_z\sigma_y = 2i\sigma_x, \\ \text{(c)} & \sigma_z\sigma_x - \sigma_x\sigma_z = 2i\sigma_y. \end{array}$$

From (18.21) and the anticommutation relations (18.17b) we find that

$$(18.22) \quad \begin{array}{ll} \text{(a)} & \sigma_x\sigma_y = -\sigma_y\sigma_x = i\sigma_z, \\ \text{(b)} & \sigma_y\sigma_z = -\sigma_z\sigma_y = i\sigma_x, \\ \text{(c)} & \sigma_z\sigma_x = -\sigma_x\sigma_z = i\sigma_y. \end{array}$$

We now proceed to find σ_x and σ_y in a representation in which σ_z has the representation (18.10a). Writing

$$(18.23) \qquad\qquad \sigma_x = \begin{pmatrix} p' & r' \\ q' & s' \end{pmatrix}$$

we find that the anticommutation relation $\sigma_x\sigma_z = -\sigma_z\sigma_x$ requires

$$(18.24) \qquad \begin{pmatrix} p' & r' \\ q' & s' \end{pmatrix} \begin{pmatrix} 1 & 0 \\ 0 & -1 \end{pmatrix} = \begin{pmatrix} -1 & 0 \\ 0 & 1 \end{pmatrix} \begin{pmatrix} p' & r' \\ q' & s' \end{pmatrix}.$$

Performing the matrix multiplication, we must have

$$(18.25) \qquad \begin{pmatrix} p' & -r' \\ q' & -s' \end{pmatrix} = \begin{pmatrix} -p' & -r' \\ q' & s' \end{pmatrix}.$$

This requires that $p' = 0$, $s' = 0$. Then, imposing the condition $\sigma_x^2 = 1$, we find that we must have $q'r' = 1$. We take $q' = 1$, $r' = 1$. Then

$$(18.26) \qquad \sigma_x = \begin{pmatrix} 0 & 1 \\ 1 & 0 \end{pmatrix}.$$

Finally, from (18.10a), (18.22c), and (18.26) we compute

$$(18.27) \quad \sigma_y = i \begin{pmatrix} 0 & 1 \\ 1 & 0 \end{pmatrix} \begin{pmatrix} 1 & 0 \\ 0 & -1 \end{pmatrix} = i \begin{pmatrix} 0 & -1 \\ 1 & 0 \end{pmatrix} = \begin{pmatrix} 0 & -i \\ i & 0 \end{pmatrix}.$$

In conclusion, by taking $\begin{pmatrix} 1 \\ 0 \end{pmatrix}$ and $\begin{pmatrix} 0 \\ 1 \end{pmatrix}$ as eigenvectors of σ_z for $\sigma_z = +1$ and -1, respectively, and by requiring that $\sigma_{z'}^2 = 1$ for all directions z' and that $\mathbf{\sigma} \times \mathbf{\sigma} = 2i\mathbf{\sigma}$, we have obtained the *Pauli spin matrices:*

$$(18.28) \quad \sigma_x = \begin{pmatrix} 0 & 1 \\ 1 & 0 \end{pmatrix}, \qquad \sigma_y = \begin{pmatrix} 0 & -i \\ i & 0 \end{pmatrix}, \qquad \sigma_z = \begin{pmatrix} 1 & 0 \\ 0 & -1 \end{pmatrix}.$$

Since the Pauli spin matrices are Hermitean, their eigenvalues are real.

The total angular momentum **J** is defined in terms of the orbital angular momentum **M** and the spin angular momentum $\mathbf{s} = (\hbar/2)\mathbf{\sigma}$ by vector addition:

$$(18.29) \qquad \mathbf{J} = \mathbf{M} + \mathbf{s} = \mathbf{M} + (\hbar/2)\mathbf{\sigma},$$

where, in the two-component Pauli formalism, the components of **M** are to be represented by 2×2 matrices

$$(18.30) \quad M_x = \begin{pmatrix} M_x & 0 \\ 0 & M_x \end{pmatrix}, \qquad M_y = \begin{pmatrix} M_y & 0 \\ 0 & M_y \end{pmatrix}, \qquad M_z = \begin{pmatrix} M_z & 0 \\ 0 & M_z \end{pmatrix}.$$

The addition in (18.29) is ordinary matrix addition (as in (17.13)). Spin independent operators, i.e. operators such as M_x, M_y, and M_z which operate on the position coordinates only, commute with spin operators, such as s_x, s_y, and s_z.

In order to introduce a useful terminology, let us consider the results of several special types of operators on two-component wave functions:

$$(18.31) \quad \begin{array}{ll} \text{(a)} & \begin{pmatrix} p & 0 \\ 0 & s \end{pmatrix} \begin{pmatrix} \psi_+ \\ \psi_- \end{pmatrix} = \begin{pmatrix} p\psi_+ \\ s\psi_- \end{pmatrix}, \\[2ex] \text{(b)} & \begin{pmatrix} 0 & r \\ q & 0 \end{pmatrix} \begin{pmatrix} \psi_+ \\ \psi_- \end{pmatrix} = \begin{pmatrix} r\psi_- \\ q\psi_+ \end{pmatrix}, \\[2ex] \text{(c)} & \begin{pmatrix} p & r \\ q & s \end{pmatrix} \begin{pmatrix} \psi_+ \\ \psi_- \end{pmatrix} = \begin{pmatrix} p\psi_+ + r\psi_- \\ q\psi_+ + s\psi_- \end{pmatrix}. \end{array}$$

In case (a), a state in which $s_z = +1$ (in which $\psi_- = 0$) is transformed into a state in which $s_z = +1$ and a state in which $s_z = -1$ (in which $\psi_+ = 0$) is transformed into a state in which $s_z = -1$. In case (b), a state in which $s_z = +1$ is transformed into a state for which $s_z = -1$ and a state in which $s_z = -1$ is transformed into a state in which $s_z = +1$. In case (c), a state in which $s_z = +1$ is transformed into a mixed state and a state in which $s_z = -1$ is transformed into a mixed state. Operators of type (a) are called *even operators*, those of type (b) are called *odd operators*, and those of type (c) are called *mixed operators*.

Problem 18.1: Show that

$$(18.32) \quad \begin{array}{ll} \text{(a)} & (\mathbf{\sigma} \cdot \mathbf{B})\mathbf{\sigma} = \mathbf{B} + i\mathbf{\sigma} \times \mathbf{B}, \\ \text{(b)} & \mathbf{\sigma}(\mathbf{\sigma} \cdot \mathbf{B}) = \mathbf{B} - i\mathbf{\sigma} \times \mathbf{B}, \\ \text{(c)} & (\mathbf{\sigma} \cdot \mathbf{B})(\mathbf{\sigma} \cdot \mathbf{C}) = \mathbf{B} \cdot \mathbf{C} + i\mathbf{\sigma} \cdot (\mathbf{B} \times \mathbf{C}), \\ \text{(d)} & (\mathbf{\sigma}, \mathbf{\sigma} \cdot \mathbf{B}) = -2i\mathbf{\sigma} \times \mathbf{B}, \end{array}$$

where $\mathbf{B}$ and $\mathbf{C}$ are any vectors that commute with $\mathbf{\sigma}$.

Problem 18.2: Show that

$$(18.33) \quad \begin{array}{llll} \text{(a)} & (J_i, M_i) = 0, & \text{(f)} & (J_i, s_i) = 0, \\ \text{(b)} & \mathbf{J} \times \mathbf{M} = i\hbar \mathbf{M}, & \text{(g)} & \mathbf{J} \times \mathbf{s} = i\hbar \mathbf{s}, \\ \text{(c)} & (J_i, M^2) = 0, & \text{(h)} & (J_i, s^2) = 0, \\ \text{(d)} & (J^2, \mathbf{M}) = 2i\hbar \mathbf{M} \times \mathbf{s}, & \text{(i)} & (J^2, \mathbf{s}) = -2i\hbar \mathbf{M} \times \mathbf{s}, \\ \text{(e)} & (J^2, M^2) = 0, & \text{(j)} & (J^2, s^2) = 0. \end{array}$$

Problem 18.3: Show that

$$(18.34) \quad \text{(a)} \quad (J^2, J_i) = 0, \qquad \text{(b)} \quad \mathbf{J} \times \mathbf{J} = i\hbar \mathbf{J}.$$

Problem 18.4: Show that $H = p^2/2m + V(r)$, J^2, M^2, and J_z commute in pairs, and that any simultaneous eigenfunction of J^2 and M^2 is also an eigenfunction of $\mathbf{M} \cdot \mathbf{s} = \dfrac{\hbar \mathbf{M}}{2} \cdot \mathbf{\sigma}$.

Problem 18.5: Using the Pauli matrices (18.28), obtain a matrix representation of $\sigma_{z'}$, (18.14). Answer:

$$(18.35) \qquad \sigma_{z'} = \begin{pmatrix} \gamma & \alpha - i\beta \\ \alpha + i\beta & -\gamma \end{pmatrix}.$$

Problem 18.6: Obtain the eigenvalues and normalized eigenvectors of $\sigma_{z'}$ in the Pauli representation (18.35). Answers:

$$(18.36) \quad \text{(a)} \quad u_1 = \lambda \begin{pmatrix} \alpha - i\beta \\ 1 - \gamma \end{pmatrix}, \qquad \text{(b)} \quad u_2 = \lambda \begin{pmatrix} \gamma - 1 \\ \alpha + i\beta \end{pmatrix},$$

are eigenvectors of $\sigma_{z'}$ for $\sigma_{z'} = +1$ and $\sigma_{z'} = -1$, respectively. When $\gamma \neq 1$, these are normalized by taking $|\lambda|^2 = 1/2(1 - \gamma)$.

Problem 18.7: Obtain the eigenvalues and normalized eigenfunctions of σ_x in the Pauli representation. Answers:

$$(18.37) \qquad u_1 = \frac{1}{\sqrt{2}} \begin{pmatrix} 1 \\ 1 \end{pmatrix}, \qquad u_2 = \frac{1}{\sqrt{2}} \begin{pmatrix} 1 \\ -1 \end{pmatrix},$$

are normalized eigenfunctions of σ_x for $\sigma_x = +1$ and for $\sigma_x = -1$, respectively.

Problem 18.8: Obtain the eigenvalues and normalized eigenfunctions of σ_y in the Pauli representation. Answers:

$$(18.38) \qquad u_1 = \frac{1}{\sqrt{2}} \begin{pmatrix} 1 \\ i \end{pmatrix}, \qquad u_2 = \frac{1}{\sqrt{2}} \begin{pmatrix} 1 \\ -i \end{pmatrix},$$

are normalized eigenfunctions of σ_y for $\sigma_y = +1$ and for $\sigma_y = -1$, respectively.

Problem 18.9: Let $\boldsymbol{\pi} = \mathbf{p} - (e/c)\mathbf{A}$. Show that

$$(18.39) \qquad \boldsymbol{\pi} \times \boldsymbol{\pi} = -\frac{e}{c}(\mathbf{p} \times \mathbf{A} + \mathbf{A} \times \mathbf{p}) = \frac{i\hbar e \mathbf{B}}{c}$$

and that

$$(18.40) \qquad (\boldsymbol{\sigma} \cdot \boldsymbol{\pi})^2 = \pi^2 - 2m_0 \boldsymbol{\mu}_s \cdot \mathbf{B} = \pi^2 + 2m_0 G_s \mathbf{s} \cdot \mathbf{B},$$

where $\mathbf{B} = \text{Curl } \mathbf{A}$ and

$$(18.41) \qquad \boldsymbol{\mu}_s = -G_s \mathbf{s} = \frac{e}{m_0 c} \mathbf{s} = \frac{e\hbar}{2m_0 c} \boldsymbol{\sigma},$$

(see (14.81b)).

Problem 18.10: Using the Pauli matrices (18.28), obtain a matrix representation of $\mathbf{M} \cdot \boldsymbol{\sigma} = M_x \sigma_x + M_y \sigma_y + M_z \sigma_z$. Answer:

$$(18.42) \qquad \mathbf{M} \cdot \boldsymbol{\sigma} = \begin{pmatrix} M_z & M_- \\ M_+ & -M_z \end{pmatrix}$$

where $M_+ = M_x + iM_y$, $M_- = M_x - iM_y$.

18.2. Inner Products and Expectation Values. It is readily verifiable that the inner product

$$(18.43) \qquad (f,g) = \int (f_+^* g_+ + f_-^* g_-) \, d\mathbf{r}$$

of two two-component functions $f = \begin{pmatrix} f_+ \\ f_- \end{pmatrix}$ and $g = \begin{pmatrix} g_+ \\ g_- \end{pmatrix}$ satisfies the basic requirements (6.6). In case the two components of f depend on xyz in the same way and the two components of g depend on xyz in the same way, that is, in case f and g assume the forms

$$(18.44) \qquad f = f_1(xyz) \begin{pmatrix} c_+ \\ c_- \end{pmatrix}, \qquad g = g_1(xyz) \begin{pmatrix} d_+ \\ d_- \end{pmatrix},$$

the inner product (18.43) becomes

(18.45) $(f,g) = (c_+{}^*d_+ + c_-{}^*d_-) \int f_1 g_1 \, d\mathbf{r}.$

Then, for functions $u = \begin{pmatrix} c_+ \\ c_- \end{pmatrix}$ and $v = \begin{pmatrix} d_+ \\ d_- \end{pmatrix}$ entirely in spin space, we may appropriately define the inner product (u,v) by

(18.46) $(u,v) = (c_+{}^*d_+ + c_-{}^*d_-).$

Two spin vectors u and v are *orthogonal* if $(u,v) = 0$. The norm of a function u entirely in spin space is

(18.47) $N(u) = (u,u) = |c_+|^2 + |c_-|^2.$

A spin vector u is *normalized* if $N(u) = 1$.

In a state represented by a spin vector u, the expectation value of a spin observable A is

(18.48) $\langle A \rangle = \dfrac{(u, A u)}{(u,u)}$

where, in the right-hand member, A is the 2×2 matrix representation of the spin operator A.

Let u_1 and u_2 be orthonormal eigenfunctions of a Hermitean spin operator A. Then any two-component spin function u may be represented in the form

(18.49) $u = c_1 u_1 + c_2 u_2,$

where, as a consequence of the orthonormality of u_1 and u_2,

(18.50) $c_1 = (u_1, u), \qquad c_2 = (u_2, u), \qquad (u,u) = |c_1|^2 + |c_2|^2 = c^2.$

Then, according to Postulate IV (Section 12.4, see in particular (12.22)),

(18.51) $P(a_1) = |c_1|^2/c^2, \qquad P(a_2) = |c_2|^2/c^2,$

where a_1 and a_2 are the eigenvalues of A.

Problem 18.11: Calculate the expectation value and the probability distribution of σ_x for a state in which $\sigma_z = -1$. (Hint: Use (18.37), (18.41)-(18.51), and the appropriate eigenvector of σ_z.) Answers: $\langle \sigma_x \rangle = 0$, $P(+1) = P(-1) = \frac{1}{2}$.

Problem 18.12: Calculate the expectation values of σ_x, σ_y, and σ_z for a spin state in which $\sigma_{z'} = 1$. Also calculate the probability distributions for σ_z, σ_y, and σ_z for such a state. (Hint: Use (18.36a), (18.37), (18.38), the eigenvectors of σ_z, and (18.48)-(18.51).) Answers:

(a)	$\langle \sigma_x \rangle = \alpha$; for $\sigma_x, P(+1) = (1 + \alpha)/2, P(-1) = (1 - \alpha)/2,$	
(18.52)	(b)	$\langle \sigma_y \rangle = \beta$; for $\sigma_y, P(+1) = (1 + \beta)/2, P(-1) = (1 - \beta)/2,$	
(c)	$\langle \sigma_z \rangle = \gamma$; for $\sigma_z, P(+1) = (1 + \gamma)/2, P(-1) = (1 - \gamma)/2.$	

18.3. The Normal Zeeman Effect in the Pauli Theory. An explanation of the anomalous Zeeman effect requires that interaction between spin and orbital magnetic momenta be taken into account. In this section, we neglect this spin-orbit interaction but include interaction between the spin magnetic moment and an external magnetic field, thus obtaining a more detailed explanation of the normal Zeeman effect than was given in Section 15.12.

The interaction between spin magnetic moment and an external magnetic field $\mathbf{B}$ may be included by supplementing the Hamiltonian (15.85) for a hydrogen atom in a magnetic field by a term giving the effect of the spin on the energy. We may write

$$
\begin{align}
\text{(a)} \quad & W_M = -\mathbf{\mu}_M \cdot \mathbf{B} = G\mathbf{M} \cdot \mathbf{B}, \\
\text{(b)} \quad & W_s = -\mathbf{\mu}_s \cdot \mathbf{B} = G_s\mathbf{s} \cdot \mathbf{B},
\end{align}
\tag{18.53}
$$

for the energies of interaction between the magnetic field $\mathbf{B}$ and the orbital and spin magnetic moments $\mathbf{\mu}_M$ and $\mathbf{\mu}_s$, respectively. $G = -e/2m_0c$ and $G_s = -e/m_0c$ are the orbital and spin gyromagnetic ratios (14.81), respectively. We then have

$$
H = H_0 + G\mathbf{M} \cdot \mathbf{B} + G_s\mathbf{s} \cdot \mathbf{B} = H^{(1)} + G_s\mathbf{s} \cdot \mathbf{B}
\tag{18.54}
$$

where

$$
H^{(1)} = H_0 + G\mathbf{M} \cdot \mathbf{B} = p^2/2m_0 + eV + G\mathbf{M} \cdot \mathbf{B}.
\tag{18.55}
$$

In the Pauli two-component wave theory, any spin independent operator, such as $H^{(1)}$, is represented by an *even* 2×2 matrix:

$$
H^{(1)} = \begin{pmatrix} H^{(1)} & 0 \\ 0 & H^{(1)} \end{pmatrix}.
\tag{18.56}
$$

Replacing $\mathbf{M}$ in (18.42) by $\mathbf{B}$, we have also

$$
\mathbf{s} \cdot \mathbf{B} = \frac{\hbar}{2}\mathbf{\sigma} \cdot \mathbf{B} = \frac{\hbar}{2}\begin{pmatrix} B_z & B_- \\ B_+ & -B_z \end{pmatrix},
\tag{18.57}
$$

where $B_+ = B_x + iB_y$, $B_- = B_x - iB_y$. Combining (18.56) and (18.57) as required by (18.54), we obtain

$$
H = \begin{pmatrix} H^{(1)} - \dfrac{e\hbar B_z}{2m_0c} & B_- \\ B_+ & H^{(1)} + \dfrac{e\hbar B_z}{2m_0c} \end{pmatrix}.
\tag{18.58}
$$

To simplify further calculations, we take the z axis parallel to $\mathbf{B}$. Then

$B_x = 0$, $B_y = 0$, $B_+ = 0$, $B_- = 0$, and $B_z = B$. In this coordinate system the Hamiltonian is an even operator:

$$(18.59) \qquad H = \begin{pmatrix} H^{(1)} - \dfrac{e\hbar B}{2m_0 c} & 0 \\ 0 & H^{(1)} + \dfrac{e\hbar B}{2m_0 c} \end{pmatrix}.$$

For the Hamiltonian (18.59) the energy eigenvalue equation $H\psi = E\psi$, where ψ is a two-component wave function $\begin{pmatrix} \psi+ \\ \psi- \end{pmatrix}$, separates into independent equations

$$(18.60) \qquad \begin{array}{ll} \text{(a)} & (H^{(1)} - e\hbar B/2m_0 c)\psi_+ = E\psi_+, \\ \text{(b)} & (H^{(1)} + e\hbar B/2m_0 c)\psi_- = E\psi_-. \end{array}$$

Writing (18.60) in the form

$$(18.61) \qquad \begin{array}{ll} \text{(a)} & H^{(1)}\psi_+ = (E + e\hbar B/2m_0 c)\psi_+, \\ \text{(b)} & H^{(1)}\psi_- = (E - e\hbar B/2m_0 c)\psi_-. \end{array}$$

we see that ψ_+ and ψ_- are separately eigenfunctions of $H^{(1)}$, but for different eigenvalues.

For the hydrogen atom, the functions $\psi_{nl}{}^m$ given in (15.41) were found in Section 15.12 to be simultaneous eigenfunctions of $H^{(1)}$, M^2, and M_z for $H^{(1)} = E_{nm}$ (see (15.88)), $M^2 = l(l+1)\hbar^2$ and $M_z = m\hbar$. Note that $H^{(1)}$ (18.55) is identical with H (15.85) when the z axis is taken parallel to $\mathbf{B}$. Since generally the difference between $E + e\hbar B/2m_0 c$ and $E - e\hbar B/2m_0 c$, viz. $e\hbar B/m_0 c$, will not be equal to the difference between two of the eigenvalues (15.88) of $H^{(1)}$, the system (18.61) can in general only be satisfied by taking $\psi_- = 0$ and $\psi_+ = \psi_{nl}{}^m$, or by taking $\psi_+ = 0$ and $\psi_- = \psi_{nl}{}^m$. Thus we obtain the two two-component wave functions

$$(18.62) \qquad \text{(a)} \quad \Psi_{nl+}{}^m = \begin{pmatrix} \psi_{nl}{}^m \\ 0 \end{pmatrix}, \qquad \text{(b)} \quad \Psi_{nl-}{}^m = \begin{pmatrix} 0 \\ \psi_{nl}{}^m \end{pmatrix},$$

which are simultaneous eigenfunctions of H (the Hamiltonian (18.59)), M^2, M_z, and s_z, the former for $H = E_{nm} - e\hbar B/2m_0 c$, $s_z = \hbar/2$, the latter for $H = E_{nm} + e\hbar B/2m_0 c$, $s_z = -\hbar/2$, both for $M^2 = l(l+1)\hbar^2$, $M_z = m\hbar$.

In the absence of a magnetic field, (18.62) gives simultaneous eigenfunctions of H, M^2, M_z, and s_z for $H = -Rch/n^2$, $M^2 = l(l+1)\hbar^2$, $M_z = m\hbar$, and $s_z \pm \hbar/2$.

18.4. Eigenfunctions of Hydrogen for the Stern-Gerlach Experiment. In a Stern-Gerlach experiment with atomic hydrogen, atoms in, say, the first or second excited states are separated according to the values of a component of $\mathbf{J} = \mathbf{M} + \mathbf{s}$, call it J_z. Rather than simultaneous eigenfunctions of $H = p^2/2m + e^2/r$, M^2, M_z, and s_z we are interested in simultaneous eigenfunctions of H, J^2, M^2, and J_z. We see quite readily that, since

$$(18.63) \qquad J^2 = \left(\mathbf{M} + \frac{\hbar}{2}\,\mathbf{\sigma}\right)^2 = M^2 + \hbar\mathbf{M} \cdot \mathbf{\sigma} + 3\hbar^2/4$$

is a mixed operator (see (18.31c) and (18.42)), the two-component wave functions (18.62) are not eigenfunctions of J^2.

As a complete set of commuting operators we take H, J, M^2, and J_z. Calculations may be shortened by including $\mathbf{M} \cdot \mathbf{\sigma}$ in the set when we look for simultaneous eigenfunctions (see Problem 18.4). Starting with M^2 and J_z, we must have, for some λ and μ,

$$(18.64) \quad \begin{aligned} &\text{(a)} \quad M^2 \begin{pmatrix} \psi_+ \\ \psi_- \end{pmatrix} = \lambda \begin{pmatrix} \psi_+ \\ \psi_- \end{pmatrix}, \\ &\text{(b)} \quad J_z \begin{pmatrix} \psi_+ \\ \psi_- \end{pmatrix} = (M_z + s_z) \begin{pmatrix} \psi_+ \\ \psi_- \end{pmatrix} \\ &\qquad\qquad = \begin{pmatrix} M_z + \hbar/2 & 0 \\ 0 & M_z - \hbar/2 \end{pmatrix} \begin{pmatrix} \psi_+ \\ \psi_- \end{pmatrix} = \mu \begin{pmatrix} \psi_+ \\ \psi_- \end{pmatrix}. \end{aligned}$$

This gives the system of four equations

$$(18.65) \quad \begin{aligned} &\text{(a)} \quad M^2\psi_+ = \lambda\psi_+, \qquad \text{(b)} \quad M_z\psi_+ = \left(\mu - \frac{\hbar}{2}\right)\psi_+, \\ &\text{(c)} \quad M^2\psi_- = \lambda\psi_-, \qquad \text{(d)} \quad M_z\psi_- = \left(\mu + \frac{\hbar}{2}\right)\psi_-. \end{aligned}$$

Hence ψ_+ and ψ_- are eigenfunctions of M^2 for $M^2 = \lambda$ and of M_z for $M_z = \mu - \hbar/2$ and $M_z = \mu + \hbar/2$, respectively. Since the eigenvalues of M^2 and of M_z are $l(l + 1)\hbar^2$ and $m\hbar$, we must take $\lambda = l(l + 1)\hbar^2$ and $\mu - \hbar/2 = m\hbar$, $\mu + \hbar/2 = (m + 1)\hbar$, $\mu = (m + \frac{1}{2})\hbar$, for some m, $-l \le m \le l$. Then

$$(18.66) \qquad \psi = \begin{pmatrix} f_+(r)\,Y_l{}^m(\theta,\varphi) \\ f_-(r)\,Y_l{}^{m+1}(\theta,\varphi) \end{pmatrix},$$

where $f_+(r)$ and $f_-(r)$ remain to be determined, is a simultaneous eigenfunction of M^2 and J_z for $M^2 = l(l + 1)\hbar^2$ and $J_z = (m + \frac{1}{2})\hbar$.

A relation between $f_+(r)$ and $f_-(r)$ may be obtained by requiring that (18.66) be an eigenfunction of $\mathbf{M} \cdot \mathbf{\sigma}$. Writing $\mathbf{M} \cdot \mathbf{\sigma}\psi = u\hbar\psi$ and using (18.42) and (18.66), we have

$$(18.67) \qquad \begin{pmatrix} M_z & M_- \\ M_+ & -M_z \end{pmatrix} \begin{pmatrix} f_+Y_l{}^m \\ f_-Y_l{}^m \end{pmatrix} = u\hbar \begin{pmatrix} f_+Y_l{}^m \\ f_-Y_l{}^m \end{pmatrix}.$$

That is,

$$(18.68) \quad \begin{aligned} &\text{(a)} \quad M_z(f_+Y_l{}^m) + M_-(f_-Y_l{}^{m+1}) = u\hbar f_+Y_l{}^m, \\ &\text{(b)} \quad M_+(f_+Y_l{}^m) - M_z(f_-Y_l{}^{m+1}) = u\hbar f_-Y_l{}^{m+1}. \end{aligned}$$

But M_z, M_+, and M_- commute with $f_+(r)$ and $f_-(r)$ (see (14.11)). Further,

(18.69)
$$\begin{aligned}
&\text{(a)}\quad M_z Y_l^m = m\hbar Y_l^m,\\
&\text{(b)}\quad M_- Y_l^{m+1} = c_l^m Y_l^m,\\
&\text{(c)}\quad M_z Y_l^{m+1} = (m+1)\hbar Y_l^{m+1},\\
&\text{(d)}\quad M_+ Y_l^m = c_l^m Y_l^{m+1}
\end{aligned}$$

(see (14.48), (14.57), and (14.58)). Hence, substituting from (18.69) into (18.68), we obtain

(18.70)
$$\begin{aligned}
&\text{(a)}\quad m\hbar f_+ + c_l^m f_- = u\hbar f_+,\\
&\text{(b)}\quad c_l^m f_+ - (m+1)\hbar f_- = u\hbar f_-.
\end{aligned}$$

Using (14.57), we find that these relations between f_+ and f_- are consistent only if $u = l$ or $u = -l - 1$.

For the case $u = l$, (18.70) is satisfied if

$$(18.71) \qquad \sqrt{l - m}\, f_+ = \sqrt{l + m + 1}\, f_-.$$

Observing from (18.63) that $J^2 = (l + \tfrac{1}{2})(l + \tfrac{3}{2})\hbar^2$ when $M^2 = l(l + 1)\hbar^2$ and $\mathbf{M} \cdot \boldsymbol{\sigma} = l\hbar$, we conclude that the two-component wave function

$$(18.72) \qquad \psi_1 = g_1(r)\begin{pmatrix} \sqrt{l + m + 1}\; Y_l^m(\theta,\varphi) \\ \sqrt{l - m}\; Y_l^{m+1}(\theta,\varphi) \end{pmatrix}$$

where $g_1(r)$ is arbitrary, is a simultaneous eigenfunction of J^2, M^2, and J_z for $J^2 = j(j + 1)\hbar^2$, $M^2 = l(l + 1)\hbar^2$ and $J_z = (m + \tfrac{1}{2})\hbar$ where $j = l + \tfrac{1}{2}$ and $-l \le m \le l$.

For the case $u = -l - 1$, (18.70) is satisfied if

$$(18.73) \qquad \sqrt{l + m + 1}\, f_+ = -\sqrt{l - m}\, f_-.$$

Observing from (18.63) that $J^2 = (l - \tfrac{1}{2})(l + \tfrac{1}{2})\hbar^2$ when $M^2 = l(l + 1)\hbar^2$ and $\mathbf{M} \cdot \boldsymbol{\sigma} = -(l + 1)\hbar$, we conclude that the two-component wave function

$$(18.74) \qquad \psi_2 = g_2(r)\begin{pmatrix} \sqrt{l - m}\; Y_l^m(\theta,\varphi) \\ -\sqrt{l + m + 1}\; Y_l^{m+1}(\theta,\varphi) \end{pmatrix}$$

where $g_2(r)$ is arbitrary, is a simultaneous eigenfunction of J^2, M^2, and J_z for $J^2 = j(j + 1)\hbar^2$, $M^2 = l(l + 1)\hbar^2$ and $J_z = (m + \tfrac{1}{2})\hbar$ where $j = l - \tfrac{1}{2}$ and $-l \le m \le l$.

The preceding formulas remain valid when $m = l$ and when $m = -l - 1$ if we put $Y_l^m = 0$ for $|m| > l$. However $j = \tfrac{1}{2}$ only when $l = 0$.

For the Hamiltonian H we take the form (15.19). We note that H is an even operator. Since the two two-component wave functions (18.72) and (18.74) are eigenfunctions of M^2 for $M^2 = l(l + 1)\hbar^2$, we see quite readily that they are also eigenfunctions of H if $g_1(r)$ and $g_2(r)$ satisfy (15.20).

For the hydrogen atom, for which $V(r) = -e^2/r$, we have previously found that (15.20) possesses a solution with finite norm provided E_{in} is one of the energy eigenvalues $E_{in} = E_n = -Rch/n^2$. Thus, according to the Pauli two-component theory, the Bohr energy levels are not affected by the introduction of the electron spin hypothesis. In this theory, no allowance is made for interaction between spin and orbital magnetic momenta.

Problem 18.13: Calculate $\langle M_z \rangle$ for the eigenstates (18.72) and (18.74).

Answers: For (18.72), $\langle M_z \rangle = \dfrac{l(2m + 1)\hbar}{(2l + 1)}$; for (18.74),

$$\langle M_z \rangle = \frac{(l + 1)(2m + 1)\hbar}{(2l + 1)}.$$

Problem 18.14: Show that, for a free particle, for which $H = p^2/2m$, $\mathbf{p}$ and $\mathbf{p} \cdot \mathbf{s}$ are compatible constants of the motion. Using (18.32c), show that $\mathbf{p} \cdot \mathbf{s} = \pm (\hbar/2)p_0$ when $\mathbf{p} = \mathbf{p}_0$. This means that, for an eigenstate of $\mathbf{p}$, the projection of $\mathbf{s}$ along $\mathbf{p}$ is equal to $\pm \hbar/2$. Find normalized simultaneous eigenfunctions of $\mathbf{p}$ and $\mathbf{p} \cdot \mathbf{s}$. (Hint: Take the z' axis parallel to $\mathbf{p}$. Then, in (18.35), $\alpha = p_x/p$, $\beta = p_y/p$, and $\gamma = p_z/p$.) Answer:

$$(18.75) \quad (a) \quad \chi = \lambda e^{i\mathbf{p}\cdot\mathbf{r}/\hbar} \begin{pmatrix} p_x - ip_y \\ p - p_z \end{pmatrix}, \quad (b) \quad \varphi = \lambda e^{i\mathbf{p}\cdot\mathbf{r}/\hbar} \begin{pmatrix} p_z - p \\ p_x + ip_y \end{pmatrix}$$

are simultaneous eigenfunctions for $\mathbf{p} \cdot \mathbf{s} = (\hbar/2)p$ and for $\mathbf{p} \cdot \mathbf{s} = -(\hbar/2)p$, respectively. When $p_z \neq p$, these are normalized in spin space by taking $\lambda = 1/2p(p - p_z)$.

18.5. The Anomalous Zeeman Effect. In the *anomalous Zeeman effect*, a magnetic field splits spectral lines into more than the three components observed in the normal Zeeman effect. The electron spin hypothesis was suggested in 1928 by Uhlenbeck and Goudsmit primarily in attempting to explain this effect.

In addition to the orbital magnetic moment $\mathbf{\mu}_M = -G\mathbf{M}$ associated with the orbital angular momentum $\mathbf{M}$, an electron is attributed an intrinsic magnetic moment $\mathbf{\mu}_s = -G_s\mathbf{s}$ associated with its spin angular momentum $\mathbf{s}$. Then the total magnetic moment is

$$(18.76) \qquad \mathbf{\mu} = \mathbf{\mu}_M + \mathbf{\mu}_s = -G\mathbf{M} - G_s\mathbf{s}.$$

We recall (see (14.81)) that $G_s = 2G = -e/m_0c$ where e is numerically negative for an electron.

Neglecting interaction between $\mathbf{\mu}_M$ and $\mathbf{\mu}_s$, the potential energy of an electron in a magnetic field $\mathbf{B}$, due to the magnetic moment of the electron is (see (18.53))

$$(18.77) \qquad W = -\mathbf{\mu} \cdot \mathbf{B} = G\mathbf{M} \cdot \mathbf{B} + G_s\mathbf{s} \cdot \mathbf{B}.$$

Except in the presence of very strong magnetic fields, the coupling between $\mathbf{\mu}_M$ and $\mathbf{\mu}_s$ is so great that it can not be neglected. It is found that this coupling can be properly accounted for by a very simple vector model relating the orbital and spin angular moments and magnetic momenta. (*Landé's vector model*.) The model (Fig. 18.1) is a rigid vector structure in which $\mathbf{M}$ and $\mathbf{s}$ precess around $\mathbf{J} = \mathbf{M} + \mathbf{s}$ so rapidly that in (18.77) the only effective part of $\mathbf{\mu}$ is the component of $\mathbf{\mu}$ along $-\mathbf{J}$. Then, in place of (18.77) we write

$$(18.78) \qquad W = gG\mathbf{J} \cdot \mathbf{B}$$

where $gGJ = \mu \cos(\mathbf{\mu}, \mathbf{J})$ is the component of $\mathbf{\mu}$ along $-\mathbf{J}$. The usefulness

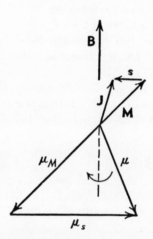

Fig. 18.1. The Landé vector model.

of the factor g, called the *Landé g factor*, was discovered by Landé in 1923,[2] before the introduction of electron spin.

To evaluate g with $G_s = 2G$, we write

$$(18.79) \quad gGJ^2 = -\mathbf{\mu} \cdot \mathbf{J} = (G\mathbf{M} + G_s\mathbf{s}) \cdot \mathbf{J} = G(\mathbf{M} + 2\mathbf{s}) \cdot (\mathbf{M} + \mathbf{s})$$
$$= G(M^2 + 3\mathbf{M} \cdot \mathbf{s} + 2|s|^2).$$

Eliminating $\mathbf{M} \cdot \mathbf{s}$ by using the relation $J^2 = M^2 + 2\mathbf{M} \cdot \mathbf{s} + |s|^2$, we obtain

$$(18.80) \qquad g = (3J^2 - M^2 + |s|^2)/2J^2.$$

Upon introducing the eigenvalues $J^2 = j(j+1)\hbar^2$, $M^2 = l(l+1)\hbar^2$, $|s|^2 = s(s+1)\hbar^2$, we obtain, in conventional form

$$(18.81) \qquad g = 1 + \frac{j(j+1) + s(s+1) - l(l+1)}{2j(j+1)}.$$

For the hydrogen atom, $j = l \pm \frac{1}{2}$ ($j = \frac{1}{2}$ when $l = 0$) and $s = \frac{1}{2}$.

[2] A. Landé, Z. *Physik*, **5**, 231 (1921); **7**, 398 (1921); **11**, 353 (1922); **15**, 189 (1923); **19**, 112 (1923).

Taking the z axis parallel to $\mathbf{B}$, we may write $W = gGJ_zB$. Since the eigenvalues of J_z are $m_J\hbar$ where $m_J = m + \frac{1}{2}$, the eigenvalues of W are $W = gm_JGB$. In a transition the change in W is $\Delta W = GB\Delta(gm_J)$ where $\Delta(gm_J) = g'm_J' - gm_J$ is to be calculated, using values of g and g' obtained from the Landé formula (18.81).

18.6. References for Supplementary Reading.

Section 18.1: Bohm, 387–406; Born, 151–5, 185–8; Dirac, 149–52; Houston, 99–106; Kemble, 510–19; Kramers, 238–45; Mandl, 109–16; McConnell, 84–90; Mott and Sneddon, 89–90, 92–8; Persico, 391–8.

Section 18.2: McConnell, 90–96.

Section 18.3: Houston, 106–8; Persico, 261–5, 398–400.

Section 18.4: Dirac, 152–9; Houston, 108–12; Kramers, 245–52; Peaslee and Mueller, 257–72.

Section 18.5: Born, 155–63, 368–9; Dirac, 181–4; French, 233–8; Frenkel, 279–97; Houston, 124–32; Mott and Sneddon, 84–5, 91–2, 98–101; Peaslee and Mueller, 272–82; Schaefer, 167–74; Shankland, 126–31.

CHAPTER 19

RELATIVISTIC QUANTUM MECHANICS

19.1. The Klein-Gordon Equation. Schroedinger's discovery in 1925 of a nonrelativistic wave equation led immediately to the suggestion, by Schroedinger and by a number of other physicists, that a relativistic wave equation could be obtained by making the substitutions (5.38) and (5.39) into the relativistic energy-momentum relation (5.42). This gives the Klein-Gordon equation (5.43).

The Klein-Gordon equation fails to account for electron spin and the formalism of nonrelativistic quantum mechanics cannot be applied since the Hamiltonian operator no longer plays a central role. For a time the equation was discredited due to difficulties arising in interpreting solutions,[1] but in recent years its significance in the theory of particles of spin zero and its close relation to wave equations for particles with spin have been more fully appreciated.

Problem 19.1: What two difficulties arise in interpreting solutions of the Klein-Gordon equation?[1]

Problem 19.2: By setting $E = E' + m_0c^2$ in the relativistic energy-momentum relation (5.42) and assuming that $2m_0c^2 \gg E - e\phi$, obtain its nonrelativistic approximation (4.13).

Problem 19.3: By setting

$$(19.1) \qquad \psi = e^{-m_0c^2t/\hbar}\psi'$$

in the Klein-Gordon equation (5.43) and assuming that $(E - e\phi)^2\psi$ may be neglected in comparison with $2m_0c^2(E - e\psi)\psi$, where $E = i\hbar\dfrac{\partial}{\partial t}$, obtain a nonrelativistic approximation to the Klein-Gordon equation. (Answer: See (7.42)).

19.2. Dirac's Relativistic Wave Equation. In order to obtain a relativistic wave equation which avoids the difficulties encountered with the Klein-Gordon equation, we might solve the relativistic energy-momentum relations (5.42) for E:

$$(19.2) \qquad E = c\left\{\left(\mathbf{p} - \frac{e}{c}\mathbf{A}\right)^2 + m_0c^2\right\}^{1/2} + V, \qquad V = e\phi,$$

[1] See N. F. Mott and I. N. Sneddon, *Wave Mechanics and Its Applications*, Oxford, 1948, p. 295; H. Feshbach and P. Villars, *Revs. Modern Phys.*, **30**, 25 (1958).

and then introduce operator representations (5.38) for **p** and E. The resulting equation

(19.3) $\qquad c\left\{\left(i\hbar \operatorname{grad} + \dfrac{e}{c}\mathbf{A}\right)^2 + m_0^2 c^2\right\}^{1/2}\psi + V\psi = E\psi,$

is of the first order in differentiation with respect to the time. Thus one of the earlier objections to the Klein-Gordon equation has been eliminated. Serious interpretative difficulty arises, however, due to the "square root" operator in (19.3). Yet progress has been made, since (19.3) may be written in the form (8.2) of the Schroedinger wave equation if we let

(19.4) $\qquad H = c\{\pi^2 + m_0^2 c^2\}^{1/2} + V, \qquad \pi = \mathbf{p} - \dfrac{e}{c}\mathbf{A}.$

This suggests that the formalism of nonrelativistic quantum mechanics might still be utilized provided some means were discovered for interpreting the square root operator in (19.4).

Dirac[2] accomplished this in 1928 by writing

(19.5) $\qquad\qquad \{\pi^2 + m_0^2 c^2\}^{1/2} = \boldsymbol{\alpha} \cdot \boldsymbol{\pi} + m_0 c\beta,$

where, quite evidently, $\boldsymbol{\alpha} = \alpha_1, \alpha_2, \alpha_3$, and β are not ordinary numbers. Their nature we proceed to investigate.

Squaring both sides of (19.5), and assuming that the α's and β commute with the components of $\boldsymbol{\pi}$ but not with each other, we obtain, upon setting $\mathbf{A} = 0$, $\boldsymbol{\pi} = \mathbf{p}$ for brevity of writing,

(19.6) $\quad p_x^2 + p_y^2 + p_z^2 + m_0^2 c^2 = \alpha_1^2 p_x^2 + \alpha_2^2 p_y^2 + \alpha_3^2 p_z^2 + m_0^2 c^2 \beta^2$
$\qquad + (\alpha_1\alpha_2 + \alpha_2\alpha_1)p_x p_y + (\alpha_2\alpha_3 + \alpha_3\alpha_2)p_y p_z + (\alpha_3\alpha_1 + \alpha_1\alpha_3)p_z p_x$
$\qquad + m_0 c\{(\alpha_1\beta + \beta\alpha_1)p_x + (\alpha_2\beta + \beta\alpha_2)p_y + (\alpha_3\beta + \beta\alpha_3)p_z\}.$

This is an identity if

(19.7)
$\quad$ (a) $\quad \alpha_i^2 = 1, \qquad i = 1, 2, 3,$
$\quad$ (b) $\quad \alpha_i\alpha_j + \alpha_j\alpha_i = 0,\ i, j = 1, 2, 3,\ i \neq j,$
$\quad$ (c) $\quad \alpha_i\beta + \beta\alpha_i = 0,\ i = 1, 2, 3,$
$\quad$ (d) $\quad \beta^2 = 1.$

Only recently has it been realized that the further theory may be developed without introducing any concrete representation for the α's and β. However, because of its importance in the literature and because of its helpfulness in gaining an understanding of Dirac's theory, we proceed to develop Dirac's matrix representation. In this representation the Pauli spin matrices (18.28) play a central role.

---

[2] P. A. M. Dirac, *Proc. Roy. Soc. (London)*, **117A**, 610 (1928); *Principles of Quantum Mechanics*, fourth edition, Oxford, 1958, Ch. XI.

19.3. The Dirac Matrices. Dirac found that the relations (19.7) can be satisfied by square matrices of order 4, but not by matrices of lower order. Let us start with the Pauli spin matrices (18.28) and the 2×2 identity matrix $\mathbb{1}$:

$$\text{(a)} \quad \sigma_x = \begin{pmatrix} 0 & 1 \\ 1 & 0 \end{pmatrix}, \qquad \text{(b)} \quad \sigma_y = \begin{pmatrix} 0 & -i \\ i & 0 \end{pmatrix},$$

(19.8)

$$\text{(c)} \quad \sigma_z = \begin{pmatrix} 1 & 0 \\ 0 & -1 \end{pmatrix}, \qquad \text{(d)} \quad \mathbb{1} = \begin{pmatrix} 1 & 0 \\ 0 & 1 \end{pmatrix}.$$

Extending these to 4×4 matrices by writing

$$\text{(a)} \quad \alpha_1 = \begin{pmatrix} 0 & \sigma_x \\ \sigma_x & 0 \end{pmatrix} = \begin{pmatrix} 0 & 0 & 0 & 1 \\ 0 & 0 & 1 & 0 \\ 0 & 1 & 0 & 0 \\ 1 & 0 & 0 & 0 \end{pmatrix},$$

$$\text{(b)} \quad \alpha_2 = \begin{pmatrix} 0 & \sigma_y \\ \sigma_y & 0 \end{pmatrix} = \begin{pmatrix} 0 & 0 & 0 & -i \\ 0 & 0 & i & 0 \\ 0 & -i & 0 & 0 \\ i & 0 & 0 & 0 \end{pmatrix},$$

(19.9)

$$\text{(c)} \quad \alpha_3 = \begin{pmatrix} 0 & \sigma_z \\ \sigma_z & 0 \end{pmatrix} = \begin{pmatrix} 0 & 0 & 1 & 0 \\ 0 & 0 & 0 & -1 \\ 1 & 0 & 0 & 0 \\ 0 & -1 & 0 & 0 \end{pmatrix},$$

$$\text{(d)} \quad \beta = \begin{pmatrix} \mathbb{1} & 0 \\ 0 & -\mathbb{1} \end{pmatrix} = \begin{pmatrix} 1 & 0 & 0 & 0 \\ 0 & 1 & 0 & 0 \\ 0 & 0 & -1 & 0 \\ 0 & 0 & 0 & -1 \end{pmatrix},$$

we may readily verify, either by direct multiplication of the 4×4 matrices in pairs or by multiplication of the intermediate 2×2 block matrices and use of the properties (18.17) and (18.22) of Pauli's spin matrices that the conditions (19.7) are satisfied.

It may be noted that each of the Dirac matrices (19.9) is Hermitean and has vanishing trace (sum of diagonal elements).

Problem 19.4: Verify that the Dirac matrices (19.9) satisfy (19.7).

Problem 19.5: Define 4×4 matrices σ_1, σ_2, and σ_3 by

(19.10) $\sigma_1 = -i\alpha_2\alpha_3, \qquad \sigma_2 = -i\alpha_3\alpha_1, \qquad \sigma_3 = -i\alpha_1\alpha_2.$

Show that

(19.11) $$\sigma_i = \begin{pmatrix} \sigma_i & 0 \\ 0 & \sigma_i \end{pmatrix}, \qquad i = 1, 2, 3,$$

where $\sigma_1 = \sigma_x, \sigma_2 = \sigma_y, \sigma_3 = \sigma_z$.

Problem 19.6:   Show that

$$
\begin{array}{lll}
\text{(a)} & (\sigma_i, \alpha_i) = 0, & \text{(b)} \quad (\sigma_i, \alpha_j) = 2i\alpha_k, \\
\text{(c)} & \sigma_i \alpha_j = -\alpha_j \sigma_i = i\alpha_k, \\
\text{(d)} & \mathbf{\sigma} \times \mathbf{\sigma} = 2i\mathbf{\sigma}, & \text{(e)} \quad (\sigma_i, \beta) = 0,
\end{array}
$$

(19.12)

where i, j, $k = 1$, 2, 3 cyclically permuted.

Problem 19.7:   Define a 4×4 matrix ρ by

$$\rho = -i\alpha_1 \alpha_2 \alpha_3. \tag{19.13}$$

Show that

$$
\text{(a)} \quad \rho = \begin{pmatrix} 0 & \mathbb{1} \\ \mathbb{1} & 0 \end{pmatrix} = \begin{pmatrix} 0 & 0 & 1 & 0 \\ 0 & 0 & 0 & 1 \\ 1 & 0 & 0 & 0 \\ 0 & 1 & 0 & 0 \end{pmatrix},
$$

(19.14)

$$
\text{(b)} \quad \rho^2 = \begin{pmatrix} \mathbb{1} & 0 \\ 0 & \mathbb{1} \end{pmatrix} = \begin{pmatrix} 1 & 0 & 0 & 0 \\ 0 & 1 & 0 & 0 \\ 0 & 0 & 1 & 0 \\ 0 & 0 & 0 & 1 \end{pmatrix},
$$

$$
\begin{array}{ll}
\text{(c)} & \alpha_i = \rho\sigma_i = \sigma_i\rho, \\
\text{(d)} & \sigma_i = \rho\alpha_i = \alpha_i\rho, \\
\text{(e)} & \rho\beta = -\beta\rho.
\end{array}
$$

Problem 19.8:   Let **B** and **C** be any two vectors that commute with $\mathbf{\sigma}$. Show that

$$
\begin{array}{ll}
\text{(a)} & (\mathbf{\sigma} \cdot \mathbf{B})\mathbf{\sigma} = \mathbf{B} + i\mathbf{\sigma} \times \mathbf{B}, \\
\text{(b)} & \mathbf{\sigma}(\mathbf{\sigma} \cdot \mathbf{B}) = \mathbf{B} - i\mathbf{\sigma} \times \mathbf{B}, \\
\text{(c)} & (\mathbf{\sigma} \cdot \mathbf{B})(\mathbf{\sigma} \cdot \mathbf{C}) = \mathbf{B} \cdot \mathbf{C} + i\mathbf{\sigma} \cdot (\mathbf{B} \times \mathbf{C}) \\
\text{(d)} & (\mathbf{\sigma}, \mathbf{\sigma} \cdot \mathbf{B}) = -2i\mathbf{\sigma} \times \mathbf{B}.
\end{array}
$$

(19.15)

19.4. The Dirac Equations.   From (19.4) and (19.5) we see that the Hamiltonian H in Dirac's relativistic wave equation $H\psi = E\psi$ is

$$H = c\mathbf{\alpha} \cdot \mathbf{\pi} + m_0 c^2 \beta + V, \ \mathbf{\pi} = \mathbf{p} - \frac{e}{c} \mathbf{A}. \tag{19.16}$$

By means of (19.9) we find that

$$
\begin{aligned}
\mathbf{\alpha} \cdot \mathbf{\pi} &= \begin{pmatrix} 0 & \sigma_x \\ \sigma_x & 0 \end{pmatrix} \pi_x + \begin{pmatrix} 0 & \sigma_y \\ \sigma_y & 0 \end{pmatrix} \pi_y + \begin{pmatrix} 0 & \sigma_z \\ \sigma_z & 0 \end{pmatrix} \pi_z \\
&= \begin{pmatrix} 0 & \mathbf{\sigma} \cdot \mathbf{\pi} \\ \mathbf{\sigma} \cdot \mathbf{\pi} & 0 \end{pmatrix}.
\end{aligned}
$$

(19.17)

Next, using (19.8), we find

$$(19.18) \quad \boldsymbol{\delta} \cdot \boldsymbol{\pi} = \begin{pmatrix} 0 & 1 \\ 1 & 0 \end{pmatrix} \pi_x + \begin{pmatrix} 0 & -i \\ i & 0 \end{pmatrix} \pi_y + \begin{pmatrix} 1 & 0 \\ 0 & -1 \end{pmatrix} \pi_z$$

$$= \begin{pmatrix} \pi_z & \pi_- \\ \pi_+ & -\pi_z \end{pmatrix}, \quad \pi_\pm = \pi_x \pm i\pi_y.$$

Substituting from (19.18) into (19.17) we obtain

$$(19.19) \quad \boldsymbol{\alpha} \cdot \boldsymbol{\pi} = \begin{pmatrix} 0 & 0 & \pi_z & \pi_- \\ 0 & 0 & \pi_+ & -\pi_z \\ \pi_z & \pi_- & 0 & 0 \\ \pi_+ & -\pi_z & 0 & 0 \end{pmatrix}.$$

In (19.16), V is to be represented by a 4×4 scalar matrix in which the only nonzero elements are V's along the principal diagonal. Then, substituting from (19.19) into (19.16) and recalling the representation (19.9d) of β, we find

$$(19.20) \quad \frac{H}{c} = \begin{pmatrix} \dfrac{V}{c} + m_0 c & 0 & \pi_z & \pi_- \\ 0 & \dfrac{V}{c} + m_0 c & \pi_+ & -\pi_z \\ \pi_z & \pi_- & \dfrac{V}{c} - m_0 c & 0 \\ \pi_+ & -\pi_z & 0 & \dfrac{V}{c} - m_0 c \end{pmatrix}.$$

Sometimes convenient is a 2×2 block representation of H/c, obtainable by using (19.17) and the 2×2 block representation of β given in (19.9d):

$$(19.21) \quad \frac{H}{c} = \begin{pmatrix} 0 & \boldsymbol{\delta} \cdot \boldsymbol{\pi} \\ \boldsymbol{\delta} \cdot \boldsymbol{\pi} & 0 \end{pmatrix} + m_0 c \begin{pmatrix} \mathbb{1} & 0 \\ 0 & -\mathbb{1} \end{pmatrix} + \frac{V}{c} \begin{pmatrix} \mathbb{1} & 0 \\ 0 & \mathbb{1} \end{pmatrix}$$

$$= \begin{pmatrix} \left(\dfrac{V}{c} + m_0 c\right)\mathbb{1} & \boldsymbol{\delta} \cdot \boldsymbol{\pi} \\ \boldsymbol{\delta} \cdot \boldsymbol{\pi} & \left(\dfrac{V}{c} - m_0 c\right)\mathbb{1} \end{pmatrix}.$$

Inasmuch as Dirac operators are 4×4 matrices, Dirac wave functions must consist of four components. Using (19.20) and representing ψ by a column with four components ψ_1, ψ_2, ψ_3, and ψ_4, we may write Dirac's wave equation $H\psi = E\psi$ in the form

$$(19.22) \quad \begin{bmatrix} \dfrac{V}{c} + m_0c & 0 & \pi_z & \pi_- \\[2mm] 0 & \dfrac{V}{c} + m_0c & \pi_+ & -\pi_z \\[2mm] \pi_z & \pi_- & \dfrac{V}{c} - m_0c & 0 \\[2mm] \pi_+ & -\pi_z & 0 & \dfrac{V}{c} - m_0c \end{bmatrix} \begin{pmatrix} \psi_1 \\ \psi_2 \\ \psi_3 \\ \psi_4 \end{pmatrix} = \frac{E}{c} \begin{pmatrix} \psi_1 \\ \psi_2 \\ \psi_3 \\ \psi_4 \end{pmatrix}.$$

This is equivalent to a system of four equations:

$$(19.23) \quad \begin{aligned} &\text{(a)} \quad \left(\frac{V}{c} + m_0c - \frac{E}{c}\right)\psi_1 + \pi_z\psi_3 + \pi_-\psi_4 = 0, \\[2mm] &\text{(b)} \quad \left(\frac{V}{c} + m_0c - \frac{E}{c}\right)\psi_2 + \pi_+\psi_3 - \pi_z\psi_4 = 0, \\[2mm] &\text{(c)} \quad \pi_z\psi_1 + \pi_-\psi_2 + \left(\frac{V}{c} - m_0c - \frac{E}{c}\right)\psi_3 = 0, \\[2mm] &\text{(d)} \quad \pi_+\psi_1 - \pi_z\psi_2 + \left(\frac{V}{c} - m_0c - \frac{E}{c}\right)\psi_4 = 0. \end{aligned}$$

Alternatively, or as an intermediate step, we may represent the four-component wave function ψ in terms of two components χ and φ, where χ and φ each have two components:

$$(19.24) \quad \psi = \begin{pmatrix} \chi \\ \varphi \end{pmatrix}, \quad \chi = \begin{pmatrix} \psi_1 \\ \psi_2 \end{pmatrix}, \quad \varphi = \begin{pmatrix} \psi_3 \\ \psi_4 \end{pmatrix}.$$

Then, using (19.21), we obtain the wave equation $H\psi = E\psi$ in the form

$$(19.25) \quad \begin{pmatrix} \left(\dfrac{V}{c} + m_0c\right)\mathbb{1} & \boldsymbol{\delta} - \boldsymbol{\pi} \\[2mm] \boldsymbol{\delta} \cdot \boldsymbol{\pi} & \left(\dfrac{V}{c} - m_0c\right)\mathbb{1} \end{pmatrix} \begin{pmatrix} \chi \\ \varphi \end{pmatrix} = \frac{E}{c}\begin{pmatrix} \chi \\ \varphi \end{pmatrix}.$$

This is equivalent to the two equations

$$(19.26) \quad \begin{aligned} &\text{(a)} \quad \left(\frac{V}{c} + m_0c - \frac{E}{c}\right)\chi + \boldsymbol{\delta} \cdot \boldsymbol{\pi}\varphi = 0, \\[2mm] &\text{(b)} \quad \boldsymbol{\delta} \cdot \boldsymbol{\pi}\chi + \left(\frac{V}{c} - m_0c - \frac{E}{c}\right)\varphi = 0 \end{aligned}$$

relating the two two-component functions χ and φ.

In concluding this section on the derivation of Dirac's relativistic wave equation, we prove the theorem that if a four-component wave function ψ satisfies Dirac's wave equation for a free particle, then each component of ψ satisfies the Klein-Gordon equation for a free particle,

(5.43) with $\mathbf{A} = 0$, $\phi = 0$. The elimination necessary to prove this is most readily effected by operating on both members of Dirac's equation for a free particle in the form

$$(19.27) \qquad c(\boldsymbol{\alpha} \cdot \mathbf{p} + m_0 c \beta)\psi = E\psi$$

with the operator $c(\boldsymbol{\alpha} \cdot \mathbf{p} + m_0 c \beta)$. Recalling that $c(\boldsymbol{\alpha} \cdot \mathbf{p} + m_0 c \beta)$ commutes with E, we obtain

$$(19.28) \qquad c^2(\boldsymbol{\alpha} \cdot \mathbf{p} + m_0 c \beta)^2\psi = cE(\boldsymbol{\alpha} \cdot \mathbf{p} + m_0 c \beta)\psi.$$

Substituting from (19.5) (where now $\boldsymbol{\pi} = \mathbf{p}$) into the left-hand member of (19.28), and from (19.27) into the right-hand member, we find that

$$(19.29) \qquad c^2(p^2 + m_0{}^2c^2)\psi = E^2\psi.$$

Since $c^2(p^2 + m_0{}^2c^2)$ and E^2 are scalar matrices, (19.29) is equivalent to the four equations

$$(19.30) \qquad c^2(p^2 + m_0{}^2c^2)\psi_i + E^2\psi_i, \ i = 1, 2, 3, 4.$$

This proves the theorem.

Problem 19.9: Obtain a matrix representation of $\boldsymbol{\delta} \cdot \boldsymbol{\pi}$. Answer:

$$(19.31) \quad \boldsymbol{\delta} \cdot \boldsymbol{\pi} = \begin{pmatrix} \boldsymbol{\delta} \cdot \boldsymbol{\pi} & 0 \\ 0 & \boldsymbol{\delta} \cdot \boldsymbol{\pi} \end{pmatrix}, \quad \boldsymbol{\delta} \cdot \boldsymbol{\pi} = \begin{pmatrix} \pi_z & \pi_- \\ \pi_+ & -\pi_z \end{pmatrix}, \quad 0 = \begin{pmatrix} 0 & 0 \\ 0 & 0 \end{pmatrix}.$$

19.5. The Pauli Theory as a Nonrelativistic Approximation to the Dirac Theory.

Substituting

$$(19.32) \qquad \begin{aligned} \text{(a)} \quad & \psi = e^{-im_0c^2t/\hbar}\psi', \\ \text{(b)} \quad & E\psi = i\hbar \frac{\partial \psi}{\partial t} = e^{-im_0c^2t/\hbar}(E + m_0c^2)\psi', \end{aligned}$$

where ψ and ψ' are four component wave functions, into the Dirac equation $H\psi = E\psi$, we obtain as the wave equation for ψ',

$$(19.33) \qquad H\psi' = (E + m_0c^2)\psi'.$$

Now letting

$$\psi' = \begin{pmatrix} \chi' \\ \varphi' \end{pmatrix}, \quad \chi' = \begin{pmatrix} \psi_1' \\ \psi_2' \end{pmatrix}, \quad \varphi' = \begin{pmatrix} \psi_3' \\ \psi_4' \end{pmatrix},$$

and referring to (19.21) for the Dirac Hamiltonian H, we write (19.33) in the form

$$(19.34) \qquad \begin{pmatrix} \left(\dfrac{V}{c} + m_0c\right)\mathbb{1} & \boldsymbol{\delta} \cdot \boldsymbol{\pi} \\ \boldsymbol{\delta} \cdot \boldsymbol{\pi} & \left(\dfrac{V}{c} - m_0c\right)\mathbb{1} \end{pmatrix} \begin{pmatrix} \chi' \\ \varphi' \end{pmatrix} = \left(\frac{E}{c} + m_0c\right)\begin{pmatrix} \chi' \\ \varphi' \end{pmatrix}.$$

This is equivalent to

$$\text{(a)} \quad \left(\frac{V-E}{c}\right)\chi' + \vec{\sigma}\cdot\pi\varphi' = 0,$$

$$(19.35)$$

$$\text{(b)} \quad \vec{\sigma}\cdot\pi\chi' + \left(\frac{V-E}{c} - 2m_0 c\right)\varphi' = 0.$$

Assuming now that $2m_0 c^2 \gg E - V$, we obtain from (19.35),

$$(19.36) \quad \text{(a)} \quad \vec{\sigma}\cdot\pi\varphi' = \left(\frac{E-V}{c}\right)\chi', \qquad \text{(b)} \quad \vec{\sigma}\cdot\pi\chi' = 2m_0 c\varphi',$$

as the nonrelativistic approximation to (19.35). Eliminating φ' from (19.36), we find that χ' must satisfy

$$(19.37) \qquad \frac{1}{2m_0}(\vec{\sigma}\cdot\pi)^2\chi' + V\chi' = E\chi',$$

in the nonrelativistic limit. Substituting from (18.40), we obtain

$$(19.38) \qquad \left\{\frac{1}{2m_0}\pi^2 + V + G_s \mathbf{s}\cdot\mathbf{B}\right\}\chi' = E\chi'.$$

The Hamiltonian in (19.38) contains in addition to its spin independent part $H^{(1)} = \pi^2/2m_0 + V$ a spin dependent part $G_s \mathbf{s}\cdot\mathbf{B}$, in full agreement with the Pauli theory (see (18.54)). Thus, in the nonrelativistic limit, the Dirac four-component wave theory reduces to Pauli's two-component wave theory. Unfortunately, spin-orbit interaction is lost in the process of taking the nonrelativistic limit.

19.6. Plane Wave Solutions for a Free Dirac Particle.   For the Dirac equation for a free particle,

$$(19.39) \qquad H\psi = i\hbar\frac{\partial\psi}{\partial t}$$

where

$$(19.40) \qquad H = c\boldsymbol{\alpha}\cdot\mathbf{p} + m_0 c^2\beta,$$

we try to obtain solutions of the form

$$(19.41) \qquad \psi(\mathbf{r},t) = f(t)\psi(\mathbf{r})$$

where $\psi(\mathbf{r})$ is a four-component time independent wave function. Separation of the time variable leads to

$$(19.42) \qquad \text{(a)} \quad H\psi(\mathbf{r}) = E\psi(\mathbf{r}), \qquad \text{(b)} \quad i\hbar\frac{df}{dt} = Ef$$

where E is a separation constant. Solving (19.42b), we find that from any four-component energy eigenfunction $\psi(\mathbf{r})$ and energy eigenvalue E we can form a stationary state wave function

$$(19.43) \qquad \psi(\mathbf{r},t) = e^{-iEt/\hbar}\psi(\mathbf{r}).$$

We proceed to determine simultaneous eigenfunctions of $\mathbf{p}$ and H, which are readily verified to be commuting operators. Starting with $\mathbf{p}$, we find that the eigenvalue equation

(19.44)
$$\mathbf{p}\psi = \hbar\mathbf{k}\psi,$$

where ψ is a four-component function and $\mathbf{p} = -i\hbar$ grad, has solutions

(19.45)
$$\psi(\mathbf{r}) = Be^{i\mathbf{k}\cdot\mathbf{r}},$$

where B is a four-component function with constant components B_1, B_2, B_3, and B_4.

Substituting from (19.45) into (19.22), in which we place $V = 0$ and $\pi = -i\hbar$ grad, we find that the energy eigenvalue equation (19.42a) implies that

(19.46)
$$\begin{pmatrix} m_0c & 0 & p_z & p_- \\ 0 & m_0c & p_+ & -p_z \\ p_z & p_- & -m_0c & 0 \\ p_+ & -p_z & 0 & -m_0c \end{pmatrix} \begin{pmatrix} B_1 \\ B_2 \\ B_3 \\ B_4 \end{pmatrix} = \frac{E}{c} \begin{pmatrix} B_1 \\ B_2 \\ B_3 \\ B_4 \end{pmatrix}$$

where now $\mathbf{p} = \hbar\mathbf{k}$ represents the observable $\mathbf{p}$ rather than the differential operator $-i\hbar$ grad.

The system of four linear, homogeneous equations has a solution other than $B = 0$ if and only if $\mathbf{p}$ and E are so related that $\Delta(E) = 0$ where

(19.47)
$$\Delta(E) = \begin{vmatrix} m_0c - E/c & 0 & p_z & p_- \\ 0 & m_0c - E/c & p_+ & -p_z \\ p_z & p_- & -m_0c - E/c & 0 \\ p_+ & -p_z & 0 & -m_0c - E/c \end{vmatrix}.$$

To avoid the labor of expanding the determinant (19.47), we recall the theorem (Section 19.4) that each component of any solution of the Dirac equation for a free particle satisfies the Klein-Gordon equation for a free particle. Substituting any component

(19.48)
$$\psi_j(\mathbf{r},t) = e^{i(\mathbf{p}\cdot\mathbf{r}-Et)/\hbar}B_j, \quad j = 1, 2, 3, \text{ or } 4,$$

into the Klein-Gordon equation (5.43), where now $\mathbf{A} = 0$ and $\phi = 0$, we find that

(19.49)
$$E^2 = c^2p^2 + m_0{}^2c^4.$$

Thus E and $\mathbf{p}$ must satisfy the relativistic energy-momentum relation, which we might have expected.

Dirac,[3] in observing that, in order to obtain a complete set of eigenfunctions, the negative as well as the positive roots of the right-hand

[3] P. A. M. Dirac, loc. cit. p. 274f.

member of (19.49) must be included as energy eigenvalues, was led to predict the existence of particles now called *positrons*. We discuss this theory in the next section, proceeding here to complete the calculations for both the positive and the negative energy solutions.

From (19.49) we must have

$$(19.50) \qquad E = \pm\epsilon, \; \epsilon = +\sqrt{c^2 p^2 + m_0{}^2 c^4}.$$

For the *positive energy solutions*, we write $E = +\epsilon$ in (19.46) obtaining the equations

$$
(19.51) \quad
\begin{aligned}
&\text{(a)} & (m_0 c - \epsilon/c)B_1 && + p_z B_3 && + p_- B_4 && = 0, \\
&\text{(b)} & && (m_0 c - \epsilon/c)B_2 + p_+ B_3 && - p_z B_4 && = 0, \\
&\text{(c)} & p_z B_1 + && p_- B_2 - (m_0 c + \epsilon/c)B_3 && && = 0, \\
&\text{(d)} & p_+ B_1 - && p_z B_2 && - (m_0 c + \epsilon/c)B_4 && = 0.
\end{aligned}
$$

For ϵ as given in (19.50), it may be verified that every third-order determinant formed from coefficients in (19.51) vanishes, that is, the matrix of the coefficients is of rank two. This implies that any two of the B's may be expressed in terms of the other two. For example, we might choose to solve (a) and (b) above for B_1 and B_2 in terms of B_3 and B_4, or we might choose to solve (c) and (d) for B_3 and B_4 in terms of B_1 and B_2. The first choice involves division by $m_0 c - \epsilon/c$, the second choice involves division by $m_0 c + \epsilon/c$. Quite naturally, then, we describe B_1 and B_2 as *large components*, B_3 and B_4 as *small components*. It is customary to solve for the small components in terms of the large components.

Solving (19.51c and d) for B_3 and B_4, we obtain, for the positive energy solutions, $E = +\epsilon$,

$$(19.52) \quad \text{(a)} \quad B_3 = \frac{p_z B_1 + p_- B_2}{m_0 c + \epsilon/c}, \qquad \text{(b)} \quad B_4 = \frac{p_+ B_1 - p_z B_2}{m_0 c + \epsilon/c}.$$

From (19.52) we may obtain in many ways two particular positive energy solutions in terms of which any other positive energy solution may be expressed. For example, for one positive energy solution we might choose $B_1 = m_0 c + \epsilon/c$, $B_2 = 0$, and for another, $B_1 = 0$, $B_2 = m_0 c + \epsilon/c$. In this way we obtain the two independent positive energy solutions

$$
(19.53) \quad
\begin{aligned}
\text{(a)} \quad u_1 &= e^{\frac{i(\mathbf{p}\cdot\mathbf{r} - \epsilon t)}{\hbar}}
\begin{pmatrix} m_0 c + \epsilon/c \\ 0 \\ p_z \\ p_+ \end{pmatrix}, \\[2em]
\text{(b)} \quad u_2 &= e^{\frac{i(\mathbf{p}\cdot\mathbf{r} - \epsilon t)}{\hbar}}
\begin{pmatrix} 0 \\ m_0 c + \epsilon/c \\ p_- \\ -p_z \end{pmatrix}.
\end{aligned}
$$

Then the most general positive energy eigenfunction may be written in the form

(19.54) $$u_+ = c_1 u_1 + c_2 u_2.$$

In Problem 19.11, there are to be found the two negative energy solutions

(19.55)

(a) $$u_3 = e^{\frac{i(\mathbf{p} \cdot \mathbf{r} + \epsilon t)}{\hbar}} \begin{pmatrix} -p_z \\ -p_+ \\ m_0 c + \epsilon/c \\ 0 \end{pmatrix},$$

(b) $$u_4 = e^{\frac{i(\mathbf{p} \cdot \mathbf{r} + \epsilon t)}{\hbar}} \begin{pmatrix} -p_- \\ p_z \\ 0 \\ m_0 c + \epsilon/c \end{pmatrix},$$

and the most general negative energy solution

(19.56) $$u_- = c_3 u_3 + c_4 u_4.$$

Problem 19.10: Show that

(19.57) $$\Delta(E) = (E^2/c^2 - p^2 - m_0^2 c^2)^2.$$

Problem 19.11: Obtain the negative energy solutions (19.55).

Problem 19.12: Obtain the eigenvalues and four independent eigenfunctions of $\mathbf{\delta} \cdot \mathbf{p}$. (Hint: Use (19.31), with $\pi = \mathbf{p}$.) Answers:

(19.58) (a) $v_1 = \begin{pmatrix} \chi \\ 0 \end{pmatrix}$, (b) $v_2 = \begin{pmatrix} 0 \\ \chi \end{pmatrix}$,

are eigenfunctions of $\mathbf{\delta} \cdot \mathbf{p}$ for $\mathbf{\delta} \cdot \mathbf{p} = p$, and

(19.59) (a) $v_3 = \begin{pmatrix} \varphi \\ 0 \end{pmatrix}$, (b) $v_4 = \begin{pmatrix} 0 \\ \varphi \end{pmatrix}$,

are eigenfunctions of $\mathbf{\delta} \cdot \mathbf{p}$ for $\mathbf{\delta} \cdot \mathbf{p} = -p$, where χ and φ are the two-component Pauli wave functions (18.75). Any linear combinations

(19.60)

(a) $$v_+ = c_1 v_1 + c_2 v_2 = \begin{pmatrix} c_1 \chi \\ c_2 \chi \end{pmatrix},$$

(b) $$v_- = c_3 v_3 + c_4 v_4 = \begin{pmatrix} c_3 \varphi \\ c_4 \varphi \end{pmatrix},$$

are eigenfunctions of $\mathbf{\delta} \cdot \mathbf{p}$ for $\mathbf{\delta} \cdot \mathbf{p} = p$ and for $\mathbf{\delta} \cdot \mathbf{p} = -p$, respectively.

Problem 19.13: Show that $\mathbf{\delta} \cdot \mathbf{p}$ commutes with the Dirac Hamiltonian (19.40). Hence $\mathbf{\delta} \cdot \mathbf{p}$ and H possess a complete set of simultaneous eigenfunctions (see Theorem IV, Section 13.4). Determine c_1, c_2, c_3, and c_4 in (19.60) so that v_+ and v_- will be eigenfunctions of H. (Hint: Use (19.21) with $\pi = \mathbf{p}$, $V = 0$.)[4]

Problem 19.14: Show that if $(\psi_1, \psi_2, \psi_3, \psi_4)$ is an eigenfunction of H for $H = +\epsilon$, then $(-\psi_3, -\psi_4, \psi_1, \psi_2)$ is an eigenfunction of H for $H = -\epsilon$. (Hint: In (19.23) replace ψ_1 by $-\psi_3$, ψ_2 by $-\psi_4$, ψ_3 by ψ_1, ψ_4 by ψ_2, and E by $-E$. Observe that the result is equivalent to interchanging (a) and (c), (b) and (d) in (19.23).)[5]

Problem 19.15: From the point of view of classical relativistic mechanics, reversal of the sign of E is equivalent to reversal of the sign of the rest mass, since

$$(19.61) \qquad E = mc^2 = m_0 c^2 / \sqrt{1 - v^2}.$$

This is not exactly true in relativistic quantum mechanics. In (19.23), replace m_0 by $-m_0$, interchange ψ_1 and ψ_3, and interchange ψ_2 and ψ_4. Observe that the result is equivalent to interchanging (a) and (c), (b) and (d) in (19.23). However, it must not be concluded that $(\psi_3, \psi_4, \psi_1, \psi_2)$ is an eigenfunction of H when $(\psi_1, \psi_2, \psi_3, \psi_4)$ is an eigenfunction of H, since H is not invariant under reversal of the sign of m_0.[6]

Problem 19.16: Taking the z axis parallel to $\mathbf{p}$, verify that the energy eigenfunctions (19.53) and (19.55) are eigenfunctions of $\boldsymbol{\sigma} \cdot \mathbf{p}$.

19.7. Dirac's Theory of the Positron.[7] In classical relativistic mechanics, negative energy values $E = -\epsilon = -\sqrt{c^2 p^2 + m_0^2 c^4}$ are not considered since, owing to the continuity of variation of classical dynamical observables, transitions between positive and negative energy values cannot occur (see Fig. 19.1). In the quantum theory, discontinuous transitions may take place and, further, negative energy eigenfunctions are needed to obtain complete sets of energy eigenfunctions. Hence it is not permissable to ignore negative energy states.

By a calculation known as *charge conjugation*, Dirac showed that the negative energy solutions refer to the motion of a particle having the mass of an electron and the opposite charge. Such particles have been observed experimentally and are called *positrons* (see Section 2.5). However, as Dirac points out, the negative energy solutions do not

---

[4] See L. de Broglie, *Théorie Général des Particles á Spin*, Gauthier-Villars, 1943, p. 85; S. M. Neamtan, *Am. J. Phys.*, **20**, 450 (1952).

[5] See J. Frenkel, *Wave Mechanics, Advanced General Theory*, Dover, 1950, p. 278.

[6] Ibid. p. 279.

[7] P. A. M. Dirac, op. cit. p. 273f.; for remarks on the existence of antimatter and for the history of particles and antiparticles, see M. A. Ruderman and A. H. Rosenfeld, *Am. Scientist*, **48**, 209 (1960); T. D. Lee, *Physics Today*, **13**, 30 (1960); E. Segrè, *Science*, **132**, 9 (1960).

represent positrons, since this interpretation would lead to ludicrous conclusions, such as a negative kinetic energy and a relativistic energy E decreasing as p^2 increases. It is equally incorrect to interpret the negative energy solutions as representing particles of negative mass.

In order to obtain an interpretation of the negative energy solutions in agreement with experimental evidence, Dirac introduced two basic assumptions regarding these solutions:

(1) Nearly all negative energy states are occupied with electrons.

(2) An electron in a negative energy state is not observable, but unoccupied negative energy states are observed as positrons.

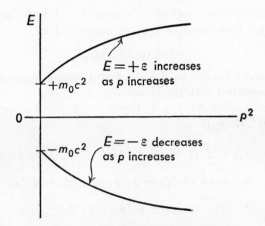

Fig. 19.1. Graph of E as a function of p^2.

According to Dirac's first assumption, negative energy solutions represent electrons in unobservable states. Consider an electron in a negative energy state, $E = -\epsilon \leqslant -m_0c^2$. Raising it to a positive energy state, with, $E' = +\epsilon \geqslant m_0c^2$, requires energy $E' - E \geqslant 2m_0c^2$. The previously unobservable electron becomes observable as a positive energy electron, and the unoccupied *hole* which it vacates is observable as a positron. This, in brief, is Dirac's famous *hole theory* which quite satisfactorily accounts for *pair production* (see Section 2.5).

19.8. Inner Products and Expectation Values. In order to give full physical content to Dirac's relativistic wave equation, we need to define inner products and expectation values in terms of four-component wave functions and Dirac operators (4 $\times$ 4 matrices). Then the formalism of the Schroedinger nonrelativistic wave mechanics may be carried over *in toto*. In particular (8.41) will be applicable, and observables associated with time independent operators which commute with the Dirac Hamiltonian will be quantum mechanical constants of the motion.

Let $f = (f_1, f_2, f_3, f_4)$ and $g = (g_1, g_2, g_3, g_4)$ be two four-component wave functions such that each of the components of f and each of the components of g are square integrable. Then the inner products (f,g) and the norm of f, $N(f)$, defined by

$$
(19.62) \quad
\begin{aligned}
\text{(a)} \quad & (f,g) = \int (f_1^* g_1 + f_2^* g_2 + f_3^* g_3 + f_4^* g_4) \, dr, \\
\text{(b)} \quad & N(f) = (f,f),
\end{aligned}
$$

exist. Further a constant c may be determined so that $N(f') = 1$, where $f' = cf$. If $(f,g) = 0$, f and g are said to be *orthogonal*. If $N(f) = 1$, f is said to be *normalized*.

The expectation value $\langle A \rangle$ of an observable A is defined for a state represented by a four-component wave function ψ by

$$(19.63) \qquad \langle A \rangle = (\psi, A\psi)/(\psi, \psi)$$

where, on the right-hand side, A is the 4×4 matrix representation of the operator A associated with the observable A.

Problem 19.17: Let $N(\psi) = 1$. Using the Dirac σ operators (19.11), (see also (19.8)), show that

$$
(19.64) \quad
\begin{aligned}
\text{(a)} \quad & \langle \sigma_1 \rangle = \int (\psi_1^* \psi_2 + \psi_2^* \psi_1 + \psi_3^* \psi_4 + \psi_4^* \psi_3) \, dr, \\
\text{(b)} \quad & \langle \sigma_2 \rangle = i \int (\psi_1^* \psi_2 - \psi_2^* \psi_1 + \psi_3^* \psi_4 - \psi_4^* \psi_3) \, dr, \\
\text{(c)} \quad & \langle \sigma_3 \rangle = \int (\psi_1^* \psi_1 - \psi_2^* \psi_2 + \psi_3^* \psi_3 - \psi_4^* \psi_4) \, dr.
\end{aligned}
$$

Problem 19.18:   Define inner products and norms for wave functions whose four components do not depend on xyz. Answer:

$$
(19.65) \quad
\begin{aligned}
\text{(a)} \quad & (u,v) = c_1^* d_1 + c_2^* d_2 + c_3^* d_3 + c_4^* d_4, \\
\text{(b)} \quad & N(u) = (u,u),
\end{aligned}
$$

where $u = (c_1, c_2, c_3, c_4)$ and $v = (d_1, d_2, d_3, d_4)$.

Problem 19.19:   Verify that the four positive and negative energy solutions (19.53) and (19.55) are orthogonal in pairs. Normalize them.

19.9. Spin Angular Momentum and Magnetic Moment.   One of the most remarkable successes of Dirac's theory is the natural way in which spin angular momentum and spin magnetic moment are correctly predicted by the Dirac equation.

For a particle in a central field $V(r)$, the Dirac Hamiltonian is, according to (19.16),

$$(19.66) \qquad H = c\boldsymbol{\alpha} \cdot \mathbf{p} + m_0 c^2 \beta + V(r).$$

It might be expected, in conformity with the Schroedinger theory, that H and $\mathbf{M} = \mathbf{r} \times \mathbf{p}$ commute. In determining whether this is correct, we need work with only one component of $\mathbf{M}$, say M_z. Since M_z commutes with $m_0 c^2 \beta$ and with $V(r)$, (see (14.11)), we have

(19.67) $\qquad (M_z, H) = c\{\alpha_1(M_z, p_x) + \alpha_2(M_z, p_y) + \alpha_3(M_z, p_z)\}.$

Using (14.16), we find from (19.67) that

(19.68) $\qquad\qquad (M_z, H) = i\hbar c(\alpha_1 p_y - \alpha_2 p_x).$

From this we may write

(19.69) $\qquad\qquad (\mathbf{M}, H) = i\hbar c \boldsymbol{\alpha} \times \mathbf{p}.$

Hence $\mathbf{M}$ does not commute with H, and is not a constant of the motion, as it was in the Schroedinger theory.

On physical grounds we might expect that there exists some vector, akin to $\mathbf{M}$, which commutes with H. Let us try $\boldsymbol{\sigma}$. Working for convenience with only one component of $\boldsymbol{\sigma}$, say σ_3, we have, from (19.66)

(19.70) $\qquad (\sigma_3, H) = c\{(\sigma_3, \alpha_1)p_x + (\sigma_3, \alpha_2)p_y + (\sigma_3, \alpha_3)p_z\},$

since σ_3 commutes with $V(r)$ and with $m_0 c^2 \beta$ (see (19.12e)). Using (19.12), we find that

(19.71) $\qquad\qquad (_3, \sigma H) = ic(\alpha_2 p_x - \alpha_1 p_y).$

From this we write

(19.72) $\qquad\qquad (\boldsymbol{\sigma}, H) = -2ic\boldsymbol{\alpha} \times \mathbf{p}.$

From (19.69) and (19.72) we readily see that the operator

(19.73) $\qquad\qquad \mathbf{J} = \mathbf{M} + (\hbar/2)\boldsymbol{\sigma}$

commutes with the Dirac Hamiltonian for a particle in a central field. Since $\mathbf{M}$ represents orbital angular momentum, it is quite natural now to interpret

(19.74) $\qquad\qquad \mathbf{s} = (\hbar/2)\boldsymbol{\sigma}$

as spin angular momentum and $\mathbf{J}$ as total angular momentum. Since $\mathbf{J}$ commutes with H, $\mathbf{J}$ is a quantum mechanical constant of the motion.

To show that

(19.75) $\qquad\qquad \boldsymbol{\mu} = \dfrac{e}{m_0 c}\,\mathbf{s} = \dfrac{\hbar e}{2m_0 c}\,\boldsymbol{\sigma}$

represents the intrinsic magnetic moment of an electron, Dirac squared the Hamiltonian for a particle in a magnetic field $\mathbf{B} = \text{Curl } \mathbf{A}$. From (19.4) and (19.5) we find that

(19.76) $\begin{aligned} (H/c)^2 &= (\boldsymbol{\alpha} \cdot \boldsymbol{\pi} + m_0 c\beta)(\boldsymbol{\alpha} \cdot \boldsymbol{\pi} + m_0 c\beta) \\ &= (\boldsymbol{\alpha} \cdot \boldsymbol{\pi})^2 + m_0 c\{\beta(\boldsymbol{\alpha} \cdot \boldsymbol{\pi}) + (\boldsymbol{\alpha} \cdot \boldsymbol{\pi})\beta\} + m_0^2 c^2. \end{aligned}$

By using (19.7c and d) we readily reduce this to

(19.77) $$(H/c)^2 = (\boldsymbol{\alpha} \cdot \boldsymbol{\pi})^2 + m_0{}^2 c^2.$$

However, from (18.39), (19.14a and b) and (19.15c) we find that

(19.78) $$(\boldsymbol{\alpha} \cdot \boldsymbol{\pi})^2 = \pi^2 - \frac{\hbar e}{c} \boldsymbol{\mathfrak{d}} \cdot \mathbf{B}.$$

Hence

(19.79) $$\left(\frac{H}{c} + m_0 c\right)^2 = \pi^2 - \frac{\hbar e}{c} \boldsymbol{\mathfrak{d}} \cdot \mathbf{B} + m_0{}^2 c^2,$$

where $H_1 + m_0 c^2 = H$. Assuming that $H_1 \ll m_0 c^2$, we obtain from (19.79),

(19.80) $$H_1 = \pi^2/2m_0 - \frac{\hbar e}{2 m_0 c} \boldsymbol{\mathfrak{d}} \cdot \mathbf{B}.$$

Since the energy of a dipole of magnetic moment $\boldsymbol{\mu}$ in a magnetic field $\mathbf{B}$ is $-\boldsymbol{\mu}\mathbf{B}$, it is natural, in view of (19.80), to attribute the electron an intrinsic magnetic moment (19.75). This agrees with experimental evidence and with the Uhlenbeck-Goudsmit hypothesis. In the Dirac theory no extraneous hypothesis is needed for the introduction of electron spin.

Problem 19.20: Show that

(19.81)   (a) $\mathbf{J} \times \mathbf{J} = i\hbar \mathbf{J}$,
           (b) $(J^2, \mathbf{J}) = 0$.

Problem 19.21: Show that

(19.82)   (a) $(\beta, H) = 2c\beta\boldsymbol{\alpha} \cdot \mathbf{p}$,
           (b) $(\boldsymbol{\mathfrak{d}} \cdot \mathbf{M}, H) = -2\hbar c \boldsymbol{\alpha} \cdot \mathbf{p} - 2ic\boldsymbol{\alpha} \cdot (\mathbf{p} \times \mathbf{M})$,
           (c) $(\beta\boldsymbol{\mathfrak{d}} \cdot \mathbf{M}, H) = -2\hbar c \beta \boldsymbol{\alpha} \cdot \mathbf{p}$,

where H is the Dirac Hamiltonian (19.66) for a particle in a spherically symmetric field. (Hint: Make full use of (6.22d), (19.69), (19.72), and other relations between operators.)

Problem 19.22: Defining an operator K by

(19.83) $$K = \beta\boldsymbol{\mathfrak{d}} \cdot \mathbf{M} + \hbar\beta,$$

show that

(19.84)   (a) $(K, \mathbf{J}) = 0$,
           (b) $(K, J^2) = 0$,
           (c) $(K, H) = 0$,

and that

$$
\text{(19.85)} \quad
\begin{array}{ll}
\text{(a)} & \boldsymbol{\delta} \cdot \mathbf{M} = \beta K - \hbar, \\
\text{(b)} & M^2 = K^2 - \hbar \beta K, \\
\text{(c)} & J^2 = K^2 - \hbar^2/4.
\end{array}
$$

Problem 19.23:   Obtain 4×4 matrix representations of J_z and of K.
Answers:

$$
\text{(19.86)} \quad J_z = \begin{pmatrix}
M_z + \hbar/2 & 0 & 0 & 0 \\
0 & M_z - \hbar/2 & 0 & 0 \\
0 & 0 & M_z + \hbar/2 & 0 \\
0 & 0 & 0 & M_z - \hbar/2
\end{pmatrix},
$$

$$
\text{(19.87)} \quad K = \begin{pmatrix}
M_z + \hbar & M_- & 0 & 0 \\
M_+ & -M_z - \hbar & 0 & 0 \\
0 & 0 & -M_z - \hbar & -M_- \\
0 & 0 & -M_+ & M_z - \hbar
\end{pmatrix}.
$$

19.10. Angular Momentum Eigenvalues and Eigenfunctions.

In preparation for solving the problem of an electron in a radially symmetric electrostatic field (Section 19.11), one of the most important, early results of the Dirac theory, we obtain simultaneous eigenfunctions of J^2 and J_z. These two operators have previously been found to commute (see (19.81b)). From (19.85c) we see that any eigenfunction of K is also an eigenfunction of J^2.

From (19.86) we find that $\psi = (\psi_1, \psi_2, \psi_3, \psi_4)$ is an eigenfunction of J_z for $J_z = \mu \hbar$ only if

$$
\text{(19.88)} \quad
\begin{array}{ll}
\text{(a)} & M_z \psi_{1,3} = (\mu - \tfrac{1}{2}) \hbar \psi_{1,3}, \\
\text{(b)} & M_z \psi_{2,4} = (\mu + \tfrac{1}{2}) \hbar \psi_{2,4}.
\end{array}
$$

Hence ψ_1 and ψ_3 must be eigenfunctions of M_z for $M_z = (\mu - \tfrac{1}{2})\hbar$, and ψ_2 and ψ_4 must be eigenfunctions of M_z for $M_z = (\mu + \tfrac{1}{2})\hbar$.

Now let ψ be an eigenfunction of K for $K = k\hbar$. From (19.85b) we find that

$$
\text{(19.89)} \quad M^2 \psi = (k^2 - k\beta)\hbar^2 \psi,
$$

since $K\psi = k\hbar\psi$. Using the 4×4 matrix representation (19.9d) of β, we see from (19.89) that

$$
\text{(19.90)} \quad
\begin{pmatrix}
M^2 & 0 & 0 & 0 \\
0 & M^2 & 0 & 0 \\
0 & 0 & M^2 & 0 \\
0 & 0 & 0 & M^2
\end{pmatrix}
\begin{pmatrix}
\psi_1 \\ \psi_2 \\ \psi_3 \\ \psi_4
\end{pmatrix}
$$

$$
= \hbar^2 \begin{pmatrix}
k^2 - k & 0 & 0 & 0 \\
0 & k^2 - k & 0 & 0 \\
0 & 0 & k^2 + k & 0 \\
0 & 0 & 0 & k^2 + k
\end{pmatrix}
\begin{pmatrix}
\psi_1 \\ \psi_2 \\ \psi_3 \\ \psi_4
\end{pmatrix}.
$$

From (19.90) we find that

$$(19.91) \quad \begin{array}{ll} \text{(a)} & M^2\psi_{1,2} = k(k - 1)\hbar^2\psi_{1,2}, \\ \text{(b)} & M^2\psi_{3,4} = k(k + 1)\hbar^2\psi_{3,4}, \end{array}$$

if $K\psi = k\hbar\psi$. Hence ψ_1 and ψ_2 must be eigenfunctions of M^2 for $M^2 = k(k - 1)\hbar^2$, and ψ_3 and ψ_4 must be eigenfunctions of M^2 for $M^2 = k(k + 1)\hbar^2$. These conditions are necessary but not sufficient that $K\psi = k\hbar\psi$.

Using (19.87), we find that $\psi = (\psi_1,\psi_2,\psi_3,\psi_4)$ is an eigenfunction of K for $K = k\hbar$ only if

$$(19.92) \quad \begin{array}{ll} \text{(a)} & M_z\psi_1 + M_-\psi_2 = (k - 1)\hbar\psi_1, \\ \text{(b)} & M_+\psi_1 - M_z\psi_2 = (k - 1)\hbar\psi_2, \\ \text{(c)} & -M_z\psi_3 - M_-\psi_4 = (k + 1)\hbar\psi_3, \\ \text{(d)} & -M_+\psi_3 + M_z\psi_4 = (k + 1)\hbar\psi_4. \end{array}$$

The simultaneous eigenfunctions of M^2 and M_z are the well-known and much-studied surface spherical harmonics $Y_l^m(\theta,\varphi)$, (see (14.55)), multiplied by arbitrary functions of the radial coordinate r. For Y_l^m, $M^2 = l(l + 1)\hbar^2$ and $M_z = m\hbar$.

Writing $k(k - 1) = l(l + 1)$, we obtain $k = -l$ or $k = l + 1$. Writing $k(k + 1) = l(l + 1)$, we obtain $k = l$ or $k = -l - 1$. We obtain all possible solutions of (19.88) and (19.91) by taking $\mu - \frac{1}{2} = m$, $\mu + \frac{1}{2} = m + 1$, and the two values $k = -l$ and $k = l$.

Taking $\mu = m + \frac{1}{2}$, $k = -l$ in (19.88) and (19.91), we readily find from our knowledge of the properties of the surface spherical harmonics $Y_l^m(\theta,\varphi)$ that (19.88) and (19.91) are satisfied by

$$(19.93) \quad \psi_{-l} = \begin{pmatrix} \psi_1 \\ \psi_2 \\ \psi_3 \\ \psi_4 \end{pmatrix} = \begin{pmatrix} f_1(r)\,Y_l^m(\theta,\varphi) \\ f_2(r)\,Y_l^{m+1}(\theta,\varphi) \\ f_3(r)\,Y_{l-1}^m(\theta,\varphi) \\ f_4(r)\,Y_{l-1}^{m+1}(\theta,\varphi) \end{pmatrix}$$

where the f's are arbitrary functions of r. Next, substituting from (19.93) into (19.22), and using (14.48), (14.58) and the eigenvalue relation $M_z Y_l^m(\theta,\varphi) = m\hbar Y_l^m(\theta,\varphi)$, we find that ψ_{-l} is an eigenfunction of K for $K = -l\hbar$ provided

$$(19.94) \quad \begin{array}{ll} \text{(a)} & m\hbar f_1 + c_l^m f_2 = -(l + 1)\hbar f_1, \\ \text{(b)} & c_l^m f_1 - (m + 1)\hbar f_2 = -(l + 1)\hbar f_2, \\ \text{(c)} & -m\hbar f_3 - c_{l-1}^m f_4 = -(l - 1)\hbar f_3, \\ \text{(d)} & -c_{l-1}^m f_3 + (m + 1)\hbar f_4 = -(l - 1)\hbar f_4. \end{array}$$

By means of (14.57), we find that the system (19.94) is consistent and may be satisfied by setting

(19.95)
$$
\begin{aligned}
&\text{(a)}\quad f_1 = \sqrt{l - m}\, f(r),\\
&\text{(b)}\quad f_2 = -\sqrt{l + m + 1}\, f(r),\\
&\text{(c)}\quad f_3 = \sqrt{l + m}\, F(r),\\
&\text{(d)}\quad f_4 = \sqrt{l - m - 1}\, F(r),
\end{aligned}
$$

where $f(r)$ and $F(r)$ remain arbitrary.

Finally, combining (19.93) and (19.95), we have that

(19.96)
$$
\psi_{-l} = \begin{pmatrix}
\sqrt{l - m} & f(r)\, Y_l{}^m(\theta,\varphi)\\
-\sqrt{l + m + 1} & f(r)\, Y_l{}^{m+1}(\theta,\varphi)\\
\sqrt{l + m} & F(r)\, Y_{l-1}{}^m(\theta,\varphi)\\
\sqrt{l - m - 1} & F(r)\, Y_{l-1}{}^{m+1}(\theta,\varphi)
\end{pmatrix}
$$

is a simultaneous eigenfunction of J_z and K for $J_z = (m + \frac{1}{2})\hbar$ and $K = -l\hbar$.

In a similar manner, taking $\mu = m + \frac{1}{2}$ and $k = l$ in (19.88), (19.91), and (19.92), it is to be found that (Problem 19.24)

(19.97)
$$
\psi_l = \begin{pmatrix}
\sqrt{l + m} & g(r)\, Y_{l-1}{}^m(\theta,\varphi)\\
\sqrt{l - m - 1} & g(r)\, Y_{l-1}{}^{m+1}(\theta,\varphi)\\
\sqrt{l - m} & G(r)\, Y_l{}^m(\theta,\varphi)\\
\sqrt{l + m + 1} & G(r)\, Y_l{}^{m+1}(\theta,\varphi)
\end{pmatrix}
$$

where $g(r)$ and $G(r)$ are arbitrary functions of r, is a simultaneous eigenfunction of J_z and K for $J_z = (m + \frac{1}{2})\hbar$ and $K = l\hbar$.

By means of (19.85), we readily see that the four-component wave functions ψ_{-l} and ψ_l, (19.96) and (19.97), are simultaneous eigenfunctions of J_z and J^2 for $J_z = (m + \frac{1}{2})\hbar$ and $J^2 = j(j + 1)\hbar^2$, where $j = l - \frac{1}{2}$.

The functions $f(r)$, $F(r)$, $g(r)$, and $G(r)$ in (19.96) and (19.97) remain to be determined by the requirement that ψ_{-l} and ψ_l be eigenfunctions of the Dirac Hamiltonian (19.66). Solution for $V(r) = -e^2/r$, giving energy eigenvalues and four-component wave functions for the hydrogen atom, is completed in the next section.

Problem 19.24: Obtain (19.97), starting by substituting $\mu = m + \frac{1}{2}$, $k = l$ in (19.88), (19.91), and (19.92).

19.11. Solution for the Hydrogen Atom. As with other problems in which there is spherical symmetry, the eigenvalues and eigenfunctions of the Dirac Hamiltonian (19.66) are most readily found by using a spherical coordinate system. The first part of the problem is to express $\boldsymbol{\alpha} \cdot \mathbf{p}$ in (19.66) in spherical coordinates.

Letting $\mathbf{B} = \mathbf{r}$, $\mathbf{C} = \mathbf{p}$, $\mathbf{B} \times \mathbf{C} = \mathbf{r} \times \mathbf{p} = \mathbf{M}$ in (19.15c) we find that

$$(19.98) \qquad (\mathbf{\delta} \cdot \mathbf{r})(\mathbf{\delta} \cdot \mathbf{p}) = \mathbf{r} \cdot \mathbf{p} + i\mathbf{\delta} \cdot \mathbf{M}.$$

Then letting $\mathbf{B} = \mathbf{C} = \mathbf{r}$, $\mathbf{B} \times \mathbf{C} = \mathbf{r} \times \mathbf{r} = 0$, we find from (19.15c) that

$$(19.99) \qquad (\mathbf{\delta} \cdot \mathbf{r})^2 = r^2.$$

Hence when (19.98) is multiplied through from the left by $\rho\mathbf{\delta} \cdot \mathbf{r}$ we obtain, since $\rho\mathbf{\delta} = \mathbf{\alpha}$, (see (19.14b)),

$$(19.100) \qquad r^2\mathbf{\alpha} \cdot \mathbf{p} = (\mathbf{\alpha} \cdot \mathbf{r})(\mathbf{r} \cdot \mathbf{p}) + i(\mathbf{\alpha} \cdot \mathbf{r})(\mathbf{\delta} \cdot \mathbf{M}).$$

By substituting from (19.100) into (19.66) we obtain a representation of H in spherical coordinates

$$(19.101) \quad H = \frac{c}{r^2} \{ (\mathbf{\alpha} \cdot \mathbf{r})(\mathbf{r} \cdot \mathbf{p}) + i(\mathbf{\alpha} \cdot \mathbf{r})(\mathbf{\delta} \cdot \mathbf{M}) \} + m_0 c^2 \beta + V(r).$$

Using (19.85a) to eliminate $\mathbf{\delta} \cdot \mathbf{M}$, we find

$$(19.102) \quad H = \frac{c}{r^2} (\mathbf{\alpha} \cdot \mathbf{r}) \{ (\mathbf{r} \cdot \mathbf{p}) + i\beta K - i\hbar \} + m_0 c^2 \beta + V(r).$$

The next major step is to obtain a 2×2 block matrix representation of H. First, replacing $\mathbf{\pi}$ in (19.19) by $\mathbf{r} = (x,y,z)$, we find that

$$(19.103) \qquad \mathbf{\alpha} \cdot \mathbf{r} = \begin{pmatrix} 0 & r\tau \\ r\tau & 0 \end{pmatrix}$$

where

$$(19.104) \quad \tau = \begin{pmatrix} z/r & (x - iy)/r \\ (x + iy)/r & -z/r \end{pmatrix} = \begin{pmatrix} \cos\theta & e^{-i\varphi}\sin\theta \\ e^{i\varphi}\sin\theta & -\cos\theta \end{pmatrix}$$

depends on θ and on φ, but not on r. Simple calculation gives

$$(19.105) \qquad (\mathbf{\alpha} \cdot \mathbf{r})\beta = \begin{pmatrix} 0 & r\tau \\ r\tau & 0 \end{pmatrix} \begin{pmatrix} \mathbb{1} & 0 \\ 0 & -\mathbb{1} \end{pmatrix} = \begin{pmatrix} 0 & -r\tau \\ r\tau & 0 \end{pmatrix}.$$

Substituting from (19.103) and (19.105) into (19.102), we find that, *for an eigenfunction of K, for which $K = k\hbar$,*

$$(19.106) \quad \frac{H}{c} = \frac{1}{r} \left\{ \begin{pmatrix} 0 & \tau \\ \tau & 0 \end{pmatrix} [\mathbf{r} \cdot \mathbf{p} - i\hbar] + ik\hbar \begin{pmatrix} 0 & -\tau \\ \tau & 0 \end{pmatrix} \right\}$$

$$+ m_0 c \begin{pmatrix} 1 & 0 \\ 0 & -1 \end{pmatrix} + \frac{V}{c} \begin{pmatrix} 1 & 0 \\ 0 & 1 \end{pmatrix}$$

$$= \begin{pmatrix} \left(m_0 c + \dfrac{V}{c} \right) 1 & \dfrac{\tau}{r} [\mathbf{r} \cdot \mathbf{p} - i(k+1)\hbar] \\ \dfrac{\tau}{r} [\mathbf{r} \cdot \mathbf{p} + i(k-1)\hbar] & \left(-m_0 c + \dfrac{V}{c} \right) 1 \end{pmatrix}.$$

Writing $\psi = \begin{pmatrix} \chi \\ \varphi \end{pmatrix}$ where $\chi = \begin{pmatrix} \psi_1 \\ \psi_2 \end{pmatrix}$ and $\varphi = \begin{pmatrix} \psi_3 \\ \psi_4 \end{pmatrix}$, we obtain from (19.106) and the energy eigenvalue equation $H\psi = E\psi$ the equations

(19.107) (a) $(\hbar a_1 + V/c)\chi + (1/r)[\mathbf{r} \cdot \mathbf{p} - i(k+1)\hbar]\tau\varphi = 0,$

          (b) $(1/r)[\mathbf{r} \cdot \mathbf{p} + i(k-1)\hbar]\tau\chi - (\hbar a_2 - V/c)\varphi = 0,$

where

(19.108) (a) $a_1 = (m_0 c^2 - E)/\hbar c,$ (b) $a_2 = (m_0 c^2 + E)/\hbar c.$

In writing (19.107), we have commuted τ and $\mathbf{r} \cdot \mathbf{p}$, which is permissible since τ does not depend on r and $\mathbf{r} \cdot \mathbf{p}$ depends only on r, not on θ or φ. Since, further $\tau^2 = 1$, we may, upon multiplying (19.107b) from the left by τ, write (19.107) in the form

(19.109) (a) $(\hbar a_1 + V/c)\chi + (1/r)[\mathbf{r} \cdot \mathbf{p} - i(k+1)\hbar]\tau\varphi = 0,$

          (b) $(1/r)[\mathbf{r} \cdot \mathbf{p} + i(k-1)\hbar]\chi - (\hbar a_2 - V/c)\tau\varphi = 0.$

To initiate the solution of (19.109), we make the substitutions

(19.110) (a) $\chi = u/r,$ (b) $\varphi = i\tau v/r,$

where u and v are two two-component wave functions, functions of r only. Since

(19.111) (a) $(\mathbf{r} \cdot \mathbf{p} - i\hbar)u/r = -i\hbar \left(r\dfrac{\partial}{\partial r} + 1 \right) u/r = -i\hbar u',$

          (b) $(\mathbf{r} \cdot \mathbf{p} - i\hbar)(iv/r) = \hbar v',$

we readily obtain

(19.112) (a) $(a_1 + V/\hbar c)u + (v' + kv/r) = 0,$

          (b) $(u' - ku/r) + (a_2 - V/\hbar c)v = 0.$

Solution of (19.112) is facilitated by utilizing its approximate solution for large values of r. If $V(r) \to 0$ as $r \to \infty$, as is the case of the Coulomb potential $V(r) = -e^2/r$, (19.112) is approximated for large values of r by

(19.113) (a) $a_1 u + v' = 0,$ (b) $u' + a_2 v = 0.$

Since the bounded solutions of (19.113) are proportional to e^{-ar} where

(19.114) $$a^2 = a_1 a_2 = m_0{}^2 c^2 - E^2/c^2,$$

we proceed to make the substitutions

(19.115) (a) $u = e^{-ar} P(r),$ (b) $v = e^{-ar} Q(r)$

in (19.112). Also making change of independent variable by letting $s = ar$, we obtain, for the Coulomb potential $V(r) = -e^2/r$,

(19.116)
(a) $\left(\dfrac{a_1}{a} - \dfrac{\alpha}{s} \right) P + \left(\dfrac{\partial}{\partial s} - 1 + \dfrac{k}{s} \right) Q = 0,$

(b) $\left(\dfrac{\partial}{\partial s} - 1 - \dfrac{k}{s} \right) P + \left(\dfrac{a_2}{a} + \dfrac{\alpha}{s} \right) Q = 0,$

where $\alpha = e^2/\hbar c$ is the *fine structure constant* (see (4.48)).
Substituting

(19.117) (a) $P = \displaystyle\sum_{j=0}^{\infty} p_j s^{j+\lambda},$ (b) $Q = \displaystyle\sum_{j=0}^{\infty} q_j s^{j+\lambda},$

into (19.116), we obtain after division by s^λ,

(19.118)
(a) $\displaystyle\sum_{j=0}^{\infty} \left(\dfrac{a_1}{a} p_j - q_j \right) s^j - \sum_{j=0}^{\infty} (\alpha p_j - [j + \lambda + k] q_j) s^{j-1} = 0,$

(b) $\displaystyle\sum_{j=0}^{\infty} ([j + \lambda - k] p_j + \alpha q_j) s^{j-1} - \sum_{j=0}^{\infty} \left(p_j - \dfrac{a_2}{a} q_j \right) s^j = 0.$

These equations are satisfied for all positive values of s only if the coefficients of the various powers of s vanish separately. Equating the coefficients of s^{-1} to zero, we find that we must have

(19.119)
(a) $\alpha p_0 - (\lambda + k) q_0 = 0,$
(b) $(\lambda - k) p_0 + \alpha q_0 = 0.$

These equations are consistent only if $\lambda^2 = k^2 - \alpha^2$. To obtain a solution finite at $r = 0$, we take

(19.120) $$\lambda = + \sqrt{k^2 - \alpha^2}.$$

Equating the coefficients of s^{j-1} in (19.118) to zero, we find that we must have

(19.121)
$$\text{(a)} \quad \frac{a_1}{a} p_{j-1} - q_{j-1} - \alpha p_j + (j + \lambda + k)q_j = 0,$$
$$\text{(b)} \quad (j + \lambda - k)p_j + \alpha q_j - p_{j-1} + \frac{a_2}{a} q_{j-1} = 0,$$

for $j \geq 1$.

Inspection of the terms in (19.121) reveals that p_{j-1} and q_{j-1} may be eliminated by multiplying (19.121a) by a_2 and (19.121b) by a and adding the resulting equations. Using the relation $a^2 = a_1 a_2$, we thus obtain

$$(19.122) \quad ([j + \lambda - k]a - \alpha a_2)p_j + ([j + \lambda + k]a_2 + \alpha a)q_j = 0.$$

It may be shown from the preceding recurrence relations that the solutions being obtained are square integrable only if the series (19.117) terminate. From (19.121), we see that these series terminate with terms in $s^{N+\lambda}$ if

$$(19.123) \quad a_1 p_N - a q_N = 0.$$

Since (19.122) is valid for $j = N$, we also have

$$(19.124) \quad ([N + \lambda - k]a - \alpha a_2)p_N + ([N + \lambda + k]a_2 + \alpha a)q_N = 0.$$

Again using the relation $a^2 = a_1 a_2$, we find quite readily that (19.123) and (19.124) are consistent only if

$$(19.125) \quad 2(N + \lambda)a = \alpha(a_2 - a_1).$$

By means of (19.108) and the relation $a^2 = a_1 a_2$ we find that (19.125) determines the energy eigenvalues. Using (19.120), we obtain

$$(19.126) \quad E = m_0 c^2 \left\{ 1 + \left(\frac{\alpha}{N + \sqrt{k^2 - \alpha^2}} \right)^2 \right\}^{-\frac{1}{2}}.$$

When we subtract the rest energy $m_0 c^2$ and replace N by a symbol s, we observe that the resulting expression is identical with (4.50) which was derived in 1915 by Sommerfeld using the Wilson-Sommerfeld quantization.

Explicit expressions for the eigenfunctions in terms of confluent hypergeometric series were first given by Darwin[8] and by Gordon.[9] Dirac,[10] using the methods of noncommutative algebra, had already shown that Sommerfeld's formula is a consequence of the relativistic wave equation.

Problem 19.25: From (19.122), deduce that $ap_j \cong -a_2 q_j$ when j is sufficiently large and the series (19.117) do not terminate. Then, using

[8] C. G. Darwin, *Proc. Roy Soc. (London)*, **118A**, 654 (1928).
[9] W. Gordon, *Z. Physik*, **48**, 11 (1928).
[10] P. A. M. Dirac, *Proc. Roy. Soc. (London)*, **117A**, 610 (1928).

either (19.121a) or (19.121b) deduce that $jp_j \cong 2p_{j-1}$ and $jq_j \cong 2q_{j-1}$. This means that the series (19.117) behave like $s^\lambda e^{2s}$ when s is large, and the solutions (19.115), where $r = s/a$, are not square integrable.

19.12. Physical and Statistical Interpretations of Dirac Wave Functions. A natural extension of Schroedinger's physical interpretation of the nonrelativistic wave function (Section 8.2) to the Dirac four-component wave function is to assume that

$$(19.127) \qquad \rho = e\psi^*\psi = e(\psi_1^*\psi_1 + \psi_2^*\psi_2 + \psi_3^*\psi_3 + \psi_4^*\psi_4)$$

represents the density of the charge in a cloud picture of the electron. In a statistical interpretation, we assume that $J = \psi^*\psi$, as given by (19.127), represents the position probability density. These assumptions are tenable only if a conservation equation (see (8.10)) is satisfied.[11]

If ψ satisfies the Dirac equation

$$(19.128) \qquad i\hbar \frac{\partial \psi}{\partial t} = -i\hbar \operatorname{grad} (c\alpha\psi) - \frac{e}{c} \boldsymbol{\alpha} \cdot \mathbf{A}\psi + m_0c^2\beta\psi,$$

the conjugate wave function ψ^* satisfies the conjugate equation

$$(19.129) \qquad -i\hbar \frac{\partial \psi^*}{\partial t} = i\hbar \operatorname{grad} (\psi^*c\alpha) - \frac{e}{c} \psi^*\boldsymbol{\alpha} \cdot \mathbf{A} + m_0c^2\psi^*\beta.$$

In interpreting (19.128) and (19.129), we remind ourselves that each term in the former represents a column vector with four components and each term in the latter represents a row vector with four components. Further $\boldsymbol{\alpha} = \alpha_1, \alpha_2, \alpha_3$ and β are 4×4 Hermitean matrices.

Multiply (19.128) from the left by ψ^*, (19.129) from the right by ψ, subtract, and divide the result by $i\hbar$. By comparing the resulting equation,

$$(19.130) \qquad \frac{\partial}{\partial t} (\psi^*\psi) = -\operatorname{grad} (\psi^*c\alpha\psi),$$

with the conservation equation (8.10), it is readily seen that $J = \psi^*\psi$ may be interpreted as a probability density provided

$$(19.131) \qquad \mathbf{S} = \psi^*c\alpha\psi$$

is interpreted as the probability current. In the cloud picture of the electron, $\rho = eJ$ and $\mathbf{j} = e\mathbf{S}$, as in Section 8.2. When the representation (19.9) is used for $\boldsymbol{\alpha}$, it is very readily found that

$$(19.132) \quad
\begin{aligned}
\text{(a)} \quad & S_x = c(\psi_1^*\psi_4 + \psi_2^*\psi_3 + \psi_3^*\psi_2 + \psi_4^*\psi_1), \\
\text{(b)} \quad & S_y = -ic(\psi_1^*\psi_4 - \psi_2^*\psi_3 + \psi_3^*\psi_2 - \psi_4^*\psi_1), \\
\text{(c)} \quad & S_z = c(\psi_3^*\psi_1 - \psi_4^*\psi_2 + \psi_1^*\psi_3 - \psi_2^*\psi_4).
\end{aligned}$$

[11] P. A. M. Dirac, *The Principles of Quantum Mechanics*, fourth edition, Oxford, 1958, pp. 260–61.

By considering the motion of a free electron in the Heisenberg picture, Dirac was led to a very surprising and interesting result.[12] First, he observed that the momentum **p** commutes with the Hamiltonian (19.40) and is thus a constant of the motion. Next he found that the operator for the velocity is

$$(19.133) \qquad\qquad \dot{\mathbf{r}} = c\boldsymbol{\alpha}.$$

These results follow directly from (8.38), (19.40) and the Heisenberg commutation relations (7.15). The result (19.133) is also suggested by (19.131).

Dirac concluded that, since ± 1 are the only eigenvalues of α_1, α_2, and α_3, "*a measurement of a component of the velocity of a free electron is certain to lead to the result $\pm c$.*" Dirac immediately explained this surprising result in terms of the uncertainty principle and a "trembling motion" (German: *Zitterbewegung*) in which the average velocity, which is observed, is less than c, but the instantaneous velocity is always $\pm c$. This has recently been the source for several very interesting investigations.[13]

Although it may be paradoxical on first thought, on reflection it is natural that Dirac's theory, which contributes so much to our "picture" of the electron, leaves us in wonderment as to "what" the electron really is. Advanced quantum electrodynamics is beset with difficulties much more serious than interpretation of the Zitterbewegung of the electron.[14] Dirac suggests that "The difficulties, being of a profound character, can be removed only by some drastic change in the foundations of the theory, probably a change as drastic as the passage from Bohr's orbit theory to the present quantum mechanics." The change may be contingent on discoveries in mathematics, as suggested by von Neumann, as drastic as the step made by Newton and Leibnitz in discovering the calculus.

19.12. References for Supplementary Reading.

Section 19.1: Bohm, 89–90; Frenkel, 239–47; Mott and Sneddon, 290–96; Persico, 400–402; Schaefer, 445–9; Schiff, 318–23; Sherwin, 278–81; Sommerfeld, 209–17.

Section 19.2: Dirac, 254–6; McConnell, 114–16; Persico, 402–4; Schaefer, 449–50; Schiff, 323–4; Sherwin, 281–3.

Section 19.3: Dirac, 257–8; Mott and Sneddon, 298–300; Schaefer, 450–52; Schiff, 324–6; Sherwin, 283–9.

Section 19.4: Frenkel, 311–17; March, 165–7; Mott and Massey, 66–9;

---

[12] Ibid. pp. 261–3.

[13] K. Huang, *Am. J. Phys.*, **20**, 479 (1952); Z. Koba, *Nuovo cimento*, **3**, 1 (1956); Y. Aharanov and D. Bohm, *Nuovo cimento, Supplemento*, **5**, 429 (1957); H. Feshbach and F. Villars, *Revs. Modern Phys.*, **30**, 25 (1958).

[14] P. A. M. Dirac, op. cit. pp. 306–10; A. Pais, *Positron Theory*, Princeton, 1949.

Mott and Sneddon, 296–303; Persico, 406–10; Schaefer, 452–6.

Section 19.5:   Mott and Sneddon, 317–21; Persico, 410–12.

Section 19.6:   McConnell, 135–40; Persico, 420–24; Schaefer, 460–62; Schiff, 326–8; Sherwin, 289–300, 324–8.

Section 19.7:   Born, 189–94; Dirac, 273–5; March, 173–6; McConnell, 134–5; Mott and Massey, 85–7; Mott and Sneddon, 310–13; Perisco, 438–45; Schaefer, 492–500; Shankland, 214–19; Sherwin, 300–301.

Section 19.9:   Dirac, 263–7; Frenkel, 323–30; March, 170–72; McConnell, 119–24; Mott and Sneddon, 303–6; Persico, 412–20; Schaefer, 463–81; Schiff, 331–2.

Section 19.10:   Mott and Sneddon, 306–7; Schiff, 332–4.

Section 19.11:   Dirac, 267–73; Frenkel, 330–44; McConnell, 124–34; Mott and Sneddon, 323–7; Persico, 430–38; Schaefer, 481–92; Schiff, 334–9; Shankland, 95–9; White, 139–48.

Section 19.12:   Dirac, 261–3; Frenkel, 321; Kramers, 281–6; McConnell, 116–19; Persico, 404–6, 412–15.

BIBLIOGRAPHY

(A) ATOMIC AND NUCLEAR PHYSICS

1. d'Abro, *The Rise of the New Physics* (2 vols.), Dover, New York, 1951.
2. Beyer, R. T., *Foundations of Nuclear Physics*, Dover, New York, 1949.
3. Blackwood, O. H., T. H. Osgood, and A. E. Ruark, *An Outline of Atomic Physics*, Wiley, New York, third edition, 1955.
4. Born, M., *Atomic Physics*, Hafner, New York, sixth edition, 1957.
5. de Broglie, L., *Matter and Light, The New Physics*, Dover, New York, 1955.
6. Dushman, S., *Fundamentals of Atomic Physics*, McGraw-Hill, New York, 1951.
7. Eldridge, J. A., *The Physical Basis of Things*, McGraw-Hill, New York, 1934.
8. Finkelnburg, *Atomic Physics*, McGraw-Hill, New York, 1950.
9. French, A. P., *Principles of Modern Physics*, Wiley, New York, 1958.
10. Green, A. E. S., *Nuclear Physics*, McGraw-Hill, New York, 1955.
11. Halliday, D., *Introductory Nuclear Physics*, Wiley, New York, second edition, 1955.
12. Herzberg, *Atomic Spectra and Atomic Structure*, Dover, New York, second edition, 1944.
13. Jauncey, G. E. M., *Modern Physics*, Van Nostrand, New York, third edition, 1948.
14. Oldenberg, O., *Introduction to Atomic Physics*, McGraw-Hill, New York, second edition, 1954.
15. Peaslee, D. C., and H. Mueller, *Elements of Atomic Physics*, Prentice-Hall, New York, 1955.
16. Richtmyer, F. K., E. H. Kennard, and T. Lauritsen, *Introduction to Modern Physics*, McGraw-Hill, New York, fifth edition, 1955.
17. Semat, H., *Introduction to Atomic and Nuclear Physics*, Rinehart, New York, third edition, 1954.
18. Shankland, R. S., *Atomic and Nuclear Physics*, Macmillan, New York, 1955.
19. Sproull, R. L., *Modern Physics*, Wiley, New York, 1956.

(B) QUANTUM MECHANICS AND WAVE MECHANICS

20. Atkin, R. H., *Mathematics and Wave Mechanics*, Wiley, New York, 1957.

21. Bohm, D., *Quantum Theory*, Prentice-Hall, New York, 1951.
22. Dirac, P. A. M., *The Principles of Quantum Mechanics*, Oxford: Clarendon Press, fourth edition, 1958.
23. Flügge, S., and H. Marschall, "Rechenmethoden der Quantentheorie," Springer, Berlin, 1952.
24. Frenkel, J., *Wave Mechanics, Advanced General Theory*, Dover, New York, 1950.
25. Houston, W. V., *Principles of Quantum Mechanics*, Dover, New York, 1959.
26. Kemble, E. C., *The Fundamental Principles of Quantum Mechanics*, Dover, New York, 1958.
27. Kramers, H. A., *Quantum Mechanics*, Interscience, New York, 1957.
28. Landé, A., *Quantum Mechanics*, Pitman, New York, 1951.
29. Mandl, F., *Quantum Mechanics*, Butterworths, London, second edition, 1957.
30. March, A., *Quantum Mechanics of Particles and Wave Fields*, Wiley, New York, 1951.
31. McConnell, J., *Quantum Particle Dynamics*, Interscience, New York, 1958.
32. Mott, N. F., and H. S. W. Massey, *The Theory of Atomic Collisions*, Oxford: Clarendon Press, second edition, 1949.
33. Mott, N. F., and I. N. Sneddon, *Wave Mechanics and its Applications*, Oxford: Clarendon Press, 1948.
34. Pauling, L., and E. B. Wilson, *Introduction to Quantum Mechanics*, McGraw-Hill, New York, 1935.
35. Persico, E., *Fundamentals of Quantum Mechanics*, Prentice-Hall, New York, 1950.
36. Schaefer, C., "Einführung in die theoretische Physik," B. III, T. 2, Walter de Gruyter, Berlin, 1937.
37. Schiff, L. I., *Quantum Mechanics*, McGraw-Hill, New York, second edition, 1955.
38. Sherwin, C. W., *Introduction to Quantum Mechanics*, Holt, New York, 1959.
39. Sommerfeld, A., *Atombau und Spektrallinien*, Frederick Ungar, New York, 1953.
40. Weyl, H., *The Theory of Groups and Quantum Mechanics*, Dover, New York, 1931.
41. White, H. E., *Introduction to Atomic Spectra*, McGraw-Hill, New York, 1934.

INDEX OF NAMES

INDEX OF SUBJECTS